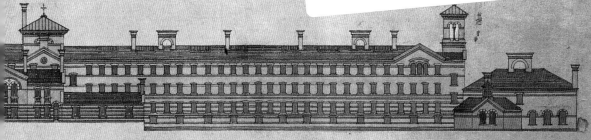

Female Wing

Working Offices (Female)

(North.)

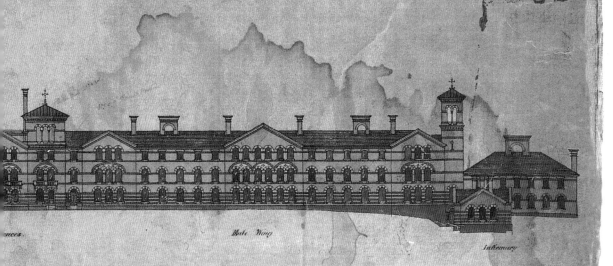

Male Wing

Infirmary

(South.)

Cris Allen

Sweet Bells Jangled Out of Tune

A History of the Sussex Lunatic Asylum (St Francis Hospital) Haywards Heath

JAMES GARDNER

ISBN 0 9536101 0 1

Published by
James Gardner, 420 Falmer Road, Woodingdean, Brighton BN2 6LG

Printed by
Biddles Limited, Guildford and King's Lynn
Typeset by
David Brown, 2 West Street Farm Cottages, Maynards Green, Heathfield, Sussex
Dustjacket design by
David Brown

In loving memory of my mother

Edna May "Kate" Gardner

CONTENTS

INTRODUCTION

James Gardner's detailed study of St Francis Hospital/Sussex county lunatic asylum at Haywards Heath is an important and rich addition to an impressive 'new wave' in the history of psychiatry in Great Britain. This new wave consists of careful studies of lunatic asylums, their patients, their staff, their triumphs and their disasters. But special attention has been given to the place of the asylum within the wider context of Poor Law provision for the insane. The research on this dimension of catering for insanity has revealed a highly differentiated local history, not just differences between England and (say) Wales but within England itself. The complex history of the relations between Poor Law workhouse provision and the county asylums has altered the historical perception of both these communities and practices – the county asylums for example may have had a far wider range of classes of patients than previously thought precisely because the asylum escaped the stigma of the workhouse. The 'mixed economy of care' was based on contractual and negotiated settlements between these various parties and was not a straightforwardly absolutist story of asylum control. Gardner's work is entirely of this kind, showing an often embattled asylum staff and an equally combative group of Brighton workhouse guardians, with all the accompanying calculations about relative costs between workhouse and asylum running alongside varieties of personal dispute and career ambition between medical men and guardians. This is now displayed in the Sussex context exactly as new historical work has portrayed it elsewhere.

Gardner brings his own personal touch to his account, having been a porter in the hospital in the early 1970s. He shows the slow and controversial origins of the institution, argued over from 1845 – the year when counties were compelled to introduce public asylums – to its eventual opening in July 1859. Sussex is revealed as the last county in England to build a county asylum and when the place eventually starts its life, a strange brigade of imported figures steps on the stage. Transfer patients come to Sussex from Bethnal Green, Hoxton, Peckham and Camberwell in London. We also meet the irascible governing figure of the Scotsman Charles Lockhart-Robertson, the asylum's first medical superintendent. Robertson suffered from ill-health throughout his time at the Sussex county asylum, especially troubled by neuralgia: he eventually came to doubt the optimistic hopes for asylum treatment, like so many of his generation, coming to favour cottage asylums and a form of home – or as we might now put it – community care. He has figured in the history of psychiatry before, not least as a translator of Griesinger, a strong defender in his early career of moral management and non-restraint and as a Lord Chancellor's Visitor in Lunacy from 1870. Gardner gives a much more detailed picture than has been available until now and the reader can see both the initial enthusiast for 'moral management' as well as a darker, angrier and exasperated alienist*, often heedless of family requests for release or specially arranged visits and a scary (if sometimes absentee) overlord. The crucial point is that the richness of this new Sussex story – the importation of dangerous cases such as the criminal lunatic George Tyron in 1860 or the exhausted and abused John Mockford who came from the Brighton workhouse in April of that year – make more understandable the unsentimental reading of Lockhart-Robertson that these pages help provide.

Gardner gives an especially detailed account of the 1860s although he continues his narrative right up until the hospital's closure in 1995. Staff sackings, staff resignations, attacks on staff, staff drunkenness – all figure. In 1867, Lockhart-Robertson had to declare the asylum 'a hospital for the treatment of disease, not a matrimonial office' because of staff behaviour. The asylum as working-class marriage market. He also stepped up his particular therapeutic enthusiasm for cold water treatment and digitalis. And of course the numbers of patients increased – 240 in 1859, 459 in 1861. Visiting was never easy as the asylum was relatively isolated but Lockhart-Robertson was not sympathetic to those who requested alternate visiting times.

In 1862 he proposed the building of a specifically middle class asylum nearby to ease with overcrowding. The plan was not realised but this is the kind of detail, about the partial acceptability of the asylum (as against the workhouse) for the bourgeoisie that makes this history so welcome and which contributes to altering the older account of the asylum as a proletarian dumping ground. Of special interest too is the conflict between the asylum and Lockhart-Robertson in particular and the Brighton workhouse governor Samuel Thorncroft. This has been a key focus of the historical work mentioned earlier, on workhouse/asylum relations and was very much a part of the Sussex asylum story. Gardner provides a peculiar and detailed twist to his vexed and combative narrative: Thorncroft went insane in 1870, the very year that Lockhart-Robertson departed from Haywards Heath to work for the Lord Chancellor's Office.

With 700 patients in 1870, a new superintendent in S D Williams (he broke down and resigned in 1887) the asylum shared in the overcrowding and

---

* Victorian term for psychiatrist

the exhaustion and the therapeutic pessimism of the latter half of the nineteenth century. West Sussex built its own asylum near Chichester in 1892 and East Sussex followed suit at Hellingly near Eastbourne in 1903. St Francis/Sussex asylum came under direct control from Brighton and after the First World War saw increases in pre- and post-admission cases, open door policies, parole for patients and after the 1930 Mental Health Treatment Act the growth of treatment without certification and out-patient clinics. The age of ECT, insulin coma treatment and then psychopharmacology and the psychiatric social worker had arrived. By 1994 there were only 100 patients left in the original building and the idea of a single 'Sussex county asylum' had changed forever. Within the year the asylum closed.

James Gardner's achievement is to bring to historical life the distresses and the struggles of county asylum history, the actual story behind the honourable and morally driven therapeutic ideal. We learn about salaries, about impossible tasks, about violence and indiscipline and about small triumphs and still endless administrative conflict. About a building in Sussex that housed large numbers of lunatics nothing to do with the county itself And about family anxiety and awkwardness, about cheap architecture and bad pay. Victorian idealism is none the poorer or less impressive for the careful attention historians have paid to the asylum realities behind that idealism. Asylum history when honestly told is about people anxious to leave, including staff and medical men and about those remaining, especially patients usually doing so because having no choice. Good histories of psychiatric institutions see both sides of the drama, its gains and losses, its painful relationship to class and to money as well as to care and to cure. This rich and heartfelt book adds to that truthfulness.

Michael Neve

Wellcome Institute for History of Medicine, London

PREFACE

One early summer's morning in 1973 I found myself driving from my home in Brighton to St Francis Hospital, Haywards Heath in order to start work as a porter for the summer holiday. As I started out on the twenty-five minute journey I felt a good deal of apprehension about what I might find at this old Victorian asylum. Like many students of that era – a period when anti-psychiatry and anti-asylums beliefs were at their height – my image of a mental hospital was almost a wholly negative one, having read about the alleged cruelty of asylum treatment as well as the dangers of institutionalisation, so well illustrated in Erving Goffman's book *Asylums*.

After I passed over the South Downs and through Ditchling village I was surprised to see what appeared, above the low morning mist, to be the outline of what I imagined a French chateau might look like. As I drove nearer, I realised that the stylish building was in fact, St Francis Hospital.

Once inside the main building, my worst preconceptions seemed to be justified. Walking down the long corridors which never seemed to end I passed several patients who were anxiously scanning the floor for cigarette ends. And I noticed signs of an environment in physical deterioration: old windows that would not open, toilets without doors and wards with beds uncomfortably close to each other. As for the patients, many seemed deeply sedated. So, at the end of my first day, I left the hospital with an overwhelming feeling of gloom.

But as the weeks passed I began to notice other aspects of asylum life. There was often a warmth and affection between staff and patients which I found surprising in such an environment. Perhaps it was a result of both groups frequently living in such close proximity. Later, I found through my research, that this special relationship went right back to the day the hospital opened.

By the time my vacation job was over at St Francis, I realised that any accurate picture of asylum life would have to include the lesser known positive aspects of the institution. An institution that many who worked there considered to be not just a community, but a large family. Although I was only at St Francis a few weeks, the experience made enough impact on me to persuade my college tutor to let me write a long essay about the hospital as part of one of my courses.

Time passed and although I lost the essay I never lost the vivid impressions which the hospital had left me with. Many years later, in 1994, I found myself on a local history course, a course which required a dissertation. And much to my surprise I discovered that very little had been written about the history of the Sussex Lunatic Asylum/St. Francis Hospital. Once I started my research I soon found that, in fact, there was an enormous amount of information about its history, especially in the mid-Victorian period when there appears to have been a penchant for gathering statistics and written records.

Its first medical superintendent Charles Lockhart Robertson, an early President of the Medico-Psychological Association, quickly came across as an important figure. From the start of his appointment at the asylum, he became involved in almost every aspect of its life; from its decoration to its regulation. He was also at the forefront of reforms and experimented with many of the most progressive ideas of the day. But it was his strong advocation of 'moral treatment', an ideology of care for patients based on kindness, which was most impressive. He wrote a journal, which is kept at the East Sussex County Records Office, and it provides fascinating reading for anyone interested in the everyday occurrences in an asylum in Mid-Victorian Britain.

Apart from Robertson, the asylum seems to have been blessed with some outstanding characters in its early years. Its first chaplain, the Rev. Henry Hawkins, arguably became the most famous asylum chaplain of his time. After leaving he later played an important part in setting up the first after-care association in the country in 1879. He also left us with some valuable written reminiscences about the asylum's early years. And then there is Robertson's assistant, Valentine Browne, who had served in the Crimean War and had then totally dedicated his life to the well-being of the mentally ill. His sudden and premature death at the asylum was deeply mourned by all the patients.

Lastly, I am aware that this book is only a partial history of the Sussex Asylum. In particular, it hardly does justice to the developments which took place there during the twentieth century. And some aspects, such as the building itself or the nurses' training school (which became one of the best in the country) probably deserve books by themselves. What I have tried to do is to give an impression of what life may have been like for people who lived and worked there. On Robertson's death in 1897, one of his obituarists predicted that his reputation would surely increase with the passage of time. This has not happened. Today, Robertson and the asylum's patients and staff are largely forgotten figures. This book is an attempt to remember them.

ACKNOWLEDGEMENTS

A special mention must be made of two people, one of whom I have known for the last six years and one whom I have never met. The latter was a remarkable woman called Sally McEwan. For many years she worked at St Francis Hospital as secretary to its medical superintendents in the 1950s, 1960s and 1970s. Before that she had worked in the same capacity for arguably two of the greatest figures of the political left in this country this century: George Orwell and Aneurin Bevan. Whilst at St Francis, she, more than anyone else, helped collect and save artifacts and official records about the hospital's history. Without these, this book most certainly could not have been written. To her, I and other students of asylum history owe an immense debt.

I also owe a great debt to Bill McNaughton who was an early inspiration for this book. Bill was a patient at St Francis for thirty years. Prior to that he served in the RAF during the Second World War. In 1992, he was, rather reluctantly, placed in a community home in Brighton. It is there that I first met him and started to listen to his observations about 'asylum life'. Bill, a gifted, studious and eloquent man, became the real starting point for this book.

I would like to thank all the people who spoke to me about the hospital and its history. They include Harold Barnett, Hazel Bartlett, Arlette Beck, Malcolm Cleroux, Eileen Cruttenden, Jayne Herriot, Joan Denley, Tony Joss, Ann Kiernan, Graeme Lee, James Mable, Kath Martin, Clive Parnes, Peter Towner, Reg Welby (who has sadly died since) and Dr Richard Wheeler. In particular, I must thank Mike Charman for not only lending me valuable material about the history of the asylum building but also for giving me a very instructive tour of the hospital grounds. I am also indebted to Sandra Williams who kindly lent me her unpublished MA thesis on the Sussex Lunatic Asylum, which clarified certain aspects of its history, and also to Helen Jones, Deborah Maddern, Judy Middleton, the Mid-Sussex NHS Trust and the Hospital Museum Trustees for providing me with much useful material.

Next, I would like to thank the following people who patiently read parts of the manuscript and gave me their constructive comments: Vic Baines, Ann Blyton, Victoria Caldarola, Lew Cope, Anne and David Crowe, Kerry Doyle, Roger and Vicky Gardner, Dianne Jones, John Lewell, Erica Mcdonald-Gibson, Mireille Mello, Andy Porter, Juliette Smith and Martin Walsh.

I would also like to thank Daphne Geering, Iris Mcleod, Eillen Muggeridge, Lillian Rogers, Harold Barnett, and my father Frank Gardner, for allowing me to use their photographs; the County Archivist for permission to use their documents; and to my uncle, James L. Gardner for his financial support. And I would like to thank David Brown, Peter Gillies and Carole King for their help, advice and skill in producing this book.

I am greatly indebted to the support and encouragement given to me by Dr Michael Neve of the Wellcome Institute who made me aware of the 'wider picture' of asylum history and who kindly offered to write the Introduction.

I owe an immense debt to the staffs of the Wellcome Institute in London, the West Sussex Records Office, the Brighton Reference Library, and finally, most of all, to the staff of the East Sussex Records Office in Lewes who patiently provided me with the bulk of my research material over a period of four years. And lastly, I would like to thank my family for their support and encouragement, particularly my brother Steve Gardner and his wife Jo, without whose help this book could definitely not have been written. To them I owe the greatest debt.

Chapter One

THE RISE OF THE ASYLUM MOVEMENT

On November 23rd, 1667, a Mr Arthur Coga made his way to Arundel House in London. There he was met by two of the most famous anatomists of their day, Dr Richard Lower and Dr Edmund King. Coga, for the payment of £1, was to allow these two men to perform the first transfusion of blood into a human body attempted in this country. It was a dangerous experiment and a Frenchman in Paris had already died that year after a similar transfusion, for the transfused blood came from a sheep. Coga received approximately twelve fluid ounces of sheep's blood in one minute. Nine days later Coga visited Arundel House again to see the eminent physicians. He told them he felt better but was a bit "cracked" in the head. The experiment was repeated several times before eventually Coga tired of it. Unlike the Frenchman, Coga lived, but they did have one thing in common – both were considered to be mad.

Coga, an educated man, was in fact a patient at Bethlem Hospital (also known as 'Bethlehem' and 'Bedlam') which since the fourteenth century had been the only institution for the insane in the country. Choosing an insane man, like Coga, for this experiment was indicative of how madness was perceived in the 17th century. Despite sometimes genuine attempts to understand insanity, the chronic insane were generally regarded at this time as a lost cause and there-fore proper objects for medical experiments, especially if they could be described as therapeutic. Experiments that would not have been morally acceptable on a sane person were permissible on an insane one. So when in 1667 a technique for transfusing blood from one animal to another had been developed, it was natural to choose a lunatic in the first attempt to transfuse animal blood into a man.

Coga was living in difficult times for the treatment of the insane but they were not much better for sane people who fell physically ill. Some two years before Coga had his transfusion, Charles II of England became ill on 1st November 1665. Despite being attended by fourteen doctors, none of them diagnosed what was wrong with him. But this did not stop the treatment. Charles was purged, his head was shaved, his scalp burnt with a piece of hot metal, he was given pepper to make him sneeze, he was told to eat the powdered skull of a man who had died a violent death, his shoulders were cut and purged, and finally, he was forced to eat a stone from the stomach of a wild goat. Not surprisingly, Charles died four days later. His original illness had probably been related to the heart but until the eighteenth century most doctors had no clear idea about the function of different organs, and the treatment they gave was largely ineffectual. Their only diagnostic guide was the pulse. The treatment of the insane, which was often brutal, should be seen within this context of ignorance and guesswork.

The understanding and treatment of the mentally ill in medieval England was either humane or fearfully barbaric. The harshness of their treatment – bleeding, cupping, whipping etc. – was tempered by the belief that the insane were less sensitive to pain and discomfort than sane people. The slightly afflicted and permanently subnormal were often give the freedom to wander around their own village or town. But it would be easy to romanticize a picture of 'community care' in this period. Such literary evidence that survives suggests that life was often a torment and that many of them joined the hordes of beggars and vagabonds who swarmed about the countryside. A few of the worst cases were often looked after in the rare religious hospitals of the day. Others fared less well as the periodic crazes of persecution, the witch-hunts, swept Europe. 'Idiots' and 'lunatics' (between which there was no distinction until the nineteenth century) were often caught up in this mania.

In the Middle Ages, it was commonly believed that the 'mad' were possessed by the devil and involved in witchcraft. It was also held that the insane were affected by astrological events, particularly the full moon, and that indeed the insane were literally *luna*tics. It was a notion that hundreds of years later was examined by the second chaplain of the Sussex Asylum, Thomas Crallan. In a detailed study in 1871 he concluded that the moon had little effect on mental illness. The belief that it did lasted until modern times and even today it is possible to find ex-mental hospital staff who believe it.

From the Middle Ages to the sixteenth century pauper lunatics, whose care was financed wholly or in part from public funds, were generally classed with vagrants, beggars and disorderly persons and were dealt with in the same way – beaten and whipped. Apart from Bethlem (which then only housed about thirty lunatics), their only refuge was the monastery; their only comfort, the clergy. This was logical as, until the birth of psychology and psychiatry, the Church claimed the exclusive right to decide whether someone was sane or insane. Charles Lockhart Robertson, the first Medical Superintendent of the Sussex Lunatic Asylum, would later observe that many of the early public asylum buildings (with their long corridors) were modelled on the monastery design.

In the sixteenth century there was apparently as much difference of opinion as there is today about whether mental illness should be treated by physical or psychotherapeutic means. Alongside the dramatic aspects of treatment such as whipping and witch-hunting there was also often a humane interest in patients. In 1584, a Kent Squire and MP, Reginald Scott, wrote *The Discovery of Witchcraft* in which he claimed that often both the accused and the accusers were ill and he recommended that witches should be studied medically and psychologically rather than be persecuted. He also made the important discovery that self-accusations and confessions, even when made voluntarily, may be delusional.

In 1602, for the first time, a physician, Dr Edward Jorden, was allowed to give psychiatric evidence for the defence at a criminal trial. The accused was an old charwoman called Liz Jackson, who was alleged to have bewitched a fourteen year old girl, Mary Glover, causing her to become temporarily speechless, blind and to have fits. Expert witnesses were called on both sides and disagreed fundamentally on psychiatric issues. Although the defence was ultimately unsuccessful, the trial had focused attention on the great ignorance and uncertainty about mental illness.

Witches and other people considered insane were treated in similar ways. Whilst not being drowned, as some witches were; the latter group were often submerged in cold water in an attempt to shock their system and return them to sanity. Again, this was a treatment that in one form or another continued well into the nineteenth century. The principle of 'shocking' insanity out of a person gained ground in the eighteenth century when men like John Wesley, the founder of Methodism, used the sparks of electrical machines to treat patients. Careful only to treat chronic cases, he found the machines to be highly effective in 'curing' nervous disorders and immensely popular as the huge queues to experience it testified. Although he did not understand how it worked, Wesley described the value of electric shock as a "thousand medicines in one". Until the opening of the nineteenth century shock treatment by whipping was still regularly employed in cases of undisputed insanity. Its effectiveness was possibly due to the sub-conscious mind of the victim developing a fear of having the treatment repeated.

The last witch was hanged in 1684 and the crime of witchcraft was repealed by the 1736 Witchcraft Act which also gave the insane official status. Twenty years earlier, the Vagrancy Act of 1714, had specifically excluded lunatics from being whipped (as other vagrants were) before being returned to their own parishes. It also required two magistrates' signatures to certify that a person was insane rather than a vagrant. Despite the Acts, the fear and superstition engendered by the idea of witchcraft continued to be attached to mental illness.

Until St Lukes Hospital, London, opened in 1751, Bethlem Hospital was the only public institution for the insane. In the history of asylums, Bethlem has become synonymous with brutality but it had been attempting to cure its patients rather than merely imprison them since the fifteenth century. Some patients were cured, a fact that surprised some of its observers. In 1632, Donald Lupton wrote in *London and the Country Carbonadoed* that:

> It seems strange that any should recover here, the cryings, screechings, roarings, bawlings, shaking of chaines, swarings, frettings, chaffing, are so many, so hideous, so great, that they are more able to drive a man that hath his witts, rather out of them, than to help one that never had them, or hath lost them, to find them againe.[1]

Bethlem was a public charity exclusively run for pauper lunatics. It raised money through benefactors, endowments and, more controversially, by allowing visitors in for a look at the inmates. Apparently, there was no fixed charge (although there may have been a minimum charge of one penny) and many people gave whatever they liked. It is unclear whether this method of raising money resulted from a policy or grew up by custom. We do know that the hospital often had to hire extra police on festive occasions to control the influx of casual sightseers and to restrain the teased patients. Obviously the patients were shamefully abused by this degrading spectacle but the visitors did bring in about £400 a year to the hospital in the seventeenth and eighteenth centuries – an important sum to the charity.

Bethlem's appalling historical reputation partly rests on this practice of visitor entertainment and also on the neglect and treatment of its patients. But the reality was not quite so clear-cut. As early as 1677, the Governors of Bethlem had forbidden staff from beating and abusing patients although enforcing this order was probably another matter. Of course, conditions were primitive, even barbaric, and the more violent patients were chained up (as they were all over

Europe). But the Governors still considered the hospital to be a place of cure and would release patients if they were not cured within a year and would not admit patients who were deemed incurable. In the 1720s and 1730s this policy was changed and a department for incurables was established, although it only admitted patients who were considered dangerous to themselves or to others. At Bethlem, patients were given basic medicines and were often provided with clothes and money on their release to help them survive in the outside world.

Conditions in Bethlem were undoubtedly harsh but the picture which emerges "is not a wholly unrelieved one of deliberate brutality and inhumanity".[2] It is one where brutality and kindness could quite easily coexist. Arguably, detailed histories of many other mental health institutions might reveal a similar picture.

Until the late eighteenth century the insane were generally perceived as being little better than animals and were often treated with force and coercion, and by being frightened. Old beliefs and public ignorance were the dominant mental attitudes of the period. Pauper lunatics, in particular, suffered from moral condemnation and public apathy. They were social outcasts. It was difficult for them to enter the few charitable asylums available and they were mainly excluded from the growing number of private 'madhouses'. Some were tied up and hidden away in attics and cellars by their families. Others were abandoned in prisons and workhouses or left to beg on the streets. However, wealthier lunatics were nursed at home, placed in private institutions or accompanied abroad for long holidays. Getting away from it all as a treatment seems to have been as effective as any. Generally speaking, provision for the mentally ill for most of the eighteenth century was non-institutional and scarce.

By the end of the century perceptions about mental illness had begun to change, not least as a result of the severe attacks of insanity which had afflicted George III. His first breakdown was in 1765 but it was hushed up. He suffered his next attack from October 1788 until March 1789. During this illness the doctors who attended him were repeatedly summoned before parliamentary committees and were questioned about their treatment of the king and their practical experience of insanity. Afterwards these reports were frequently reprinted in cheap editions for the general public. They revealed the wide differences of opinion amongst the 'experts' and the often barbarous nature of the treatment. At the hands of Dr Willis, the king was chained up, whipped and starved. That he temporarily recovered afterwards was a miracle. The king had further relapses in 1801 and 1804 before the final breakdown in 1810 – when the Regency was established – which lasted until his death.

George III's illness made madness more respectable: something which might happen to anyone, even a king. The topic of insanity could now be discussed in a context which excluded the attitude of moral condemnation which had previously been an obstacle for any reform. George III's suffering at the hands of his doctors highlighted the need for a greater understanding of the disorder and a more rational approach to its treatment. The insane began to be perceived as defective human beings, tragic versions of ordinary people, but people for whom there was hope of salvation. Although George III's illness had attracted a lot of attention for political reasons it nevertheless acted as a catalyst in changing public attitudes about insanity.

At the beginning of the nineteenth century serious attempts were made to discover exactly how many lunatics there were. The Parliamentary Report of 1807 found that the county returns of 1806 about how many pauper and criminal lunatics they had were extremely deficient. The total number of lunatics in England was given as 1,755 but there had been serious omissions. Hampshire completely ignored the request for returns and other counties claimed that there were no pauper lunatics within their boundaries. A parliamentary select committee investigation revealed a widespread concealment (both on paper and in practice) of lunatics and described workhouse facilities for lunatics as "revolting to humanity". It also reported that bloodletting and purging were still being widely used in charitable asylums (which were financed by public subscriptions) and in private madhouses. Counties tended to conceal the true number of their pauper lunatics for fear that the government would demand they provide adequate provision for them, a potentially costly business.

The County Asylums Act of 1808 recommended that an asylum should be set up in each county, to which both pauper and criminal lunatics might be sent. Twenty years later only nine counties had fulfilled this recommendation but the Act was an important first step towards reform. In the wake of the Act, public concern about the plight of pauper lunatics was heightened by a series of scandals. In 1814, Geoffrey Higgins, a Yorkshire magistrate, brought to light extreme fraud and cruelty at the York Asylum. A similar scandal at Bethlem echoed the abuses at York and forced the government to set up an enquiry in 1815 into the care of lunatics in workhouses, charity hospitals, county asylums and private madhouses.

The scandal at Bethlem involved financial mismanagement and the mistreatment of patients, in particular, of James Norris, an American marine. He was admitted to Bethlem on 1st February, 1800. As he failed to recover within a year he was transferred to the incurable department. The hospital's predicament is described by Patricia Allderidge in *Bedlam: Fact or Fantasy* :

> Norris seems to have been the most violent and dangerous patient that Bethlem had ever encountered. He made a number of murderous attacks on keepers and fellow patients. He was exceptionally strong and very cunning. He could not be restrained by manacles because of the peculiar conformation of his wrists and hands, the bones of the wrists being larger than those of the hands: he simply slipped them off and used them as weapons. For four years he terrorized all who came into contact with him until finally, in June, 1804, it was decided that he should be permanently confined in an iron harness, with an iron collar and chain which prevented him from ever moving further from his bed than to stand beside it.[3]

Edward Wakefield, a Quaker businessman, found Norris in this horrific contraption when he visited Bethlem in 1813 and brought it to the attention of the outside world. By then, Norris was considerably enfeebled and clearly no longer a threat to anyone.

The Norris case formed the basis of a central charge of mismanagement brought against Bethlem at the 1815 enquiry although a charge of 'deliberate cruelty' was not made against the institution. A lesser known fact about Norris was that during his nine years of confinement he was provided with books and newspapers to read, and he amused himself with his pet cat. This story illustrates the mixed picture of asylum treatment which emerges from the early part of the century and would continue at the Sussex Lunatic Asylum later.

The Parliamentary enquiry lasted two years and produced 600 pages of evidence which exposed the appalling degradation, inhuman treatment and neglect of pauper lunatics in public and private institutions. It particularly condemned the keeping of lunatics for profit and the use of mechanical restraint – chains, shackles and strait-jackets. The enquiry concluded that there was no group more urgently in need of the protection of legislation than the mentally ill. The outcome of the enquiry was the 1815 Asylums Act which allowed counties to borrow money for up to 14 years to encourage the construction of their own asylums. It also recommended that the physical restraint of patients should only be used in exceptional circumstances and that private madhouses should be better regulated. The enquiry and the 1815 Act were a resounding rejection of all the old methods and ideas and gave a green light to the reformers and their supporters.

At the forefront of the reformers was the Tuke family which had been running a small Quaker asylum in York called 'The York Retreat' since the end of the eighteenth century. In 1813, Samuel Tuke published his *Description of the*

Retreat, the first full-length description of any asylum in the country. He claimed that the insane retained their essential humanity, and that by placing them in civilized surroundings they could more readily recover their sanity. He demonstrated that a 'moral treatment' based on kindness, reason and tactful manipulation could be more effective than brutality and coercion.

The treatment was based on moral rather than medical grounds emphasizing the importance of re-education, diet and healthy daily routines. Shared activities with other inmates and staff were encouraged. Patients were classified according to their clinical state and given separate management. Moral treatment also placed demands on the asylum building itself. It had to be spacious with plenty of light. Bars, locks and high walls were to be discouraged in order to make the building seem more like a home rather than an institution. The only concessions to security were the iron window frames. Work was seen as important for its therapeutic value rather than an end product. Pet therapy, close personal contact with staff and local people and other progressive ideas were encouraged. Reformers from France, Russia and the U.S. visited the York Retreat and came away highly impressed by the regime and its results.

The Tuke family implemented ideas and practices which were already in existence. What was innovative was that they brought them all together and added a spiritual dimension. The York Retreat was run by lay people until it was obliged to appoint a medical superintendent in 1846 as a result of the 1845 Act. This meant that in its early days it relied heavily on moral rather than medical therapy. But later on, as medical science appeared to produce more effective cures, the use of medicine increased. Even in its most progressive and successful days the Retreat still used mechanical restraint for its dangerous and suicidal patients and sometimes strait-jackets, straps and seclusion were used.

The results were good but the York Retreat was only a small- to medium-sized asylum and it rarely had more than 72 patients in the early part of the century. It remained to be seen whether treatment based on moral therapy could work in much larger institutions. In addition, the Retreat had a high staff ratio of 1:8 whereas in public asylums such as Hanwell it was 1:17. When the Sussex Lunatic Asylum opened in 1859 the staff ratio was 1:15 which was considered to be better than average. The key to the success of moral treatment lay in the quality of personal relationships between staff and patients. A low staff ratio tended to make this more difficult to achieve.

In the beginning, the Retreat only accepted patients who were Quakers and critics have claimed that the particular discipline required by their way of life meant that only Quakers were ideally suited for this type of regime. Some critics have also suggested that moral treatment eventually became a more subtle form of restraint when applied to the larger pauper asylums. There, the conditioning potential of moral treatment as a socially acceptable way of enforcing conformity was stressed, rather than an emphasis on individualism and greater humanity. It was this institutional conditioning in large public asylums which would make the successful release of patients back into the community so difficult in the future. Despite the strength of some of these criticisms, the York Retreat was enormously influential and became an important model for reformers and for future medical superintendents like Charles Lockhart Robertson.

Mental health reformers in the early part of the century were not a homogeneous group and some believed, as did a section of public opinion, that asylums were by no means the only or the best solution for lunatics. A minority view was that isolated care in a domestic setting was preferable to living in secluded asylums away from family and friends. In Scotland, most patients were placed with ordinary families in cottages. But there were difficulties. Often only impoverished families accepted patients and the logistical problem presented by visiting individual patients meant that they were poorly supervised and mistreatment was thought to be rife.

John Conolly, one of the leading asylum reformers, initially had great reservations about placing lunatics in asylums. He argued (as asylum critics would do in the 1950s and 1960s) that confinement in an institution induced a self-fulfilling prophesy, intensifying and even creating the very behaviour that was its alleged justification:

> Once confined, the very confinement is admitted as the strongest of all proofs that a man must be mad. How can a treatment that would be injurious to a sane mind should tend to restore a diseased one.[4]

Conolly put these reservations behind him when in 1836 he became the medical superintendent of the largest asylum in the country, Hanwell in Middlesex. There, he successfully implemented a policy of non-restraint and eventually became one of the staunchest supporters of the new asylums. Out went the chain and shackles; in came moral management. The new approach encouraged the diagnosis and classification of mental illness and for the first time a 'cure' for many types of lunacy seemed to be attainable.

This new approach coincided with a need for more 'welfare' institutions to keep pace with demographic and industrial changes. The population almost doubled during the reign of George III (1760-1820) from seven million to twelve million. At the same time unplanned urban growth and mass unemployment intensified social distress. The number of 'socially undesirable' people such as beggars and pauper lunatics increased dramatically – the latter group from 2,248 in 1807, to 8,000 in 1828. In the new wage labour economy of the industrial age, poor families found it more difficult to support and sustain a non-productive relative.

In 1828, public asylum accommodation for pauper lunatics was still scarce and many of them were placed in workhouses and prisons. The Lunacy Acts of that year did consolidate the previous reforms by increasing the monitoring and regulation of all asylums. The Acts also forced the private asylum owners to comply with the regulations or go out of business. But they did not compel the counties to provide specialist care for their pauper lunatics nor did they have much effect on the unknown number of unlicensed houses which had sprung up.

The New Poor Law Act of 1834 had a much greater effect on the insane poor than the 1828 lunacy Acts. It aimed to amend local relief practices and imposed a uniform *national* workhouse system controlled by a central board – the Poor Law Commissioners. The aim of the law was to deter able-bodied pauperism by curtailing outdoor relief, thus depriving the poor of their traditional right to obtain relief when living in their own homes, a form of social security that had continued for two hundred years. After 1834, by law, relief could only be obtained by entering a workhouse. There, families were often segregated by sex and age, and also classified as being either able-bodied or non-able-bodied. To keep the 'maintenance rate' low inmates were expected to work for their keep. Despite widespread protests against the Act, especially in the south-east, poor relief was cut by 20% although the number of paupers actually rose.

The 1834 Poor Law Act was not always implemented and was successfully resisted by some local authorities including Brighton, which continued to pay outdoor relief for the rest of the century. Nor was it ever really abandoned nationally. But the Act did encourage workhouses to become dumping grounds for the decrepit and dependent of all descriptions, especially the elderly and the infirm. Many workhouse buildings were plainly inadequate for such a large influx and living conditions often deteriorated. At one point it was even reported at Andover Workhouse that inmates were reduced to gnawing horse bones for nourishment.

The insane were not recognized as a separate group under the new workhouse classification and although often segregated, were not provided with any specialist accommodation. By law it was forbidden to keep a dangerous lunatic or idiot in a workhouse for more than fourteen days. After this time, local authorities were required to place them in either public or private asylums. In reality, many were kept in workhouses for much longer, the motive being to save money. Inmate labour meant that in 1843 the average weekly maintenance rate for a workhouse resident was 2s. 7$\frac{1}{2}$d; for a county asylum resident, 8s. 11$\frac{1}{2}$d.

Whilst the number of lunatics in workhouses remained small they created no real problems for the workhouse authorities. But as the numbers grew – 20,893 people were classified as lunatics in 1844 – they became a threat to the workhouse ethic which required most of its residents to work. It was much more difficult to make lunatics work and large numbers of them tended to disrupt and undermine the system. Local authorities soon became faced with three choices – sending their lunatics to expensive private asylums (admissions to which were often restricted); sending them to public asylums which were few in number and sometimes in another part of the country; or building their own public county asylum. Most eventually took the third option but often reluctantly and only after, in some cases, coming under extreme pressure from central government.

The 1845 Lunatics Asylums Acts were the outcome of fifty years of agitation for lunacy reform. They compelled every county and borough in England and Wales to provide adequate accommodation for all pauper lunatics within three years. They set up a Lunacy Commission to regulate all private and public asylums. Their commissioners were allowed to visit any institution that contained the insane, including prisons and workhouses and were authorized to monitor practice and establish standards relating to medical certification, management and patient care. All asylums had to record on a weekly basis their use of restraint and seclusion. The reformers had finally triumphed but the execution of the legislation would be painfully slow, especially in Sussex.

The public asylum system arose, to a large extent, to meet the chronic shortage of accommodation for pauper lunatics during the nineteenth century. Some reformers had high hopes that they would reverse the trend of the ever increasing numbers of mentally ill people in Victorian society. Some local authorities undoubtedly saw county asylums as convenient places in which to place socially undesirable people in their care. There were also some reformers and local authorities who simply believed that there was no real alternative to large county asylums. Whatever the motivation, public asylums were here to stay and would dominate this island's landscape for the next one hundred and fifty years.

Chapter Two

LUNACY IN SUSSEX AND
THE STRUGGLE FOR A COUNTY ASYLUM

A study of the *Sussex Advertiser,* the only surviving Sussex-based newspaper of the eighteenth century, reveals little about lunacy but much about the barbaric times. In the second half of the century a man could still be publicly hanged for stealing a sheep and publicly whipped for vagrancy, a woman privately burnt and privately whipped for the same offences. In the 1770s a man was publicly whipped and imprisoned until his wounds healed and then the punishment repeated after which he was whisked off to Shoreham Harbour by a local press gang. His crime: stealing an old bonnet from a woman. In another case a woman was transported for seven years for stealing a silver spoon. It was a time when stealing was a necessity of life for many to survive and public punishment was a form of entertainment. In 1793, a crowd of 14,000 people (including 2,000 women, many well-dressed), saw three highwaymen hanged in Sussex at the scene of their crime. And communal justice, at a lower level, often ended with the guilty person having his windows broken and his effigy burnt. But it was also an age when charity was common. Frequent donations and collections were made for local paupers, debtors and even foreign sailors shipwrecked on the county's shores. But the overwhelming impression is that for perhaps the majority of people, life was a daily and never-ending struggle.

Suicides were very common, usually by hanging or by cutting one's throat. In fact, according to reports, the local surgeons seem to have been quite adept at sewing up throats just in time. Most suicides were deemed to be 'acts of lunacy' by the magistrates and only rarely do we find the description 'suicide caused by pecuniary circumstances' given as a motive. Before George III's well-publicized mental illness of 1788, the *Sussex Advertiser*, contains little about the subject of lunacy. And when mentioned, it made no distinction between 'idiocy' (learning disability) and mental illness. Lunatics were often treated like criminals. In 1767, Simon Southward owed £15 to the Duke of Richmond and was thrown into prison for non-payment. There, he protested that he was a member of the royal family and that he would only accept things that came from his cousin the king. The prison staff and inmates humoured him by calling him 'my lord'. Southward was clearly mad but the debt was never paid and he was locked up until his death, forty-three years later. Many lunatics in the eighteenth century were probably unfairly confined in prisons due to the lack of any alternative accommodation.

On 2nd June, 1777, an advertisement offering treatment for insanity appeared in the *Sussex Advertiser* for the first time.

INSANITY, &c.

HAVING never wish'd to derive any other Advantage from the Afflictions of Others than that which might conveniently accrue from their Circumstances and Situations in Life,

PERFECT,

SURGEON, at TOWN MALLING, in KENT, About 27 Miles from LONDON, and 15′ from TUNBRIDGE-WELLS, remarkable for its pleasant Situation and Salubrity of Air, with the Conveniency of a Coach and Diligence to and from London every Day in the Week:

Continues to accommodate in his House, all Degrees of Insane Persons; and cure the Hysterical, Hypochondriacal, and such as labour under any Species of FITS.—He takes this Method to repeat to the Public what he has already sedulously adhered to as the most invariable Rule of his Conduct, that he seeks no longer to experience their Patronage than he shall continue to deserve it. At the same Time that he finds himself incited by every Sense of Gratitude and tender Feeling of Humanity to unremittingly persevere in the same Line of Care and Attention to his Patients, which from his first Commencement of this Undertaking in the Year 1769, to the present Time, has been so amply and happily crowned with Success.

☞ References to unexceptionable Characters in the County of SUSSEX can be made.

Dr William Perfect from Kent, was the only doctor to advertise for Sussex patients in the newspaper for the next fifteen years. He treated them at his madhouse in West Malling and he managed to expand his business with the help of his publications which included *Insane, Epileptic, Hypochondriac, Hysteric, and Nervous Cases.* His treatment relied on using a minimum of restraint, a good diet and little medicine. On 13th March 1789, the *Sussex Advertiser* reported that two men and a boy who had been bitten by a wild dog were "placed under the care of Dr Perfect, who is distinguished for his skill in the cure of canine and other madness". Sussex seems to have been overrun with rabid dogs in this period and the newspaper sometimes blamed it on the negligence of the aristocracy. As well as Perfect, Sussex doctors such as Samuel Newington accepted patients at their own home. They believed that a cure was more likely if the patient could be separated from his environment and they encouraged families to seek help for their insane relatives rather than concealing them.

News of the king's recovery from his second attack of insanity was reported in the *Sussex Advertiser* on 16th March 1789. It recorded the celebrations throughout the county and referred to his illness as "his late alarming indisposition". At Lewes:

> On the arrival of the Gazette here on Wednesday morning last, confirming the accounts before given of the perfect restoration of His Majesty's health, many of the inhabitants resolved to celebrate the same with illuminations, and other demonstrations of joy, which the cryer immediately proclaimed throughout the town. The first signal was a Royal Salute from the Castle at noon, which animated the whole town with loyalty, and diffused a general joy that appeared visible in the countenance of every inhabitant. At seven o'clock the illumination commenced, and soon became so universal, that the whole place appeared to be in a blaze. Indeed nothing could exceed it in point of splendour and beauty, unaccompanied with the decorations of variegated lamps and emblematical devices, which there was not sufficient time to provide. During the illumination, a band of music paraded the street, playing "God save the King"; at nine o'clock some very capital fireworks were exhibited from the Town-Hall, which was also illuminated, an instance never before known on any former occasion. After the display of fireworks, many of the inhabitants retired to the Star and White Hart Inns, where many loyal and constitutional toasts were drank. Beer was distributed to the populace before the above houses, and money given to be spent at every public house in the borough.

Food and beer were given out freely throughout the county during the celebrations and perhaps for the poorer inhabitants it was an occasion made important by this liberality rather than by patriotism.

Two months later, for the first time, news of a case of suspected lunacy appeared in the *Sussex Advertiser*. On 11th May, Richard Gracemark, from Ferring near Worthing, was committed to Horsham Gaol for allegedly burning his house down along with all his furniture and another poor family's furniture on the day that his daughter was married. Almost three months later, on 3rd August, he was acquitted. Shortly after being released he killed his daughter by cutting her throat. He then sat on her body for six hours before cutting his own throat and fainting. After a while he revived and crawled into a ditch where he was found by a passer-by. He was then arrested and accused of incest, murder and attempted suicide. Reports emerged that he had had several children by his daughter whom he had made pregnant nine times. Reports concluded that he was probably insane.

Gracemark was tried and sentenced to be publicly hanged. Before this occurred, an unsigned letter from Ferring, explaining the tragedy and allocating blame, appeared in the newspaper on 5th October:

> Richard Gracemark has lived in the parish of Ferring upwards of thirty years; was always very industrious, and very healthy. I have known him upwards of two and twenty years, and have not known, or heard that he has lost a day through sickness, or even through *lunacy*, in so long a time. Indeed, no person ever suspected him to be a *lunatic*, the greater therefore was the surprise at hearing he was declared such at his trial, at the Lewes Assize, for setting fire to his dwelling-house. The origin of this unhappy affair was this: This wicked man (for so we may justly call him) had cohabited with his own daughter upwards of thirteen years, by his own confession; in which time he had several children by her, two of which children died infants, whether by natural or unnatural means, is best known to God and their unnatural parents. The officers of the parish had her examined; but, as she always positively affirmed that the fathers of them were men, either dead or lately run away, they did not wish to have her sworn, having great reason to think they belonged to her father, and therefore were not willing to be the cause of her adding the sin of perjury to that of incest. About three years since she did venture to swear one child to a labouring man, in the parish of Ferring, for which he gave bond. Since that time she proved pregnant again, and declared the same labouring man to be the father. On this the officers of the said parish, insisted on their being married, for this reason, among others, that they hoped thereby to break off the unnatural connection between the father and the daughter. The morning, on which these young people were to be married, the father went to his work as usual; and on coming home to breakfast, was informed of it. The consequence was, that he applied to the gin bottle, till he had so inflamed himself that he declared, if she went to be married, he would burn her clothes, and the house over her head. By

some means she got her children from the house, and as soon as she could disengage herself from her father, she ran off too.

Enraged at this, he fastened the door, fetched her clothes downstairs, put them in a back room, in which were near an hundred gorse, and, by his own confession, set fire to them, and because they did not burn fast enough, kicked them about the room, by which means the gorse caught fire, and the house was in a blaze in a few minutes. As soon as the house became too hot for him, he ran out of it, with a knife in his hand, and would certainly have killed the young man, who married his daughter that same day, had not another man ran after them, tripped up R. G.'s heels, and secured him, just at the instant he had put the knife to the young man's throat. And now may I ask, does there appear any symptom of lunacy in this? The culprit had often been heard to say, in his cooler moments, that he would burn his daughter's clothes, and the house too, if ever she married; and when the time came, he was as good as his word. What is there of lunacy in this? The reason he gave for this rash action, on his being asked, after he was taken up for the murder of his daughter, was – that he loved her better than he ever loved either of his wives or his mistress; and that he had lain with her upwards of thirteen years, and that though he could, and did, have access to her in the day time, as before marriage, he could not bear the thoughts of her lying with another person; and as she could not sleep with him, he was resolved she should sleep with no other person.

But let us come to the affair for which he is now in gaol: – A correspondent, in your paper, August 30th, says, that it is a strong symptom of lunacy, or loss of senses, first to kill a person, and then for the murderer to sit hours on the dead body, and afterwards to cut his own throat, I acknowledge it. But, pray, let me ask – how did this murderer lose his senses? – Was it from the hand of God, or from his own hands? I hesitate not to say – from his own hands: and I say it from his own confession. For he acknowledged, when warned that to all appearance he had but a very few days to live, that he had planned this horrid scene from the time he was discharged at the assizes; that he had not met with a favourable opportunity till that day, and that even then he could not do it till he had been to one ale-house, and drank two pints of cider, then, said he, I had worked myself up for this horrid deed, and I did it without remorse. After this, sure it must be needless to add, that this unparalelled villain acknowledged, without the least symptoms of sorrow, that he had the same unnatural connections with his daughter but a few minutes before he perpetuated the last shocking act, as he had had with her almost every day since his release from gaol.

I know that it has been asserted that the mother of this unhappy man was long confined as a lunatic: I own it. But how came she in those unfortunate circumstances? Not from a hereditary lunacy, but from the ill-treatment of a brutal husband. This she often acknowledged in her lucid intervals, and this is further confirmed by many of her relations, who are now living in this neighbourhood. This, I assure you is the truth, and nothing but the truth, relating to this melancholy affair, which has afforded so much matter for conversation: and, believe me, nothing should have obliged me to have troubled you with this tedious account, but a desire to vindicate the conduct of the parishioners of Ferring, who have been blamed for a neglect in not confining such a dangerous person.

The end of an affair, with all the tragic hallmarks of a Thomas Hardy novel, was reported in the *Sussex Advertiser* on 29th March 1790:

> On last Saturday Richard Gracemark, was executed at Horsham, pursuant to his sentence. He was brought out of the gaol about twelve o'clock, and from thence conveyed in a cart to the gallows, which he approached without betraying the least mark of sorrow or contrition for the horrid crime which his brutal and incestuous passion had prompted him to commit; nor did the further prosecution of the dismal ceremony, tend at all to awaken him to a sense of that awful change he was about to undergo, for in his last moments, and with an air of indifference, he cried aloud to the surrounding multitude, "Ladies and gentleman, I wish you all well, I meant no harm," kicked off his slippers among the crowd, and left the world exhibiting a most shocking instance of the depravity of human nature. After hanging the usual time, the body was cut down, and given to two surgeons, Messrs. Price & Popay who attended to receive it for dissection, etc. The unhappy sufferer who had killed his daughter, Jemima Martin, was about fifty years of age.

Gracemark's body was then publicly dissected at Horsham a couple of days later. The occasion attracted people interested in anatomy or those who were just curious. They watched the whole process from the first incision to the boiling of the bones. His skin, which in some parts was a quarter of an inch thick, was given to a local tanner for the purpose of manufacturing it into leather and several local people placed orders to have it used in the soles of their shoes.

The letter from the Ferring parishioner, apart from raising the question of Gracemark's sanity or insanity, also touched upon the delicate matter of community responsibility. On the first question, the correspondent obviously believed that Gracemark was bad rather than mad and that the murder was a preconceived, callous act. Up until that moment, as reported, "no person ever suspected him [Gracemark] to be a lunatic". On the matter of community responsibility and whether the parishioners should have had him confined, the writer exonerated the community on the grounds that, although Gracemark's mother may have been a lunatic, there was no proof that he was. Irrespective of whether the parishioners were at fault or not, the letter shows that there was an awareness of collective communal responsibility towards lunatics in that period and that local people played a part in the confinement or not of an individual. Reports suggest that individuals who were acknowledged as lunatics, were often left alone and even provided with single accommodation. Confinement, which in many instances meant being chained up, seems to have been very much a last resort.

Towards the end of the eighteenth century there was a boom in private madhouses which began to change their name to 'asylum', a place of refuge. This expansion was probably due to the king's apparently successful treatment raising public confidence in the ability of the specialist doctors to treat mental illness. Also, it was part of a wider expansion in advertising, service industries and the growth of health 'cures' such as spas. The growth of private licensed asylums led to what Parry-Jones[1] has called a financially rewarding "trade in lunacy" which only declined in the 1850s. In 1792, Perfect's asylum had a new rival for Sussex patients when Samuel Newington opened Ticehurst House in Ticehurst. It was located in the north-east of the county on the Sussex-Kent border; only seventeen miles from Perfect's establishment. In the weeks before the opening of Ticehurst House, first Perfect and then Newington advertised their services several times. (The story of this institution is splendidly told by Charlotte Mackenzie in her book *Psychiatry for the Rich, A History of Ticehurst Private Asylum*.)

At first, Ticehurst House catered primarily for lower middle class patients with fees starting at 21s. per week but it was selective:

> Mr Newington begs leave to inform his friends that he does not wish to receive into his house any Patients but such are of a quiet and tractable disposition, as the comfort and convenience of his Patients are what he means particularly to attend to, and, therefore, if any of a more violent turn, that such will be suitably provided for in his neighbourhood until by his management they become more tractable and proper to be received among those of the above description.[2]

In fact, Ticehurst House became famous for its comfort and physical care rather than for its cure rate.

The Newington family was a remarkable one. Samuel Newington had ten sons and five daughters. Four of his sons became surgeons and the family went on to run the asylum for four generations. At the beginning, they did take in pauper lunatics but they were always a minority as few parishes could afford their fees. Between 1792 and 1817, out of a total of 538 patients admitted, only 49 were pauper lunatics. With the fees rising to as much as two guineas per week on average in 1810, the number of paupers declined and the last one was admitted in 1825.

The asylum grew gradually: 16 patients in 1795, 33 in 1815 and 61 in 1840. At first most of its patients came from Sussex and Kent but as it expanded its geographical catchment area became wider. In 1830, Ticehurst House produced its own prospectus[3] which contained statistics to demonstrate that its cure rate compared well with that of the best establishments in the country. But it contained no information about the types of patients or their treatment. Its estate grew to cover 300 acres and included a bowling green, pagoda, cricket facilities and even a nine-hole golf course. As it began to cater for the upper and middle classes, patients were allowed to have their own servants, horses and carriages and were given a lot of personal freedom. Relatives were encouraged to board nearby during their visits and foreign holidays with staff were organised.

The staff ratio at Ticehurst House was often 1:1 and the Visitors and Lunacy Commissioners often praised it for its minimal use of restraint and coercion. But the institution was becoming increasingly expensive and exclusive. In 1845, sixty-four patients were paying on average 63s. per week at a time when the national average was between 15s. and 42s. per week. Despite being a progressive establishment its cure rate remained low although this may have been partly due to its high degree of comfort, providing a deterrent to patients leaving. But not all patients were content to stay there. John Perceval, son of a former prime minister, was briefly a patient at Ticehurst House in the 1830s paying one of the highest rates, six guineas a week. He subsequently complained about the poor food, cold rooms and the inefficient management of the institution. Ticehurst House is still open today as a private establishment although the Newington family's active involvement in its management ended in 1917.

By 1830 there were only two licensed asylums in Sussex and both were in the eastern part of the county. One was Ticehurst House and the other was in Ringmer. In terms of patient treatment they were poles apart. If Ticehurst House was similar to the York Retreat, Ringmer Asylum was more comparable with Bethlem.

Ringmer Asylum had started off as a private house in Rottingdean in 1825 but had moved to the old barracks at Ringmer – about ten miles inland from Brighton – in 1829. It catered mainly for pauper lunatics. Both its owners lived in Brighton. It was supervised by a Mr James William Ivory and his wife Anne. Ringmer Asylum was the sole institutional accommodation for pauper lunatics in Sussex, providing for sixteen paupers in 1830 at a cost of 15s. each per week to their respective parishes. Fifteen were regarded as incurable and mechanical restraint in the form of leg locks, hand locks and strait waistcoats was used on half of them. By the standards of the day Ringmer Asylum seems to have been fairly typical of accommodation for pauper lunatics and it adopted few of the enlightened ideas being pioneered in other institutions.

The 1828 Lunacy Acts required that all asylums must be regularly monitored by a Committee of Visitors (made up of local magistrates) and that they had to write annual reports on each institution. In their report on Ringmer Asylum for 1830, the Visitors criticized the charges for being expensive and found the accommodation and medical attention totally inadequate. They further recommended that a place should be found "where a considerable greater number of pauper patients can be placed under the same roof and where the building has been fitted up expressly for these purposes".[4] Their damning report led to the eventual demise of this asylum. By January 1831, the parishes had withdrawn their pauper lunatics and sent most of them to the cheaper London private asylums. The last pauper to stay there was in 1836, but only for a few weeks before being transferred to Hoxton Asylum, London, which charged only 10s. per week.

Between 1833 and 1845 only 45 patients were admitted into Ringmer Asylum, and some were readmissions. Generally it only had four or five patients at any one time as its reputation declined. In March 1844, the Visitors reported that the patients refused to answer any of their questions. Seven years later they found that the patients were more tranquil and that restraint was much diminished although one had been kept without clothes for years. Their visit was rather spoilt when a patient, Catherine Williamson, hit one of their members several times in the face. The final nail in the coffin of Ringmer Asylum was the visit of the Lunacy Commissioners in December 1851. They found it in an appalling condition with rotten chairs tied to window bars, filthy mattresses and beds, the bath filled with rubbish and evidently rarely used, and a woman patient "padlocked" into a dress. They also discovered a large accumulation of instruments of restraint in a nurse's cupboard despite receiving assurances from staff that mechanical restraint was no longer being used.

In August 1853, the Lunacy Commissioners wrote to the Visitors complaining about the "great mismanagement" of the asylum and recommended that they must "take measures to put it on a better footing and to secure better treatment for the unfortunate patients".[5] Two years later it was refused a licence and closed down. In order to try and attract a better clientele Ringmer Asylum had overcharged its pauper lunatics but at the same time, because of its poor facilities, had attracted few wealthy clients.

One other private licensed asylum in Sussex, Knole House, near Worthing opened briefly in 1846 with only one male and one female patient. The man apparently went for regular walks and the woman went for regular carriage rides. By December of that year it was empty as the man had died and the woman had been discharged cured! A year later there was just one patient living there after which we have no more records of its existence. In 1854, an application for a licence to open a small asylum at Stillwood House, Brighton, was turned down despite elaborate plans being produced.

Before the 1845 Asylums Acts, specialist provision for pauper lunatics within Sussex had been virtually non-existent. In 1831 the county, administratively divided into the Western and Eastern Divisions, were compelled by the government to provide statistics about their numbers. Out of a county population of 272,300, two hundred and ten were classified as pauper lunatics. They were kept in four main places:[6]

> 2% in public asylums at an average cost of 8s. 6d. per week
> 13% in private asylums at an average cost of 11s. 2d. per week.
> 36% with relatives/friends at an average cost of 3s. 6d. per week.
> 49% in workhouses at an average cost of 3s. 6d. per week

The dearth of asylum accommodation within the county meant that all but one of those in asylums were held in London. Because of the distance and expense involved only lunatics classified as 'dangerous' were sent away. For example, in 1832,[7] Brighton had twelve pauper lunatics. Nine were described as dangerous and were held in two private London asylums – Hoxton House and Bethnal Green – whilst two "harmless" cases were held in the workhouse and a boy of thirteen was given 5s. a week and allowed to live with his father on a farm. One of those sent to Hoxton House was Liz Allen, aged 47. She was described thus:

> … health good, a dangerous lunatic, without any prospect of her regaining her sanity, requires almost constantly the use of the "Strait Waistcoat".[8]

In that particular period, the Brighton Workhouse was experiencing some problems of indiscipline and, as has been mentioned before, a violent lunatic was a threat to the order and ethos of the workhouse system.

The 1831 statistics must be treated cautiously as many lunatics were probably undisclosed by their local authorities in order to avoid providing more expensive specialist accommodation. The statistics show that very few of the 'official' lunatics were properly provided for. The 1834 Poor Law Amendment Act, which required workhouse authorities to remove dangerous lunatics to an asylum within fourteen days, accelerated the use of asylums. By 1854 Sussex was sending 45% of its pauper lunatics to asylums, all of which were outside the county and becoming increasingly expensive.

Leonard Smith, in a recent book[9], has written about the 'mixed economy of care' which existed in England from 1808 to 1845 (the year counties were compelled to build their own asylums). With parallels to today's buying and selling of health care services, it is a story of local authorities often shopping around for the cheapest accommodation they could find for their pauper lunatics. In Sussex we see parishes such as Brighton's doing exactly that; preferring to send its patients to private asylums in London rather than to the nearby but more expensive asylum at Ringmer. Both private and public asylums of that period competed to have the lowest rates in order to attract this 'trade'. But this choice of provision was effectively ended in 1845 when authorities were obliged to send their patients to their own county asylums.

The most important reason for Sussex failing to provide specialist accommodation for their pauper lunatics before the opening of the Sussex County Lunatic Asylum in 1859 was probably financial. After the Napoleonic Wars there was real economic and social distress, due to poor harvests. Grain-producing counties such as Kent, Essex and Sussex were hardest hit.[10] With little industrial development in the county, the Sussex labourer's only alternative to farm work was parish relief. By 1831 Sussex had the highest per capita relief expenditure in the country – 14% of its inhabitants were receiving help.[11] The following winter almost half of the labouring families in some parts of the county were regularly receiving parish money. Burdened, like other authorities, by heavy relief expenditure Sussex had little inclination to spend money on pauper lunatics.

The 1834 Poor Law Amendment Act which attempted to lessen the burden on ratepayers by stigmatizing relief and making it more difficult to obtain, did not necessarily help the situation. Much of the money saved by the Act was spent on trying to stem the storm of civil unrest which it caused throughout the country. Popular protest against the new workhouse system was particularly strong in Sussex. The red flag was hoisted above the workhouses at Seaford and Alfriston along with banners declaring "Death or Liberty". At Eastbourne an attempt was made to burn the workhouse down and throughout the county Relieving Officers and Workhouse Guardians were attacked. Expenditure on law and order in Sussex rose dramatically. Ironically, the Poor Law Act was successfully resisted only in places where the Guardians were against it (as in Brighton) rather than by any sensational disturbances by the poor.[12]

The following decade, 'the hungry forties', was also a time of harvest failure, industrial depression and high unemployment. Local finances became increasingly stretched. A rapid increase in building roads, bridges and highways in the first 40 years of the century had also drained county resources. The increase of civil unrest in Sussex meant that a new county prison rather than a new county asylum was a top priority. But there may have been another reason why Sussex thought it was unnecessary to build their own asylum and it's revealed in a letter written to the Home Office from the Lunacy Commission dated 9th May, 1845:

> I am directed by the Commissioners in Lunacy, with reference to the urgent want of provision for the pauper lunatics for the County of Sussex, to draw attention to the fact which has recently come to the knowledge of this Board, that the Board of Guardians of the Horsham Union (a union of town parishes) are in the practice of placing their insane poor under the charge of a person named JAMES MORRIS at Oakwood Hill, near Ockley, in the County of Surrey, the house of the said James Morris is not being licensed for that purpose… This is illegal.[13]

A copy of this letter was sent to the Duke of Richmond, the chairman of the West Sussex Visitors' Committee. The committee questioned Morris about its contents two months later. He claimed that the Horsham Union paid him 6s. per patient per week which included the cost of food and clothes. He said that all his patients were tranquil and that there was "no need for any doctors".[14]

It is unlikely that this was an isolated example of pauper lunatics being kept in an unlicensed building. It's more likely that local authorities sent their 'harmless' cases to these houses and only sent their 'dangerous' patients to the much more expensive private asylums. This letter also explains why there was such a lack of private licensed houses in Sussex apart from the over-priced Ringmer Asylum and the only-for-the-rich Ticehurst House. Cheap unlicensed accommodation was obviously a more preferable alternative for some Sussex parishes. The letter also casts a huge shadow of doubt over the reliability of pauper lunacy statistics in Sussex before the opening of its own asylum.

The 1845 Asylums Acts led to the great expansion of the public county asylum system in the late 1840's "at a time when the principles of moral treatment were in the ascendant and the non-restraint movement was making rapid headway".[15] In Chapter One, the ideology of moral treatment was epitomized by the regime at the York Retreat; non-restraint was more difficult to define. It generally meant not using any form of mechanical restraints on a patient, such as leg irons and straps. Physical restraint was only to be employed as a means of last resort. What was considered to be restraint and non-restraint tended to change throughout the nineteenth century. For example, when the use of bed straps was condemned, the York Retreat replaced them with a quilt secured to the bed by its four corners which was deemed more acceptable.

Most parishes and unions in Sussex opposed the 1845 Act on financial grounds. They were helped in their opposition by the Act permitting any two authorities to join together for the purpose of setting up an asylum. This left the door open for authorities to drag their feet in negotiations between each other and led to years of prevarication.

In October 1845, the Horsham Union suggested using the old county gaol at Horsham as the Sussex Asylum. It estimated that a simple conversion costing about £11,000 would provide for up to 200 pauper lunatics which would be a lot less than the anticipated £44,000 needed for a purpose built asylum. The idea was rejected as the county really needed accommodation for at least twice that number of patients.

In April, May and June, the local magistrates were bombarded with petitions from unions and parishes who had been invited to give their views. Nearly all were against the idea of a county asylum and they organised a campaign of protest. Petitions from Rodmell, Ringmer, Playden, East Dean, Hartfield, South Malling and Twineham were virtually identical. They claimed that there was still enough room for their lunatics in the existing licensed houses and county asylums outside Sussex and that private licensed houses had better cure rates than county asylums. Placing their patients in the latter, they argued, would prolong their families' stay in the workhouses thereby increasing the ratepayers burden. They ended their petitions with a heartfelt plea that "for the sake of humanity and economy we must fight the act".[16] They were right in their claim that, statistically, rates of cure were higher in private asylums than in county ones. In 1846, of the 1,920 pauper lunatics living in private asylums, 33.2% were deemed "curable"; of the 4,244 living in public asylums, only 15.4% were deemed so.[17] But the statistics didn't take into account the different admission policies employed. Many private establishments would only take people who had only recently become ill and some would release patients who were not cured within a year.

Some parishes protested that they had hardly any pauper lunatics and that the workhouse was the best and cheapest place for them. Out of a population of 10,000, Lewes would admit to having only three cases and Battle to only having six out of 12,000. Again, they used statistics to support their argument. Suspiciously, the number of pauper lunatics in East Sussex had gone down from 117 in 1831 to 106 in 1845, at a time when nationally the numbers had almost doubled. This counter-trend was probably due to the lack of disclosure on the part of the Sussex parishes and their use of unlicensed houses such as James Morris's in Surrey.

Rye's petition[18] claimed that they had already been over-taxed by having to pay for the new county gaol at Lewes, built in 1850. It further protested that removal to an asylum would isolate patients from their friends and family. It concluded by saying they were very sceptical about the value of medical treatment for "idiots" and "imbeciles". There was some validity in their arguments, particularly the point about patients being cut off from their families and friends, an argument which would be used by the anti-asylum lobby a hundred years later. But the petition omitted one of the key reasons for Rye and other parishes' objections to a county asylum. By law a new asylum had to be built near the centre of the county. This would obviously be a disadvantage to parishes like Rye, which were near the boundaries of Sussex, as it would involve extra expense for transporting lunatics to the new asylum.

Apart from Horsham (which had 32 of West Sussex's 77 pauper lunatics), all the petitions came from parishes with few 'declared' lunatics. The only parish which petitioned for a county asylum was Brighton which had the highest number of pauper lunatics in Sussex in 1845. Brighton's lengthy petition[19], dated 25th June 1846, outlined much of the pro-asylum case put forward by the reformers. The petition was a mixture of humanitarianism and economic expediency. But saving money was undoubtedly the main motivation. The parish – having to send most of its lunatics to London because of the lack of asylums locally or in adjoining counties – calculated that a new asylum could save them £281 per year and that the county as a whole could save £7 annually on each patient.

It may seem odd that Brighton was the only parish in favour of the construction of a county asylum for Sussex. But, apart from economic reasons Brighton had its reputation to consider. In the second decade of the nineteenth century, after Bath, Brighton was the fastest growing town in the country. Its population had risen from 2,000 in 1750 to 24,000 in 1821. In a very short period it had developed from being a small fishing village into a national, almost continental, seaside resort. It successfully attracted a wealthy clientele, so small businesses and tourism boomed. But the town's relief structure couldn't cope with the corresponding increase in unemployment, sickness and mental illness amongst its poorer inhabitants. Brighton also became quite an unruly place and even Queen Victoria refused to come to the town after local people had made funny faces at her. Pauper lunatics let loose in the town could only add to this unruliness and damage Brighton's popularity. With the workhouse already overcrowded it was convenient to place them somewhere not too near and not too far away from the town. A county asylum seemed to offer a perfect solution.

By 1847, thirty-six of the fifty-two counties had built asylums but the Sussex authorities continued to prevaricate. Three years after the 1845 Act the Western and Eastern Divisions of Sussex were still debating the desirability of building an asylum. A serious cholera epidemic at the Bethnal Green private asylum in London in 1848 put pressure on them. Sussex had 123 pauper lunatics confined there but they could not be removed out of danger as the county had nowhere for them to go. The Lunacy Commission wrote an angry letter to the Western Division chairman, the Duke of Richmond, complaining about the "total want of pauper accommodation in the county"[20] and the lack of plans to build an asylum. But the stalling continued. The following year a letter from the Eastern to the Western Division asked for a postponement of the decision for another year because of the "very unusual local distress" and the lack of funds due to more than £30,000 having been spent on the new prison at Lewes. The letter finished by saying that "the justices believe that the pauper lunatics of this Division are humanely and properly treated in private asylums". [21]

In order to save money both Divisions had hoped to unite with one of the adjoining counties which already had an asylum. But the Kent and Surrey asylums were already full and the Hampshire Asylum had high charges for pauper lunatics coming from outside their county. As the number of pauper lunatics in Sussex increased – from 375 in 1849 to 455 in 1853 – it became harder for the Sussex authorities to claim that a county asylum was unnecessary. Finally, in March 1854, the East and West Divisions agreed to unite for the purposes of building an asylum. But before the planning began there was still time for one last irony.

By the 1853 Lunacy Act, boroughs within the county did not have to participate in the project and could send their lunatics where they wished. On the other hand, parishes and unions were compelled to join the scheme and contribute towards its funding. The three Sussex boroughs all acted differently. Hastings preferred to continue sending their patients to private London asylums, Chichester declined to participate but wanted to send patients on a contract basis, and Rye, which had petitioned so strongly against an asylum, decided to join the scheme. But the greatest irony was Brighton's position. Since their petition of 1846 the Brighton magistrates had changed their minds about having a county asylum and did not want to participate in the scheme. Unfortunately for them, Brighton became a borough one month *after* the agreement between the two Divisions and therefore was annexed to East Sussex for asylum purposes.

Why had Brighton, which had petitioned so eloquently for an asylum eight years before, changed its mind? The truth was that the town had continued to grow in confidence since 1846 and wanted to build its own asylum. By being annexed to East Sussex, Brighton would have little say in the construction and supervision of the new asylum despite being expected to contribute one fifth towards its expenditure (as the town possessed one fifth of the county's pauper lunatics). The Eastern and Western Divisions were to contribute towards the building and maintenance in the proportion of roughly 2:1, reflecting the number of pauper lunatics in each Division. The asylum was to be run by a Committee of Visitors – 14 from the East, 8 from the West and 2 from Brighton. So Brighton was under-represented and over the next few years its leaders would try and exploit this grievance whenever they could. It was yet another irony that almost 50 years later Brighton would eventually become its sole owner.

So ended the struggle to establish a county asylum. To its shame Sussex had become the last county to start making proper provision for its pauper lunatics. Why had not the Lunacy Commissioners put more pressure on the Sussex magistrates and compelled them to act earlier? The fall-out from the New Poor Law of 1834 probably provides the answer. The Law had attempted to centralize relief but in doing so had often undermined local power and influence. It had been resisted (sometimes successfully) but had left a bad feeling between central government and the local authorities. The Lunacy Commissioners were reluctant to emulate the heavy-handedness of some of the Poor Law Commissioners and preferred to use persuasion rather than force to bring the Sussex magistrates into line. In the end, the magistrates had succumbed when the number of pauper lunatics in Sussex could no longer be concealed or ignored. But it was to be another five years before the Sussex Lunatic Asylum finally opened and provided much needed accommodation for the county's pauper lunatics then dotted around the country in various institutions.

Chapter Three

THE BIRTH OF THE
SUSSEX LUNATIC ASYLUM

Building site wanted for a lunatic asylum for the county of Sussex. From 50 to 100 acres on a dry soil and southern exposure, with a good supply of pure water; within two miles of a railway station on the main line, or else in a central position in regard to the divisions of the county… Parties having such land to offer, are requested to communicate full particulars, including price, to W. P. Kell Esq., Solicitor, Lewes on or before the 14th day of June 1854.

Sussex Advertiser, 31st May 1854.

*I*n August 1854 a man caught the London to Brighton train and got off at Haywards Heath at about mid-day. He was met by two well-dressed gentlemen and two labourers with spades. His name was Mr Grainger and he was a medical inspector with the government's Board of Health. The two gentlemen were members of the recently formed Committee of Visitors for the prospective Sussex Lunatic Asylum and had come to show Mr Grainger some local sites. Afterwards, his job was to write a report and recommend which one would be most suitable for the new asylum.

Haywards Heath lies roughly midway between the eastern and western boundaries of Sussex – an ideal locality for both the Divisions. Some of the countryside around was described at the time as being the most beautiful in England. Better still, Haywards Heath itself was a virtually deserted tract of open country, offering cheap land and with only about 200 inhabitants. Before Grainger's visit the committee had discounted other possible sites on the grounds of locality – one situated as far away as Farnham in Surrey – and on the grounds of expense. They had been offered a site at Preston, near Brighton but the land in that neighbourhood cost £250 per acre; the land near Haywards Heath only £70 per acre.

Mr Grainger had arrived with standardised guidelines from the Lunacy Commissioners. The most important were that the site must have a good water supply – enough to provide each resident with 40 gallons per day (equivalent to a normal bath filled to the rim) and that it must be secluded with limited public access. Mr Grainger was taken to visit four sites near Haywards Heath. At every site he asked the labourers to dig several holes to a depth of eight to ten feet in different parts in order to expose the nature of the soil. The site also had to be in an area with a good health record and a low incidence of cholera.

One of the sites visited was Kenwards Farm which was owned by one of the members of the committee, Henry Thomas, the Earl of Chichester. After his visit, Mr Grainger compiled a report and recommended that this site was the best one for building a lunatic asylum – not too far from Haywards Heath railway station, secluded and offering beautiful views from its elevated position. In addition a local doctor, Mr Bull, claimed that it was a very healthy area with only two cases of cholera reported in 28 years. Taking Mr Grainger's advice, the committee wrote to the Earl suggesting that it would be better if they named a price (£70 per acre) rather than let him do so. What happened next is a bit of a mystery.

In the minutes of the Visitor's Committee meeting held on 9th April, 1855 the members agreed that Kenwards Farm was the most eligible site. Two weeks later, at the Old Ship Hotel in Brighton on 23rd April, they decided that Hurst House Farm, owned by a Mr Henry Lane, a friend of one of the committee members, was the best choice. Surprisingly, it was a site that Mr Grainger hadn't even visited. Presumably this change of heart was due to the relative cheapness of Lane's farm – under £50 an acre – and also perhaps to avoid the embarrassing situation of the Committee buying the land off one of its own members. That same day a contract was drawn up to buy Hurst House Farm and 120 acres of farmland for £5,750.

The site had a perfect location. It was situated in the centre of the county, just over a mile from Haywards Heath station at an elevation of 281 feet above sea level. Hurst House Farm was twelve miles from the sea, but hidden from it by the range of the Sussex South Downs of which it commanded beautiful views. The first chaplain of the asylum, Henry Hawkins, poetically described the panorama fourteen years later:

> Here and there the spire and tower of a county church adds beauty to the
> scenery. Now and then the line of white vapour shows the course of a

distant train. Further off are the softly undulating South Downs hills, presenting endless varieties of beauty. They delight the eye under almost every change of season and of weather, sometimes appearing nearer to the eye – ominous, then, of bad weather – sometimes more remote; sometimes standing clear and bright in the sunshine, or overshadowed by the passing cloud, or partly shrouded by mist, or at times in winter capped or covered in snow.[1]

The next task for the Committee of Visitors was to find a suitable architect. Five experienced in building asylums were invited to submit plans to the committee; four complied. The estimates ranged from £55,000 to just under £39,000. The winner was Mr H. E. Kendall of Brunswick Square, London, the son of a famous asylum architect. Kendall was the architect of the Essex Asylum and had recently beaten sixty other competitors for the job of designing the Cambridgeshire Lunatic Asylum. He was obviously a successful architect but he was also the cheapest (by at least £10,000) and the number of defects that arose after the asylum's construction may have made the committee regret its choice.

Kendall in his "Description, specification and estimates for the building of the Sussex Lunatic Asylum"[2] claimed that he had "spared no experience or pains in personally visiting and studying the best existing asylums or pains in obtaining the views of the most eminent and experienced Superintendents, both medical and otherwise". His design was based on "economy and convenience" but took account of the principles of moral treatment.

Kendall designed an asylum capable of accommodating just over 400 patients but also made it easy for further extensions to be made to take a further 400 if the need arose in the future. A lodge and gates provided the entrance on the north side, facing Haywards Heath. All of the south front of the asylum was for the undisturbed use of the patients with no access from public or private roads. Near the north entrance Kendall designed a chapel standing by itself and sufficiently large for a congregation of 300. The asylum itself had separate entrances for male and female patients apart from a central main entrance. The building was three stories high with a female wing left of the centre and a male wing to the right on each floor. Each wing was divided into two wards. This separation of the sexes reflected the moral beliefs of the Lunacy Commissioners.

The wards were arranged in the old asylum plan of day-room, dining room and gallery, with bedrooms opening into each. There were 124 single bedded rooms and 284 beds in dormitories in accordance with the recommendations of the Lunacy Commission. B. W. Richardson in *The Medical History of England* (1864) describes the antecedents of the old asylum plan as explained to him by the future medical superintendent of the Sussex Asylum, Dr Robertson:

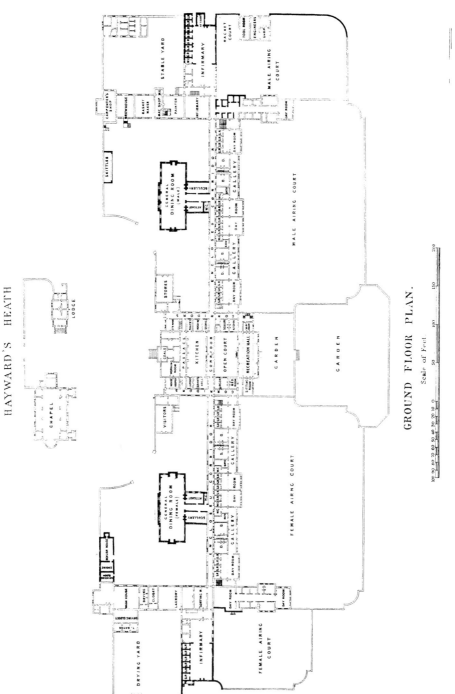

The ground floor plan. Kendall's original design has been added to in this drawing of 1868

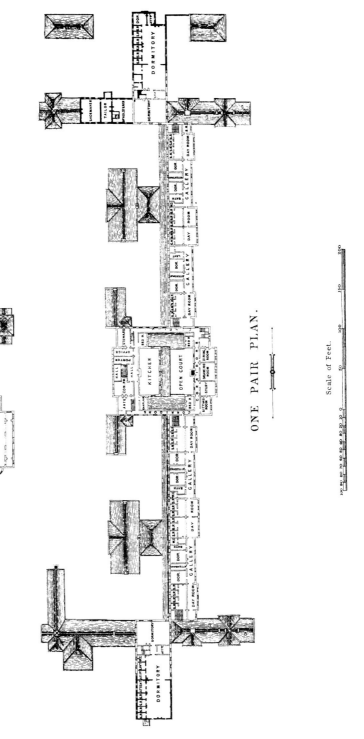

SUSSEX COUNTY LUNATIC ASYLUM.

HAYWARD'S HEATH.

Showing original building and additions.

CHAPEL

ONE PAIR PLAN.

Scale of Feet.

The First floor plan.

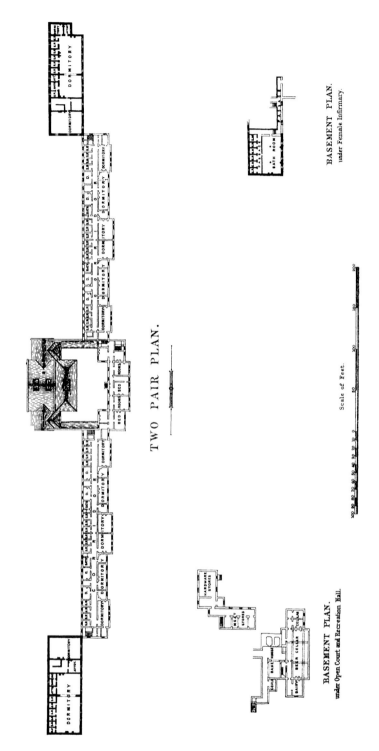

SUSSEX COUNTY LUNATIC ASYLUM.

HAYWARD'S HEATH.

TWO PAIR PLAN.

BASEMENT PLAN.
under Female Infirmary.

BASEMENT PLAN.
under Open Court and Recreation Hall.

Scale of Feet.

The second floor plan

ld in the background, a rustic couple admire the view
ecording angels at work in the bottom corners."
of 1856)

"The general prospect is a panoramic view from the South, with the Wea
from under a tree, and the whole is framed in gothic foliage, with
(Kendall's caption for his design

The earliest asylums according to Robertson were religious houses, which, at the suppression of the monasteries, were devoted to the reception of the insane. The long gallery and the cells adjoining constituted the structure of the monastery, and when the buildings were adopted to the use of the insane, they were retained, the gallery acting as a promenade for the mad. That which was a place of retirement for the exercise of religious devotion by the monks, thus became, in time, a theatre for the full development of the ravings of the insane man.[3]

The galleries which were for the patients' exercise in each ward were designed to be cheerful and light with windows which opened at the top and bottom. At one end of the ward gallery was a large bright day room and at the other end a large dining room. There were also two attendants' rooms in each ward, between the dormitories, with a small internal window for watching the patients. At the end of the wards were the bathrooms and lavatories. The whole asylum was to be heated by open fires.

Kendall's design included accommodation for the staff and officers, stables, a gas house, an engine and boiler house, a brewhouse and a number of workshops. There was also a landscaped garden in which patients could take the air and 100 acres of grounds to comply with the Lunacy Commissioners' ruling that there should be one acre of land per four patients for working and exercise purposes. Kendall finished his plan by assuring the Committee of Visitors that the asylum would be "built with the best labour, workmanship and materials, equal to any asylum yet erected".[2] His commission was to be £1,800.

By providing equal accommodation for the sexes the design did not take into account the Visitors' Committee's own findings that female patients were increasing at a higher rate than male patients and were already the majority in Sussex in 1854 – 266 women to 216 men. Despite this, Kendall's plan was officially adopted on 11th February 1856 and submitted to the Lunacy Commissioners for approval. The committee's failure to take into account the larger proportion of women at the outset seems to have been very short-sighted.

The Lunacy Commissioners made important alterations to Kendall's plan such as enlarging the working wards and extending the width of the single rooms from 6 feet 6 inches to 7 feet and insisting that all the internal brickwork must be plastered regardless of cost, a suggestion that was later ignored. Other alterations they suggested put £2,500 onto Kendall's original estimate. But the Commissioners did not show any reservations about the planned size of the asylum. Perhaps they were just relieved that Sussex was finally building its own.

The Committee of Visitors decided to cover the initial costs by borrowing £48,000 from the London Life Association at 4½% interest over thirty years.

The East Division borrowed £32,000 and the West Division, £16,000, a proportion related to the number of pauper lunatics they needed to care for. In all, the Committee believed that to build, furnish and run the asylum it might eventually cost £80,000. They accepted the tender from Rees and Ayers, a building firm from Dover, for the construction work. The builders were under an engagement to finish the entire building by 1st January 1859 although this was later changed to 1st March.

The biggest building project in the county since the construction of Lewes gaol in 1850, finally got under way just after Easter 1857. Twenty temporary buildings were quickly erected to provide accommodation and refreshment for the 200 people employed on the site. The most conspicuous of these was "The Asylum Arms", run by a Mr James Ashdown, which offered "very neat and commodious liquor" according to the *Brighton Examiner* (2/6/1857). Workmen soon began digging up 17,300 cubic yards of soil. A new road to the asylum costing £1,000 was quickly laid and in use as waggon loads of materials (including 454 doors, 440 windows and 770 yards of boundary fencing) made their way to the site.

The Visitors' Committee set up a sub-committee which met fortnightly to superintend the building work. The digging work went slowly owing to some of the ground being much harder than anticipated. In August that year the sub-committee complained about the use of inferior bricks and compelled the builders to use better ones in the future. On 31st October, Mr Bigg, the chairman of the committee, bumped into a man called Birch just as he was leaving the site. Birch, who had worked on the project as a foreman of the bricklayers, told Bigg that improper material and inferior workmanship had been used in the building. Kendall was subsequently called before the sub-committee but assured the members that the charges were "without foundation".

On Tuesday, 10th August 1858, work was suspended for the day as the building contractor, Parker Ayers, organised a summer party in an adjacent field for the workmen and their friends and families. After playing games such as cricket and jumping in the sacks, a tea was provided followed by dancing to music from a locally hired band. The day ended with Parker Ayers (who had arrived to great cheers) making a short speech in which he thanked the party-goers for being orderly and well-conducted and said that he looked forward to seeing them again. Only three workmen were missing from the festivities: two had decided that the nearby Lewes Races was a more attractive proposition, and the other one, Jeremiah Donovan, twenty-one, was languishing in a Brighton hospital. He had slipped and fallen 31 feet from scaffolding the previous week and subsequently died on the 16th August.

The question of appointing a medical superintendent was raised in January 1858 by the chairman of the Visitors, the Duke of Richmond. It was felt that the new man would be invaluable in advising and helping with the furnishing of the asylum. The Duke recommended a Dr Meyer for the job but it was decided that the post should be advertised in *The Times* at a salary of £450 per annum. The advertisement didn't stipulate any age or status requirements. Eighty-three people applied for the job of which four – all from London – were selected for interview. Only three turned up for the interview including a J. M. Winn who was the medical superintendent for Sussex House private asylum in Hammersmith, London. A sub-committee of six headed by the Earl of Chichester conducted the interviews and at the end of the day decided to appoint Charles Lockhart Robertson and asked him to start on 1st September, 1858.

Robertson, aged 34 and single, came from a distinguished Scottish medical family, his father being an eminent surgeon and his brother, Argyll Robertson, a famous ophthalmologist. After studying at Edinburgh and St Andrews, he went straight into the Army Medical Service and became assistant surgeon to the Yarmouth Army Lunatic Asylum at the age of twenty-one. But a letter printed in *The Lancet* a year after this indicates that he had already worked for a year as the resident physician at a private asylum, Dunston Lodge, in Gateshead-on-Tyne in the north of England.

After four years at Yarmouth, in 1849, Robertson applied for the post of medical superintendent at the Glasgow Royal Lunatic Asylum. He cited 24 referees, including Sir James Young Simpson, a professor of midwifery at Edinburgh University, who was instrumental in the introduction of the use of chloroform in medicine. In support of his application Robertson wrote of being awarded two prizes in 1848 and 1849 for essays about improving the conditions of the insane. He also stated that:

> I have, by visiting, made myself acquainted with the arrangements and plans of treatment adopted in the principal Lunatic Asylums in Great Britain. I have also visited several of the German public establishments for the insane…[4]

Simpson wrote:

> Few, or none, I believe, of our countrymen are more truly conversant with all that has been done and is doing in the subject, and few or none have appeared to me to have more liberal and expanded views of what may yet be obtained and reached in the improvement of this particular field of practice… Dr Robertson's manners, morals, zeal, and talents all seem to me to fit him in a most superior manner for this line of practice.[5]

Indeed, Robertson did appear to be a perfect candidate both from the intellectual and practical viewpoints but his application was unsuccessful. Next year he resigned from the army and resumed his medical studies at Cambridge where he obtained a medical degree. Afterwards, he set up a consulting practice in London.

In 1855 Robertson became the honorary secretary of the Medico-Psychological Association which was primarily for the growing number of medical officers who worked in asylums. He was also a frequent contributor to its mouthpiece *The Journal of Mental Science*, founded in 1853, and other medical journals. His contributions were often endorsements of new progressive ideas such as the growing need for half-way house accommodation for patients who had just been discharged from large public asylums but who, as yet, were not ready for the outside world.

Apart from his professional interests, Robertson was also a linguist and a great traveller who had a large circle of friends. He was a member of both the Oxford and Cambridge Clubs and the Athenaeum Club and was, according to the *British Medical Journal*, "very dependent on the refinements of life".[6] Unfortunately, Robertson suffered from frequent attacks of neuralgia throughout his life which often confined him to bed. Perhaps these attacks contributed to his making rather caustic remarks at times and being somewhat aggressive. He could be dogmatic in his beliefs and was often intolerant of those who disagreed with him. But he was a man who held progressive ideas about the treatment of mental illness and had a deep interest in the subject. In addition, according to the asylum's first chaplain, "his decisive manner and the keen glance of his eye intimated his capacity for government".[7] Overall, Robertson was a good choice for the Sussex Asylum and, in turn, it was an ideal opportunity for him to put his ideas into practice.

Robertson was so impressed when he first saw the Sussex Asylum he claimed that he had never seen a building less like an asylum and thought that the chapel was the best imitation of a Venetian church in the country. His first task was to visit other asylums such as Colney Hatch and Hanwell in London and Kendall's Essex Asylum in order to learn about the proper fittings needed. Robertson was further expected to help supervise the building work and eventually to recruit attendants and nurses.

Everything went out to tender and few articles were obtained locally. A contractor in Chelsea, London, won the tender to provide the asylum with £1,794 worth of bedding, £654 worth of men's clothes, £418 worth of women's clothes, £123 worth of shoes, and finally £600 worth of bedsteads. The latter

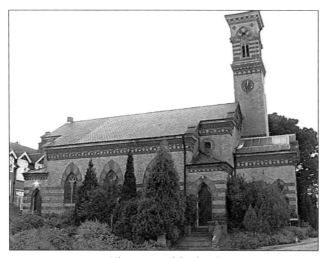

The exterior of the chapel

were made of birchwood and were French polished, with sacking bottoms and horsehair mattresses. Amongst the clothing ordered for male patients were 600 handkerchiefs for the pocket and 300 for the neck, whilst twenty extra-strong dresses were ordered for women patients who might need to be physically restrained. The Earl of Chichester himself went to Gregory's Furniture Warehouse in Finsbury Park, London in order to obtain furniture. And Kendall, the architect, provided 41 settees, 44 easy chairs, 93 chairs and 12 stools for £275. Once the asylum was up and running all the furniture in the future would be made by the patients under artisan supervision. The floors were made of pine and covered with coconut matting which, again, in the future, would be made by the inmates.

Mr Kell, the Clerk to the Visitors' Committee wrote to other asylums for advice about provisions and equipment. He asked the steward at Hanwell for advice about stores and was informed that because of asylum theft it was not advisable to keep more than one month's worth of supplies at any one time. As the completion date grew nearer attention focused on staff recruitment. The Visitors made all the important appointments.

The post of chaplain was advertised with the stipulation that the person must be under forty and that the successful candidate would have to live within two miles of the

The interior of the chapel looking west

asylum. There were nine applicants from various parts of the
country but only three, from
Kent, Sussex and Essex, were
invited for an interview. One of
the candidates, James Dunnager,
provided 43 references but he
wasn't selected. Instead, the
Oxford educated local man,
Henry Hawkins, was appointed.
Hawkins was 34 years old and
had been the curate of Cuckfield
(near Haywards Heath) and the
chaplain of the Cuckfield Union
Workhouse for the past five

The east end of the chapel

years. He was well-known to some of the magistrates on the Visitors'
Committee and his appointment may have been a foregone conclusion. One of
the other unsuccessful candidates, Mr Coombs, obviously thought so and wrote
an angry letter complaining about his and the other candidate's "unceremonious
and unsatisfactory treatment"[10] at the interview. To add insult to injury they had
been kept late by the committee which had forced them to make a mad dash
across the Heath in order to catch their train. In any event, Hawkins turned out
to be an inspired choice and arguably became the most famous asylum chaplain
in the country.

An advertisement for the post of resident Steward and Clerk was placed in
The Times and Samuel Mortlock, aged 28, from Hanwell Asylum was eventually
chosen. Mortlock went on to work at the asylum until he died there in 1901.
This length of service was surpassed by Mary Anne Buckle who arrived from the
Worcester Asylum to take up the position of head attendant on the female side,
a position she held until 1911. But her 52 years' service at the asylum is not the
record. Percy Ralfe started there as a living-in attendant in 1912 and did not
retire till 1966! William Knox, aged 36, previously at the Brentwood Asylum,
was appointed the head attendant on the male side.

One of the most important appointments was that of Thomas Gwynne
from Guys Hospital who became Robertson's assistant medical officer. He was
originally paid £80 per annum (although this was later raised to £100) and
provided with furnished apartments plus board and lodging. This was a vital
position as the assistant was expected to see each patient at least twice a day and

keep the medical superintendent informed about daily events.

The first nurses and attendants were employed in March 1859 and by the end of the year 16 women and 18 men had been recruited. Several of the nursing staff were recruited through two London employment agencies which specialized in finding asylum staff. Few of them were local. Robertson also had to recruit a variety of artisans including a tailor, a cowman, a brewer, a baker and a blacksmith. The majority of these had little asylum experience. The asylum's staff was predominantly youthful. Forty-six out of the sixty-three staff employed in the first year were thirty or under and only two were over forty.[8]

Robertson was also expected to draw up diet tables and general rules for the asylum and to submit them to the Committee of Visitors and Lunacy Commission for approval. He modelled these on those already being used at Essex Asylum. As busy as Robertson was, on 29th April 1859, the Lunacy Commissioners suggested that:

> … the Medical Superintendent should be directed to visit all asylums and workhouses containing male pauper lunatics belonging to the county of Sussex, so as to be enabled to select such as were harmless and able-bodied … who might be usefully employed in road making, levelling the ground and making the garden.[9]

Visiting the county's pauper lunatics was a time-consuming task as many of them were confined in London asylums. There is no evidence to suggest that Robertson took up their suggestion and he appears to have been scornful about the idea of using pauper lunatics as cheap labour.

The completion of the asylum building was delayed by the discovery that the existing well at Hurst House Farm was inadequate. This necessitated the sinking of an artesian well at the southern extreme of the farm to a depth of 217 feet. The hardness of the strata slowed down progress on the whole project. The Visitors' Committee was forced to borrow another £10,000 from the London Life Association as the bill for the asylum rose to over £46,000 (including Kendall's commission which had risen from £1,800 to £2,570). Completion dates came and went: January, then May 1859. The asylum building was not finally completed until November 1859, almost three months after its opening.

The Lunacy Commissioners tried to get the Visitors' Committee to open a portion of the asylum earlier in the year in order that Sussex patients could be withdrawn from other county asylums thus relieving their overcrowding problem. The committee refused the request. The commissioners also had little joy when it came to encouraging the committee to spend more on furnishings and decoration. A decision about their recommendation that £50 be spent to improve the wards with pictures and aquariums was deferred by the committee to a later date.

Four weeks before the asylum opened Robertson received some unusual advice from Mr Kell, the Clerk to the Committee, who was based in Lewes.

> I observe by your list of proposed patients to be transferred, many of them belong to Brighton. I should strongly recommend you not take Brighton patients at present for the authorities there will be sure to object to the first high (maintenance charge) average and give you some trouble… You had better take others in preference as the (Brighton) authorities also make half yearly visits and then publish reports of their visits.[10]

Kell's prediction that Robertson would have problems with the Brighton authorities would prove correct but it was impossible not to take their patients as the town was such an important financial contributor to the project.

When the asylum was finished, Kendall described the building in his completion report:

> Sufficient character is given to its exterior by picturesque treatment and outline, and varied coloured brickworks to render it cheerful and effective, such character having a beneficial effect on the patients in a curative point of view; the style of the building generally in Lombardic or Byzantine, chosen for its appropriate, effective and inexpensive character, little ornament being used beyond that conducive to utility.[11]

It was the last phrase that reflected a change – some might say a watering down – of the asylum reformers' beliefs. The very earliest asylum buildings had been designed to secure the safe confinement and imprisonment of lunatics. The new moral architecture of the first half of the nineteenth century, advocated by the Tuke family and others as vital to the success of moral treatment, made the building itself an essential part of the therapy. Asylum buildings had to be warm, homely, well-decorated and as un-prison like as possible. But by mid-Victorian times, views on moral architecture had begun to be modified by considerations of economy. The Lunacy Commission gradually became less insistent on the importance of decoration as the century progressed. Thus, the basic tenet that cheerful decoration was cost effective because patients were cured sooner, became seriously undermined. The new asylums owed more to careful budgeting and rather less to patient needs.

In many ways, Kendall's design combined both the earlier and later ideas about asylum architecture in the nineteenth century. It was cheap but also quite impressive physically and on a par with any public school or town hall built in that period. It towered proudly over the Victorian landscape twelve miles from the nearest town, Brighton. But unforeseen then, the very scale of asylum buildings (such as the Sussex Asylum) became one of their greatest limitations. It tended to emphasize the separateness of their inhabitants and increased the difficulties of their return to normal life.

According to Daniel Tuke's *Dictionary of Psychological Medicine* (1892), an asylum should be no more than three or four miles from a town for reasons of accessibility. That the Sussex Asylum was built so far away from a town had more, I believe, to do with the cheapness of land and county accessibility rather than with a deliberate desire to isolate patients. When the Sussex Asylum finally opened on St James's day, 25th July 1859 – a year which saw the publication of *The Origin of the Species* by Charles Darwin and John Brown's raid at Harpers Ferry which sparked off the American Civil War – it was, with some justification, seen as another great example of Victorian philanthropy and achievement.

By the time the asylum opened, most pauper lunatics were in purpose-built publicly maintained asylums. The simple logic of modern asylums was an attractive proposition. Firstly, the patient must be removed quickly from the family – which had nurtured the illness in the first place – and quarantined in a protective, friendly environment. Secondly, supportive staff (acting like an extended family), and the latest medical knowledge allied to a stimulating regime of a healthy diet, fresh air, sporting activities and work therapy, would enable the patient to regain his confidence and self-control, returning to the community a better, fitter person. It was of paramount importance that the 'disease' must be treated quickly. This would increase the chance of cure and save the local authorities a lot of money, money which had previously been spent on long-term confinement. The reality of county asylums, even in 1859, was a lot different and already confidence in the public asylum as the best place for treatment was being seriously undermined.

In 1856, the Lunacy Commission was already complaining about the crowded state of nearly all county asylums. The table below shows the growing increase in patient numbers for England and Wales:[12]

1st January	County Asylums	Average Number of Patients
1827	9	116
1850	24	298
1860	41	387

The reformers' ideal of a maximum asylum population of 250 was being quickly superseded as local authorities tended to send their most troublesome patients there rather than those most likely to be cured. On the other hand, due to the prevailing fear that Victorian society had about wrongful committal, some patients were undoubtedly held back from asylum treatment by cautious magistrates. And many patients who should have been sent to public asylums were kept in workhouses because local magistrates often preferred concrete savings now to hypothetical cures later on. Public asylums soon filled up with the elderly, the sick, the handicapped and the dangerous. Few arrived directly from home – only about 7% of the Sussex Asylum's first intake came from home. It gradually became clear that too many asylum patients were unsuitable for treatment and that asylum overcrowding was making a homely environment impossible.

By 1859, not only were asylums becoming overcrowded with pauper lunatics but the cure rate was in decline, from 15% in the 1840s to 11.2% by 1860 and it would continue to fall as the century progressed. Asylum doctors had little control over the criteria of admissions which were often decided by Visiting Committee members who had close links with workhouse Guardians. 'Recent insanity' admissions were increasingly outnumbered by long term workhouse admissions who had little hope of recovery.

Even one or two medical superintendents began to doubt the efficacy and desirability of the asylum system and proposed an alternative. J. C. Bucknill, the superintendent of the Devon County Asylum, developed the English Cottage system where patients were boarded 'on trial' with trustworthy cottagers and asylum staff. The superintendent of the Gloucester Lunatic Asylum, in 1864, "considered that the cottage system was the best means for treating the insane, and he proposed a plan for a colony comprising of 29 cottages".[13] Others advocated single care – one patient placed in (and looked after by) one family – although this was an option only really available to the richer classes. But some reformers still believed that the public asylum system was the best and most humane way of trying to solve a long-standing socio-medical problem. It is within these parameters of pessimism and hope that the life of the Sussex Lunatic Asylum began.

Chapter Four

1859
"STRAWBERRIES IN THE DARK"

O n its opening day, 25th July 1859, forty-two women from Bethnal
Green private asylum arrived followed by forty-two men three days
later. The first patient to be registered was Jane Woods, a 40-year-old
domestic servant who suffered from visions of angels and devils ascending and
descending in rooms. The majority were escorted on foot by asylum staff and
two policemen from Haywards Heath railway station to the asylum, about a
mile and a half away. The more difficult patients were transported by van. One
'idiot' boy tried to escape during the transfer but was soon recaptured. Another
escape attempt was reported by the *Sussex Express* on 2nd August:

> Just as the party arrived at the asylum, a hue and cry was raised, and it
> was found that an inmate had escaped. It seems that a man from Chailey,
> formerly servant to Mr Blencowe had been brought in that morning, and
> as all the officials were obliged to escort the newcomers, he was left in the
> charge of the tailor, who, having occasion to leave the room for a few
> minutes, the lunatic contrived to force open the window and gaining terra
> firma, set off like steam. Just at that moment the van arrived and a chase
> took place, the run-away being captured before he got off the grounds. He
> afterwards tried to force his way out by using a fender, but was frustrated.

Two hundred and forty patients – 115 men and 125 women – were officially
transferred to the asylum in the weeks following its opening. The overwhelming
majority came from private licensed asylums. Many arrived in a very poor condition. Robertson described them in his asylum journal on 30th July – "They are
quiet and orderly but in very indifferent health and look like persons who have
been long in confinement. Only two of forty-two females are in good health. The
female patients were clean in their clothing and person; the male patients were

rather the contrary".[1] The majority were maintained by the Sussex Unions – including 63 from Brighton – although ten were private patients.

The arrivals from the London private asylums – Peckham, Camberwell, Bethnal Green and Hoxton – were used to relatively primitive conditions. At Hoxton House the male patients had occasionally had to share the same beds. But the worst conditions seem to have been at Bethnal Green. On 13th August, Robertson wrote that "the male patients last removed from Bethnal Green are the most violent, filthy and neglected lot of patients I have ever met with in all my experiences… and that they showed long years of neglect. In viewing the patients which you will recollect the Commission recommended should be removed last autumn from Bethnal Green to finish the buildings, I have no hesitation in saying it would have been impossible to have managed them in the unfinished building, and we should have [had] to send them all back. So much for the value of theoretical advice!".[2] Three of the patients from Bethnal Green died within a few weeks.

As predicted, Robertson soon began to encounter problems with the Brighton Workhouse and its Guardians. On 10th September, a ten-year-old idiot boy, Richard Bennett, arrived from Brighton. Robertson protested that:

> He's not a fit case for this Asylum… [it would be] better to get old women from the union house to look after him. This Asylum is not adapted for the treatment of idiocy and the presence of idiots in such a house is a great injury to other patients … He breaks and destroys everything he can lay his hands on and almost requires the attention of a nurse to himself. It is impossible in this Asylum to do justice to such young children.[3]

The Brighton Guardians refused to move Bennett and he was only transferred to Redhill Asylum – which specialized in the care of 'idiocy' – on 29th October by the authority of two of the Visitors and with the sanction of the Lunacy Commission. 'Idiocy'– a severe condition affecting all the faculties – was considered to be the worst form of mental handicap. There was little specialist care for this type of patient in mid-Victorian Britain and although the boundaries of insanity were potentially wide, asylum superintendents were not keen to have them. Only 6% of the first intake at the Sussex Asylum were classified as 'idiots and imbeciles'. Many suffered from epilepsy and as there were no anti-convulsant drugs available, were treated with potassium bromides, sedatives which were not always effective. Robertson admitted the following year that medical science had little idea about the cause and treatment of epilepsy. Obviously, it was difficult to implement a non-restraint policy with patients who were sometimes uncontrollable.

Some of the arrivals from Brighton and the Brighton Workhouse were in a shocking state. Mrs Groves, a 49-year-old Mormon and labourer's wife, arrived on 13th August and died on 25th August. "She was brought here by her husband literally covered with vermin, bruises and sores. Her clothing was so filthy that I [Robertson] sent it to the oven to be burnt".[4] Another, Mrs Charlotte Trigg, had signs of violence and rough handling on her body. Meanwhile, a deputation (the Lunacy Committee) from the Brighton Workhouse Guardians, arrived on 27th August and saw every one of their patients. The *Brighton Herald* recorded that "we hear the deputation were very much pleased with their reception by the Superintendent and also with the arrangements of the Asylum". But mutual acrimony between Robertson and the Brighton Guardians was soon to break out.

On 28th September, Robertson complained about the case of Mrs Mercer, "one of the Brighton cases, who came from the union is another of those painful cases of neglect of which we have had several instances from Brighton. Her hair was crawling with vermin and also her clothing".[5] The Brighton Guardians in company with their medical officer, complained about this description and Robertson withdrew his complaint about the clothing when he discovered that the workhouse clothing had been returned to Brighton before he had seen it. But he refused to withdraw his main allegation:

> I had no intention of reflecting on the care generally bestowed by the Brighton Guardians on their poor… nevertheless the fact remains that Mrs. Mercer coming here from the Brighton Union her hair crawling with vermin and also what I did not report to the Visitors – the skin chafed from her dirty habits in the attention of the calls of nature: habits which the care and management of this asylum have instantly broken.[6]

Mrs. Mercer died soon afterwards. Six months later the friction between Robertson and the Brighton Guardians came to a head over the case of John Mockford, yet another patient who had arrived from the Brighton Workhouse in an appalling condition.

The asylum building itself was in an unsatisfactory condition. After the first week the toilets and water pipes were out of order and bursting. By the end of the first month the foul air at night emanating from the architect's rather crude wall ventilation was "undoing the benefits of our liberal diet and pure air by day". Robertson also found that his apartment floors were "yielding" and that all the doors and shutters were defective. "I desire in the strongest terms to record my dissatisfaction with the manner in which both engineering and the woodwork have been executed,"[7] he complained bitterly to the Visitor's Committee.

The patients, however, were soon organised into diverse activities. "As Sussex

was predominantly agricultural, an extensive farm and market garden was established, using existing agricultural buildings, later replaced".[8] Labourers were hired
to start the project but were soon replaced by patients, and outdoor farm labour
became the principle source of employment for male patients. Female patients
mainly worked inside; cleaning the wards, working in the kitchen and the laundry
room and doing needlework. Repairing torn clothing and sheets seems to have
been a full time occupation. Initially, few patients worked with the artisans except
those making uniform dresses for the male and female attendants. In the first six
months, thirty patients attended mixed education classes in writing, geography
and history, run by the chaplain. He also supervised music classes which produced
a band composed mainly of patients.

Regular walks were also organised and to reduce the boredom for some of
the old, infirm women, the asylum purchased a wagon that could take them for
drives in the countryside. Contact with the outside world was an important part
of the concept of moral treatment. Patients – mainly male – were encouraged to
do sports: cricket, croquet and fives. Friends and relatives could visit every
Wednesday during the daytime and at other times in cases of illness.

By the end of October the Visitors' Committee decided to permit a weekly
ball with the music to be provided by the asylum band. It was to be held every
Wednesday evening from 7.20pm - 9.15pm and cakes and a half pint of beer were
to be supplied to the attendants and the patients. Outsiders (or strangers as they
were then called) were allowed to attend if they obtained permission 48 hours
beforehand. The Committee was clear about its purpose:

> It is the wish of the Visitors that this ball be viewed entirely as a medical
> measure for the cure of the patients… It is neither their intention nor
> desire to provide amusement for the neighbouring farmers and herdsmen.[9]

Beer was part of the daily diet for all patients and was to remain so until the
end of the century. Working patients received extra beer whilst the sick received
sherry, brandy, gin and whisky. Initially the asylum bought very low quality beer
and as a result many patients went down with diarrhoea.

The beer was soon being made on the premises. The diet, whilst not extravagant, was a big improvement on the average workhouse food. The asylum farm
ensured a constant supply of fresh meat, milk, vegetables and fruit. The average
meal consisted of meat, soup, bread, butter and potatoes. Cheese was originally
only given to the working patients and fresh fish – though provided for the sick –
was not part of the normal diet until the 1890s. Sick patients did receive 'extras'
such as eggs and calf's foot jelly. Boiling was the most common method of
cooking and roast dinners did not appear until the 1880s.

The food was not weighed individually on being given to the patients but a fixed amount was sent to each ward and it was consumed in the day rooms. There were differences in the quantities of food received by male and female patients and both received less food on Sundays. As it was not a working day, it was thought that the patients needed less food and that this would also lessen the household work. Robertson lamented the fact that the asylum was not two or three miles from Brighton instead of twelve miles away. This made supplies much more expensive. If expense was not important then Robertson claimed that he would give the patients almost twice as much uncooked meat. The table below shows the asylum diet scale for 1859:[10]

SUSSEX LUNATIC ASYLUM, HAYWARD'S HEATH.

DIET SCALE.

WEEK DAYS.	BREAKFAST, At 8.0 A.M. Males.		Females.		DINNER, At 1.0 P.M. Males.								Females.								SUPPER, At 6.0 P.M. Males.			Females.		
	Bread.	Cocoa.	Bread.	Cocoa.	Bread.	Beer.	Uncooked Meat.	[illegible]	Pie.	Suet Pudding.	Mutton Broth.	Vegetables.	Bread.	Beer.	Uncooked Meat.	Dumpling.	Pie.	Suet Pudding.	Mutton Broth.	Vegetables.	Sweet Cake or Bread.	Butter	Coffee.	Sweet Cake or Bread.	Butter	Tea.
	oz.	pints.	oz.	pints	oz.	pints.	oz.	oz.	oz.	oz.	pints.	oz.	oz.	pints	oz.	oz.	oz.	oz.	pints.	oz.	oz.	oz.	pints.	oz.	oz.	pints
SUNDAY	6	1	5	1	..	½	4	..	..	12	..	..	..	½	4	..	..	8	..	..	6	½	1	5	½	1
MONDAY	6	1	5	1	6	½	4	..	..	..	1	4	[illegible]	½	4	in Batter	..	..	[illegible]	8	6	½	1	5	½	1
TUESDAY	6	1	5	1	6	½	8	[illegible]	..	..	..	12	5	½	6	[illegible]	..	..	..	8	6	½	1	5	½	1
WEDNESDAY	6	1	5	1	6	½	4	..	..	..	1	4	[illegible]	½	4	in	Batter		[illegible]	8	6	½	1	5	½	1
THURSDAY	6	1	5	1	..	½	2	..	16	..	..	8	..	½	2	..	12	..	..	..	6	½	1	5	½	1
FRIDAY	6	1	5	1	6	½	4	..	..	..	1	4	5	½	4	..	..	..	1	..	6	½	1	5	½	1
SATURDAY	6	1	5	1	5	½	8	[illegible]	..	..	..	12	5	½	6	[illegible]	..	..	..	8	6	½	1	5	½	1
WEEKLY TOTAL	42	7	35	7	~~18~~ 30	3½	34	[illegible]	16	12	3	~~44~~ 44	15	3½	30	[illegible]	12	8	[illegible]	~~16~~ 32	42	3½	7	35	3½	7

EXTRA DIET FOR SICK. (At the discretion of the Medical Superintendent:) } Extra Meat Dinner, Mutton Chop, Fish, Eggs, Mutton Broth, Beef Tea, Milk, Arrow-Root, Rice Pudding, Batter Pudding, Sago, Barley Water, Gruel, Oranges, Biscuits, Calf's Foot Jelly, Porter, Port Wine, Sherry, Brandy, Gin, Whiskey.

EXTRA DIET FOR WORKING PATIENTS. { ½ Pint Beer, 2 oz. Bread, 1 oz. Cheese, at 11 A.M., and ½ Pint Beer at 4 P.M., the Laundry Patients ½ Pint Tea. Tobacco and Snuff given as indulgences.

ATTENDANTS' AND SERVANTS' DIET. { Men, 1 lb. Uncooked Meat; Women, ¾ lb. ditto; ¾ lb. Vegetables, 1 lb. Bread, 1 Pint Coffee, 2 Pints Beer, daily. 2 oz. Tea, ½ lb. Sugar, ½ lb. Butter, 1 lb. Cheese, weekly. ¼ lb. Meat may be exchanged for Pudding or Pies, at the discretion of the Housekeeper.

COCOA FOR ONE HUNDRED PATIENTS......3½ lb. Cocoa, 6½ lb. Treacle, 3 Gallons Milk, or more if the Dairy yield it.
COFFEE DITTO ......1½ lb. Coffee, ½ lb. Chicory, 4 lb. Sugar, 13 Pints Mik.
TEA DITTO ......1 lb. Tea, 4 lb. Sugar, and 2 Gallons Milk.
MUTTON BROTH DITTO ....{ The Liquor of the Cooked Meat, Bones, &c., 25 lb. Meat, 3 lb. Scotch Barley, 4 lb. Rice, 25 lb. Turnips, Cabbage, Parsnip, Leek, Onion, or other Vegetables, Herbs, Salt and Pepper.
MEAT PIE DITTO ......Dripping Crust, 31 lb. Flour, 60 lb. Potatoes, 13 lb. Meat. Fruit Pie occasionally instead.

C. LOCKHART ROBERTSON, M.B., CANTAB.,
Medical Superintendent.

25th December, 1859.

Figure one

It is interesting to note that the only quantity which was the same for both sexes was that of beer. There were also differences in the staff diet, where, for example, the men received one pound of uncooked meat daily but the women only three-quarters of a pound.

By 8th October, Robertson was pleased with the way things were going:

> I have the satisfaction of recording that the moral machinery of the house is getting into working order; that the patients are becoming more tran-

quil and that since the opening of the Asylum not the slightest accident or injury to a patient, or an escape has occurred I can hardly hope that fortune will continue so to favour me.[11]

On 17th December, he was recording that one of the worst cases from Bethnal Green, John Petty, who had arrived on 13th August:

> … and who was dangerous and violent by day and who by night, regularly painted with his excrement the walls of his room and tore to shreds with great ingenuity all the strongest clothing… is at present employed at trade in one of the shops and he comes clean and orderly (every day)… I never saw such a chronic case so improved by treatment.[12]

But what was the treatment? Due to heavy administrative duties, Robertson probably saw little of the patients apart from when they were admitted or if they were seriously ill. His assistant, Mr Gwynne, saw more of them but presumably only for brief moments. The nursing staff, though reputedly experienced, were untrained and apparently ill-disciplined – thirteen were sacked by the end of 1859. Few drugs were used apart from painkillers and sedatives such as chloral hydrates, cannabis, digitalis and tobacco. In fact, five years later, Robertson told B. W. Richardson – who was writing *The Medical History of England* – that the patients derived more benefit from the use of tobacco as a sedative than anything else in his stock of drugs. In the asylum's first Annual Report for 1859, Robertson explained the treatment and its success in treating the patients transferred from London:

> A very marked improvement has taken place in the general health and conduct of the patients (many cases of long-standing mental disease) removed from London. The invigorating influence of the pure air and water of Haywards Heath has given light and colour to many who on admission presented a worn and dehabilitated appearance; while the order and discipline of the establishment have reduced into harmony and good conduct some of the most violent and unpromising class of insanity which the Medical Superintendent ever met with in practice.[13]

Some of the 'marked improvement' was undoubtedly due to patients being removed from far worse institutions. The scenes of some of the greatest abuses had occurred in asylums which had accommodated pauper lunatics. Bethnal Green Asylum had become infamous. In order to allow its attendants some free time at the weekends, patients there had been placed in cribs at 3pm on Saturday, secured with chains and left unattended till Monday morning.[14] These practices had died out by the time the Sussex Asylum opened, but no one was surprised to learn that many of its worst cases had arrived from Bethnal Green. A new asylum with few inmates could only be an improvement on some of the older private establishments. Besides, the alternatives to a county asylum, particularly a new one, were often a lot less attractive. "In the early days asylum life offered a significantly better quality of life than either workhouses, common lodging-houses or living from hand to mouth on the streets".[15]

THE ASYLUM STAFF

The Sussex Asylum was under the sole governance of the medical superintendent, Dr Robertson. He had control of all the officers, attendants, and servants resident in the asylum and had the authority to discharge and hire staff as he saw fit. But he had to live in the asylum and could not be absent from it for more than one night without the previous written consent of one of the Committee of Visitors. He was only answerable to the committee whom he met regularly and who paid frequent visits to the asylum. Robertson also was not allowed to do any private work. His administrative workload was extremely heavy. Apart from dealing with patients and staff, he had to meet and correspond with a wide range of people: Lunacy Commissioners, the Visitors' Committee, parish Directors and Guardians, workhouse officials and, patients' friends and families. It is not surprising that he was periodically ill – as were many of his successors who often suffered physical or mental breakdowns – and that he frequently had to ask for lengthy leave.

The personal authority vested in the medical superintendent was all-powerful and Robertson's will embraced every aspect of asylum life. The Committee of Visitors usually accepted his advice when it came to staff matters. In 1859 they gave a "£5 gratuity to William Knox, Head Attendant, on Doctor Robertson's recommendation as a mark of their approval of the ability and diligence displayed by him in the discharge of his duties".[16] They also accepted his advice that his assistant, Gwynne, should be paid £100 per annum although Gwynne had asked for £120. But the committee frequently rejected Robertson's pleas for better equipment and more amusements for the patients.

Robertson's assistant, Thomas Gwynne, was expected to see the patients at least twice a day, keep case records, make up medicines, and organise all the sporting and entertainment activities. Most importantly, he had to exercise a general control over the conduct of the attendants, and to report to Robertson any misconduct or neglect of duty on their part. Gwynne had to 'live in' and when Robertson was away he was in sole charge of the asylum.

The asylum chaplain, Henry Hawkins, was obliged to visit the wards once a week and was responsible for the spiritual guidance of not just the patients but also the staff and their families. He read daily prayers in the chapel and organised the educational classes. He was also responsible for the library and controlled the issue of books. Samuel Mortlock, the steward, was in charge of the domestic and clerical arrangements. Finally, the head attendants, Mrs Mortlock and William Knox, had the day-to-day control of the staff and the patients. They had to make sure that the asylum was kept clean and were responsible for the personal cleanliness of every patient. A good head attendant was crucially important to the smooth running of an asylum.

The new county asylums placed a lot of responsibility on the nursing staff. John Conolly, the medical superintendent of Hanwell Asylum, Middlesex, and one of the great asylum reformers, wrote in 1847:

> The character of particular patients, and all the patients of a ward, takes its colour from the character of the attendants placed in it. On their being proper or improper instruments, well or ill trained, well or ill disciplined, well or cared for, it depends whether many of the patients shall be cured or not cured; whether some shall live or die; whether frightful accidents, an increased mortality, incalculable uneasiness and suffering, and occasional suicides shall take place or not.[17]

The nursing staff were the backbone of the asylum. Their close daily proximity to the patients, their role as carers and their role as stimulators, were crucial to the process of inmate recovery. Although they did read to the patients and share their activities, much of the work of the nurses and attendants was that of a domestic servant. There was to be no proper training or qualifications for them until the 1890s. Working conditions were often exhausting with thirteen-hour days, six-day weeks and little annual leave – ten days in 1863. Ward work could be very demanding, stressful and dirty as Robertson's graphic account of the habits of John Petty testifies. After only two weeks, one attendant, Edward Bassett, fearing for his sanity on the wards, was swapped with the house porter, Fred Harper, whom Robertson found was too fond of gossiping with the female servants. Nurses were given board and lodging under their conditions of service but there was no obligation for male attendants to live in.

Some have claimed that most of the early county asylum staff were rejects from other professions. Many of the male attendants came from the services or from jobs in agriculture. Most nurses came from domestic service. Few of the initial staff intake at the Sussex Asylum were local people. On census night in 1861, only two out of the residing 26 nurses and attendants were born in Sussex.[18] Before the introduction of mental health training, job hopping amongst asylum staff seems to have been common. At the Sussex Asylum there was a wide disparity in wages between male and female staff:[19] a male attendant on average received £24 per annum whilst a nurse received between £15-£18 per annum. The lowest paid was the laundry maid, Ellen Genden, only £10 per annum whilst the artisans generally received the highest wages, between 25s. and 30s. per week.

The artisans played an important part in the practical application of moral treatment in the asylum. They worked a ten-hour day and occupied the patients in the workshops and supervised their walks. Apart from helping to make the asylum more self-sufficient, the artisans and their patient labour became a major source of profit. The therapeutic value of a good artisan was well appreciated by men like Robertson who believed strongly in the curative benefits of work.

The staff ratio at the asylum was 1:15 which Robertson believed was better than most. A good ratio was essential if all the old bad asylum practices were to be eliminated. Mechanical restraint – the indiscriminate use of leg irons and straps etc. with its low staff requirement – was officially discouraged and other more humane methods were encouraged to restrain the patients. These included individual attention, social activities, sport, education and padded cells. Preventing physical abuse was the cornerstone of the new humanitarian regimes. Robertson seems to have been relatively conscientious about trying to stop patient abuse and investigated every allegation. On 8th October, he wrote: "James Lesser reported that one of the other attendants M. Jordan was violent against William Welling. After careful investigation I found it was exaggerated"[20]. But as he became increasingly submerged by paperwork it became much harder for him to monitor exactly how much violence was going on. As the asylum grew in numbers and as the work of the staff became more demanding, there is evidence to suggest that as soon as the medical officers' backs were turned staff violence became quite frequent.

The Sussex Lunatic Asylum kept a 'Servants and Attendants Register' which recorded the names of the staff, their previous jobs and who had recommended them, their ages, starting and leaving dates and the reason for going. Not all the staff mentioned in Robertson's journal and order book are found in the register, perhaps because they may have been on a trial period. The register does record the high staff turnover at the beginning of the asylum's history. Many female staff left to get married whilst quite a few male staff seemed to have been dismissed for a variety of reasons. For 1859 the register records:[21]

Name	Age	Job	Date and Reason for Dismissal
Thomas Verral	26	Attendant	25/8/59, Slow and idle.
George Marwick	29	Attendant	No date. Idle shirker.
Edwin Eastlake	30	Attendant	14/11/59, Negligent to patients.
Will Simmonds	32	Ass. Gardener	17/12/59, Idle and useless.
Henry Green	34	Attendant	10/11/59, Drunk.
Henry Nunn	35	Tailor/Attendant	8/11/59, Useless.

Ellen Genden	28	Laundry Maid	19/11/59, Untidy, inactive.
Rufus Vizard	30	Attendant	23/9/59, Slow, disrespectful.
Liz Johnson	24	Nurse	1/11/59, Idle, impudent

Others were dismissed but their names do not appear in the register. Robertson wrote in his journal on 17th December that "Henry Gunn, one of the attendants, absented himself on the 26th November and is now before the bench at Lewes for drunkenness. I had to discharge him although he was an excellent attendant"[22]. At least five other staff left before the end of 1859. Many found the long hours and the demanding nature of asylum work unattractive.

THE PATIENTS AND MENTAL ILLNESS

The patients arrived at the Sussex Asylum with a variety of 'supposed causes of mental illnesses'. Below are some examples taken from the Admissions Register for 1859:

nervous exhaustion
mental debility
over-pressure of work
anxiety on account of illness of
    husband and excessive joy at
    his recovery
intemperance
spinal irritation
excitement on betting
hereditary

not taking sufficient food
overstudy
frightened by injury to head
religious excitement
fright from being attacked by
    cattle
run over cliff at Hastings
fear of reduced pecuniary
    circumstances.

The 'supposed causes' of insanity listed in the admission notes at the Sussex Asylum rarely cited the 'family relationships' as being the source of the problem. Instead, sudden changes in circumstances or adverse shocks were often blamed. In the case of female patients, their insanity was often thought to have its roots in gynaecological problems. The cause of 'religious excitement' was also very common. Later in the century, Alfred Newth, the asylum apothecary, claimed that they received a sudden increase in 'local' insanity cases after a visit to the area around Haywards Heath by a particularly powerful evangelical speaker.

The patients discharged are recorded in a table[23] of the asylum's first annual report, printed at the end of 1859. There, the form, length of disease and its apparent or alleged cause were all listed. It was the form of the disease that occupied and interested the medical superintendents most. The table shows that mania, acute mania, dementia, melancholia, idiot, and monomania were the principle classifications of insanity.

Mid-Victorian Britain was still largely ignorant about the causes of mental illness. Even the great social reformer, Lord Shaftesbury, (who was the chairman of the Lunacy Commissioners and whose own son Maurice suffered from severe epilepsy), believed that railway travel, commercial speculation and Catholicism were major causes. It was also a subject that was rarely spoken about and was often the source of much family shame. Shaftesbury himself was extremely embarrassed on one occasion when Maurice had a severe epileptic fit in public. He subsequently placed his son in care in Switzerland. Articles in the local Sussex newspapers of the period reflected the national interest and speculation about the causes of insanity. The following item appeared in The *Sussex Express* on 20th August 1859:

> The terrible ravages which tobacco is making on the bodies and minds of the young seem to be attracting the attention of medical men in various parts of the world. In a pamphlet just issued by Dr. Seymour, of London, on private lunatic asylums, and the causes of insanity of late years, the doctor denounces with emphasis as one of the producing causes the immoderate smoking indulged in by boys and young men at the universities and the larger schools and colleges.

And on 27th October, 1860, the *Brighton Herald* printed part of an article from the *Edinburgh Review* entitled 'Brain Difficulties'. Below is a short extract:

> It cannot be doubted that the rapid movements of the present age – the congregation of vast numbers of people together, and the fierce competition which ensues in the race for life, whether the object be to acquire riches or learning, all tend to produce a strain upon the brain which, if it does not end in insanity in the individual himself, has a detrimental effect upon the next generation.

The basic Victorian perception of mental disorder was that insanity was a disorder of the mind resulting from a structural or functional lesion of the brain. It was monomania – insanity with respect to only one mental faculty, idea or train of thought – which dominated psychological thinking for much of the nineteenth century. It was seen as an obsession with just one idea or instinct, ie. dipsomania, kleptomania, nymphomania, etc. which excluded and blocked the development of other natural instincts or feelings. Whereas the natural healthy condition of the mind was one that concentrated on many faculties; monomania made an insane person solitary and asocial. The disease could only be cured by suppressing the afflicted organs of the brain. This was to be achieved by using the other mental organs much more; thus distracting the brain from its weaker points.

This belief conveniently conformed to the reformers' conviction that phrenology – the study of the shape and size of the cranium as a supposed indication of character and mental faculties – and a positive environment could cure much insanity. Disturbed mental faculties could be improved by providing the sufferer with a healthy, activity-based environment. With time, such treatment would restore the organs of the brain to their proper balance. Phrenology, by describing mental disturbances in terms of individual organic causes, alleviated Victorian families' feelings of responsibility for the illness. Phrenology was eventually undermined by lack of scientific evidence and the advance of neurophysiology, but it did provide a framework which encouraged individual treatment and emphasized the importance of the environment in asylums. Robertson's belief in this led to his repeatedly asking the Visitors' Committee for extra money to improve the wards, to buy more books and newspapers and to provide more leisure activities.

The problem with classifications of insanity such as monomania, was that they widened the boundaries of what counted as disease. People previously considered to be sinful, or depraved, or even criminal were now judged, by at least some medical men, as being sick. Once the classifications were in place, asylum and workhouse officials (who often had very little knowledge about mental illness) tried to fit the patients into the various categories. It could be very much a hit-and-miss exercise.

THE END OF THE YEAR – 1859

By 25th December 1859,[24] there were 285 patients – 135 men and 150 women – in the asylum. Sixty-nine of them came from Brighton; nine were private patients and only two came from other counties. The maintenance rate for the contributing Sussex parishes started at 13s. per patient per week although this was reduced to 10s. 6d. by the end of the first year. The rate for non-county patients was 14s., and for private patients 16s.

By Christmas, eight patients had been discharged: four to the care of their husbands, six were pronounced cured and two were deemed unimproved. One of the cured, James Pelling, according to Robertson, was sane when he arrived although he was very "heavy and infirm". He was discharged to Lewes after a couple of weeks. It was much easier to be discharged if you had family or friends to stay with, as pauper lunatics were not entitled to any relief once they had left an asylum. Robertson recorded the gratitude of one of the patients, Mrs Anne Finch of Eastbourne: "On her departure she expressed herself most grateful for the attention and kindness she had received in the Asylum".[25] Another patient, Sarah French, who had previously spent five years in a private London asylum – Peckham House – was pronounced recovered after just three months. Robertson wrote "I attribute the recovery to this removal".[26]

TABLE III—*Shewing the Number of Patients Removed to the Asylum on its opening July 25th, 1859; Since Admitted, Discharged, and Dead; also distinguishing the Patients belonging to the different Unions, to December 25th, 1859.*

UNIONS.	Removed on the opening of the Asylum.			Since admitted for the First Time.			Total under Treatment.			Discharged Cured.			Discharged not Recovered.			Died.			Total Discharged and Dead.			Remaining in the Asylum Dec. 25, 1859.			UNIONS.
	M.	F.	T.	M.	F.	T.	M.	F.	T.	M.	F.	T.	M.	F.	T.	M.	F.	T.	M.	F.	T.	M.	F.	T.	
Arundel	1	..	1	..	1	1	1	1	2	..	..	..	..	..	..	..	..	..	..	..	..	1	1	2	Arundel.
Battle	6	1	7	1	1	2	7	2	9	..	..	..	..	..	..	1	..	1	1	..	1	6	2	8	Battle.
Brighton	23	40	63	4	6	10	27	46	73	..	..	..	1	..	1	1	2	3	2	2	4	25	44	69	Brighton.
Chailey	4	5	9	1	2	3	5	7	12	..	..	..	..	..	..	..	..	..	..	..	..	5	7	12	Chailey.
Cuckfield	4	7	11	1	1	2	5	8	13	..	..	..	..	..	..	..	1	1	..	1	1	5	7	12	Cuckfield.
Eastbourne	3	7	10	2	0	2	5	7	12	..	1	1	..	..	..	..	..	..	..	1	1	5	6	11	Eastbourne.
East Grinstead	9	2	11	..	..	..	9	2	11	..	..	..	..	..	..	1	..	1	1	..	1	8	2	10	East Grinstead.
Hailsham	5	8	13	..	..	..	5	8	13	..	..	..	..	..	..	..	..	..	..	..	..	5	8	13	Hailsham.
Hastings	3	7	10	2	2	4	5	9	14	..	..	..	..	..	..	..	..	..	..	..	..	5	9	14	Hastings.
Horsham	3	3	6	2	2	4	5	5	10	1	..	1	..	..	..	1	..	1	2	..	2	3	5	8	Horsham.
Lewes	3	4	7	..	..	..	3	4	7	1	..	1	..	..	..	..	..	..	1	..	1	2	4	6	Lewes.
Midhurst	4	5	9	..	..	..	4	5	9	..	..	..	..	..	..	..	..	..	..	..	..	4	5	9	Midhurst.
Newhaven	1	3	4	..	..	..	1	3	4	..	1	1	..	..	..	..	..	..	..	1	1	1	2	3	Newhaven.
Petworth	3	4	7	1	1	2	4	5	9	..	..	..	..	..	..	..	1	1	..	1	1	4	4	8	Petworth.
Broadwater	3	4	7	..	2	2	3	6	9	..	..	..	..	..	..	..	..	..	..	..	..	3	6	9	Broadwater
Rye	3	2	5	..	..	..	3	2	5	..	..	..	..	..	..	..	..	..	..	..	..	3	2	5	Rye.
Steyning	5	6	11	1	2	3	6	8	14	..	..	..	..	..	..	..	1	1	..	1	1	6	7	13	Steyning.
Sutton	3	1	4	..	1	1	3	2	5	..	..	..	..	..	..	..	..	..	..	..	..	3	2	5	Sutton.
Thakeham	2	2	4	..	..	..	2	2	4	..	1	1	..	..	..	..	..	..	..	1	1	2	1	3	Thakeham.
Ticehurst	5	3	8	..	1	1	5	4	9	..	1	1	..	..	..	..	..	..	..	1	1	5	3	8	Ticehurst.
Uckfield	8	3	11	1	..	1	9	3	12	..	..	..	..	..	..	..	..	..	..	..	..	9	3	12	Uckfield.
Westbourne	2	3	5	..	..	..	2	3	5	..	..	..	..	..	..	..	..	..	..	..	..	2	3	5	Westbourne.
Westfirle	3	3	6	..	1	1	3	4	7	..	..	..	..	..	..	..	1	1	..	2	2	3	2	5	Westfirle.
Westhampnett	6	8	14	2	..	2	8	8	16	..	..	..	..	..	..	..	..	..	..	..	..	8	8	16	Westhampnett.
County, Eastern	3	3	6	..	1	1	3	4	7	..	..	..	..	..	..	..	..	..	..	..	..	3	4	7	County, Eastern.
County, Western	..	1	1	..	..	..	..	1	1	..	..	..	..	..	..	..	..	..	..	..	..	..	1	1	County, Western.
Other Counties	..	..	..	1	1	2	1	1	2	..	..	..	..	..	..	..	..	..	..	..	..	1	1	2	Other Counties.
Private Patients	..	..	..	8	1	9	8	1	9	..	..	..	..	..	..	..	..	..	..	..	..	8	1	9	Private Patients.
Total	115	135	250	27	26	53	142	161	303	2	4	6	1	1	2	4	6	10	7	11	18	135	150	285	

Figure two

Ten patients had died in the asylum by 25th December. A table[27] in the first annual report shows that two of them died after less than two weeks. The average age of the dead patients was just under 46 years old. Robertson believed that the death of the five patients from London asylums was caused partly by their journey to the asylum, but mainly because they had left London in such a weak and pitiful condition. Indeed, he feared a high mortality rate in winter because of the age and weakness of the London patients and because of the asylum's poor heating. The 30 open fires were expensive to run and inefficient – they couldn't maintain an even temperature in the day and especially during the night when patients often got out of bed. In fact, the asylum caught fire on 17th December owing to the "careless and reckless way the hearth stones were laid".[28]

As Christmas approached, two reporters from the *Brighton Herald* were contemplating where to go on Christmas Eve when the postman arrived with an unexpected invitation. It was from Robertson and it invited them to attend the patient's ball at the asylum that evening. The reporters decided to accept this

A HISTORY OF THE DISCHARGES,

No. in Register.	Date of Admission.	Date of Discharge.	Age on Discharge.		DURATION OF DISORDER ON ADMISSION.				MENTAL AND PHYSICAL STATE ON ADMISSION.			
			Male.	Female.	Age at First Attack.	Number of previous Attacks.	Duration of present Attack.	Class in reference to Duration.	Form of Disease.	Particular Propensities or Hallucinations.	Original Intellect and Disposition.	Bodily Complications or Disorder.
116	August 5th, 1859	August 22nd, 1859	59		52	First	6 Years	IV.	Mania	Irritable and Eccentric	Good	Chronic Rheumatism
155	August 11th, 1859	Sept. 17th, 1859		54	53	First	1 Year	II.	Melancholia	Extreme Depression	Fair	
170	August 16th, 1859	Sept. 20th, 1859		36	36	First	3 Weeks	I.	Dementia	Violent and Incoherent	Fair	Sunstroke Paralysis
21	July 25th, 1859	Nov. 5th, 1859	59			Several	1 Year	IV.	Monomania	Desire of Drink	Good	
3	July 25th, 1859	Nov. 26th, 185J		49	35	Two	2 Years	IV.	Melancholia	Extreme Depression	Fair	
237	Sept. 8th, 1859	Nov. 23rd, 1859	10		From Birth			IV.	Idiot	Very dirty habits	Nil	
206	August 24th, 1859	Nov, 29th, 1859		46	41	First	5 Years	IV.	Acute Mania	Great Excitement	Good	
43	July 27th, 1859	Nov. 30th, 1859	20		20	First	1 Week	I.	Dementia	Utter Prostration of Mind	Fair	

Class I., First Attack, and within 3 Months.—Class II., First Attack above 3, but within 12 M

OBITUARY, FROM 25th

No. in Register.	Date of Admission.	Date of Death.	Age at Death.		DURATION OF DISORDER ON ADMISSION.				MENTAL AND PHYSICAL STATE ON ADMISSION.			
			Male.	Female.	Age at First Attack.	Number of previous Attacks.	Duration of present Attack.	Class in reference to Duration.	Form of Disease.	Particular Propensities or Hallucinations.	Original Intellect and Disposition.	Bodily Complications or Disorder.
35	July 25th, 1859	August 6th, 1859		63	63	First	6 Months	II.	Melancholia	Religious Delusions	Fair	Very debilitated, covered with ulcers, vermin, and bruises
169	August 13th, 1859	August 25th, 1859		49	49	First	1 Month	I.	Dementia	Utter Mental Prostration		
111	August 5th, 1859	Oct. 13th, 1859	43		37	First	6 Years	IV.	Dementia	Ditto		Filthy habits
219	Sept. 2nd, 1859	Oct. 25th, 1859	45		41	First	4 Months	IV.	Dementia	Propensity to Pilfering	Fair	Dirty habits
118	August 10th, 1859	Oct. 27th, 1859		65	65	First	4 Months	II.	Melancholia	Refusal of Food		Extreme debility
122	August 11th, 1859	Nov. 22nd, 1859		33	33	First	5 Months	II.	Monomania	Religious Delusions		Paralysis of left side
228	Sept. 2nd, 1859	Nov. 24th, 1859	19		Congenital	Idiot		IV.	Dementia			Habits filthy
282	Nov. 17th, 1859	Dec. 7th, 1859		56	54	Several	4 Days	III.	Mania	Extreme Incoherence		None
277	Nov. 9th, 1859	Dec. 20th, 1859	37		37	First	2 Months	I.	Dementia	Destructive		Habits dirty
239	Sept. 15th, 1859	Dec. 22nd, 1859		48	47	First	16 Months	IV.	Dementia	Extreme Mental Prostration		Habits dirty

Class I., First Attack, and within 3 Months.—Class II., First Attack above 3, but within 12 Mo

Figure three: Tables from the Annual Report of 1859 showing the history of discharges and causes of death of patients admitted in that year.

rather unusual invitation. They clambered aboard the train for Haywards Heath at Brighton station and found that half the town's population seemed to be catching the same train. They soon found themselves squeezed amongst a more than customary prevalence of babies, bonnet boxes and pocket flasks. As they alighted at Haywards Heath they were greeted with the sweet sound of the nearby Lindfield church bells.

The night was pitch black and it started to rain as the intrepid reporters stumbled along roads that once wet, were virtually impossible to walk on. They eventually managed to hire a dog-cart from the Haywards Heath Inn and plunged into the country in the direction of the asylum. As they jogged along quietly, they were met with the occasional "Good Night!" thrown at them out

ABLE III.

FROM THE 25th JULY, TO 25th DECEMBER, 1859.

CIVIL STATE ON ADMISSION.			APPARENT OR ALLEGED CAUSE.			Result.	REMARKS.
As to Marriage.	As to Religious Persuasion.	As to Occupation.	PREDISPOSING.		Exciting.		
			Hereditary.	Other Causes.			
Married	Church of England	Glazier				Recovered	Convalescent on Admission. Transfer from another Asylum at opening
Married	Church of England		Not known	Ill health	Domestic trouble	Recovered	
Married	Church of England				Sunstroke	Unimproved	To the care of her husband
Married	Church of England				Drink	Recovered	To the care of her husband. (Two month's previous out on trial.)
Married	Church of England		Not known		Not known	Recovered	To the Idiot Asylum, Redhill, with consent of Commissioners in Lunacy.
Single	Church of England			Fright of Mother during pregnancy		Unimproved	To the care of her husband.
Married	Church of England		Not known		Blow to head	Recovered	Evidently the result of an injury in a brawl
Single	Church of England					Recovered	

Months.=Class III., Not First Attack, and within 12 Months.—Class IV., Cases of more than 12 Months duration.

BLE IV.

JULY, TO 25th DECEMBER, 1859.

CIVIL STATE ON ADMISSION.			APPARENT OR ALLEGED CAUSE.			Cause of Death.	REMARKS.
As to Marriage.	As to Religious Persuasion.	As to Occupation.	PREDISPOSING.		Exciting.		
			Hereditary.	Other Causes.			
Widow	Protestant Dissenter		No information to be obtained			Bronchitis	A Transfer from Bethnal Green
Married	Mormon	Wife of Laborer			Mormonism	Exhaustion	Admitted from her own home moribund. Lived [12 Days
Married	Church of England	Bricklayer				Pyæmia	Transfer from Bethnal Green
Married	Church of England	Coachman				Sanguineous Apoplexy	Transfer from Hanwell
Widow	Church of England	Charwoman				Exhaustion	
Married	Church of England	Wife of Laborer			Over Study	Bronchitis	Transfer from Bethnal Green
Single	Church of England					Dysentery	Transfer from Hoxton House
Widow	Church of England					Valvular Disease of Heart	
Single	Church of England	Stableman				Pulmonary Apoplexy	
Widow	Romanist					Exhaustion	Admitted in a filthy unsatisfactory state

nths.—Class III., Not First Attack, and within 12 Months.—Class IV., Cases of more than 12 Months duration.

of the darkness from the roadside:

> Presently, distant lights gleamed through the bare trees; as we went on they shone more and more brightly, till at length it was not difficult to discern that they were ranged row above row – shining, in fact from the windows of the Asylum, which was lit from wing to wing. Glowing thus in the dark night, it rose on us even more like a fairy palace that it had ever done beneath the blue skies of June [on their last visit].

Though it was clearly a time of high festival, they had by no means "thrown wide the doors". On the contrary, they were fast closed and scrupulously guarded. And this trifling fact had a significance in it that struck one forcibly. Going to a ball! It was more like going to prison. The clang of the heavy door behind one, the shooting of the bolt into its socket, the close scrutiny of our credentials, the heavy tramp of the porter's feet, as we followed him down the long stone corridor – Well! the feeling it produced was not exhilarating. In point of truth the situation powerfully recalled to our mind a story we had somewhere met with of a French maquis, who, under pretence of being taken to a masquerade at Versailles, suddenly found himself in virtue of a 'lettre di cachet', lodged in the Bastille.

But the end of the corridor once reached, the aspect of affairs changed. There the word "Welcome", wrought in flowers upon a banner, re-assured us, and no less did the strain of lively music which at the moment broke upon our ears. Just then, too, Dr Robertson himself, attended by Mr Mortlock the steward, and the Head Warder, advanced to meet us, and, in his cordial reception, the gloomy impressions which had surrounded us faded away. "The Ball", the Doctor informed us, "had commenced, would we proceed at once to the Ball-room?" Certainly: but were we to mix with the patients? "By all means. They were accustomed to visitors and pleased to receive them".

Without further parley, we followed the Doctor. A few paces brought us to the Ball-room. It was a bright, cheerful scene as ballrooms are wont to be, and at the first glance had no special features to distinguish it from others. A large room – the roof supported by pillars – elegant gas-brackets around the room – the band in a raised orchestra pit at one extremity - festoons of laurel and floral designs upon the walls – people arranged in sets, dancing quadrilles. These were the salient features: these would be the features in any ball at this Christmas time. But, as one looked closer, other features were disclosed, and these gave the scene a special tone and character of its own.

The knowledge that these dancers and those spectators sitting so quietly around were all lunatics – that collectively they represented almost every form of mania with which God or their own folly has afflicted men – no doubt insensibly affected one in looking on this scene. But apart from this there was something strange and unnatural about it. It was too quiet. It was too subdued in tone. There was too little vigour in the movements of those who moved; too obvious an abstraction about those who were in repose. The dancers went through the dance with an over-sad earnestness – with a painful over-estimate of their responsibility. No natural joyous exhilaration lit up their faces – no merry twinkle of the eye finished the half-spoken jest – no merry laughter rang from the full heart. And missing all this, you missed the soul of the Ball-room. You did; but they did not. Obviously to the limit of their capacities, the 200 persons there assembled were supremely happy.

We took an opportunity of putting the question to Dr Robertson – were they really enjoying themselves? "Thoroughly" he replied. "This is their favourite amusement. We have in the Asylum every means of recreation. The inmates play at draughts and cribbage, and all kinds of games; but they have a ball every Wednesday evening, and they look forward to it with all the impatience of children. This Christmas Eve Ball is, of course, special and it has created the most intense interest among them. The whole of the decorations were done by the insane."

These decorations were most tasteful and profuse. There were tablets on the walls with inscriptions such as "A Merry Christmas and Happy New Year"; there were pendant garlands, the pillars were wreathed with evergreen, and the walls were covered with designs. We found subsequently that this was not only the case in the Ball-room but that the corridors throughout the Asylum had been adorned in like manner.

All this was revealed in hasty glances; but the great interest of the place was human interest. We could not keep our eyes from the groups who passed and re-passed before us. Their appearance was diversified: for though the majority of the inmates wore the Asylum garb – a simple blue-checked dress for the women, and grey tweed suits for the men, – some steadfastly refused to adopt that style, and appeared resplendent in scare-crow refinery. One little old lady was particularly amusing. Her mania took the form of a belief that she was Queen of England: and Her Majesty insisted on adopting a costume calculated to inspire proper deference and respect. We may note that Her Majesty's style of polking – for in that dance we first caught sight of her – was peculiar. It consisted in taking firm hold of the partner who might be honoured with a command to dance, and pursuing him, with trotting, paddling little steps, round and round. We refer to this case, because it illustrates a class – and those the most amusing – in which the insane have lost personal identity. There was another case, in which a poor fellow imagined himself Prince Rupert: and it would have been singular to see the Prince dancing with Her Majesty; but that was forbidden by the rules laid down for the management of these assemblies. Lunatics do not dance with lunatics. If the lady is insane, she dances with an attendant or a visitor; if the gentleman is of the unfortunate class, you perceive at a glance that the lady is a nurse or some one of sane mind. This adds to the diversity in the appearance of the room, to which we have alluded.

As a rule, the dancing was good, many patients having acquired the art, in all its branches, in the Asylum. It was conducted in perfect order, though without any apparent restraint; marvellous to think of when all the facts are considered. Take one fact only. A young woman, of unpromising facial angles, approached, and asked us to join her in a polka? Not from any apprehension, but perhaps from being unprepared for this advance on the part of a lady, we declined the honour. "A fort-night ago", said Dr Robertson, "that young woman was raving: she is at this moment quite harmless." Many similar cases were pointed out to us, all tending to illustrate the perfection of the system which it is possible to adopt in a thoroughly classified public institution like this.

One point we must not omit to make. Not only were we in the midst of lunatic dancers, but those who made the music for us were the most part lunatics also! It is a fact that in the orchestra the two violinists and the drummer were all insane, though quite capable of the task which they had undertaken; for this, Dr Robertson explained, is a peculiarity of minds affected with manias of any kind, – they have no consistency in maintaining them. Thus, for instance, let a poor patient believe himself to be the Czar of all the Russias, still he will willingly clean your boots for you. His dignity is not offended, and he hasn't a notion of the incongruity! In this odd little world, therefore, you can never judge of a man by his actions. The lady who invited us to accompany her into the garden to partake of strawberries – overlooking the trifling fact that people don't usually gather strawberries in the dark on Christmas Eve – might have been the Begum of Oude ; and it would not have surprised us to discover that the gentleman, who was handing round a tray of cakes and fruit for the refreshment of the dancers was the pope himself.

The saddest feature of the whole scene was to detect among the patients the haggard faces of more than one townsman whom we had known in bygone times. But we will not be tempted to enlarge on this topic. Sad at the best, let us at least quit our theme under its brightest aspects – let us be content to have dwelt on the sunnier hues of the picture – and let us entertain the hope that we shall have struck no painful chord in this rapid sketch of the Sussex Asylum Ball on Christmas Eve.[29]

1859 CONCLUDED

The 'rapid sketch' of the *Brighton Herald* reporters, in some ways, tell us a lot more about the asylum than all the official documents. It presents a mixed picture. On the one hand, there is a prison-like quality about the place – something which the reformers had been trying to eliminate – and the patients appear to be largely subdued and sad. On the other hand, there is evidence of a defiant individuality and the social occasion of the ball is undoubtedly a positive development in the treatment of patients. The article also gives an insight into the prevailing attitudes and preconceptions towards the mentally ill at that time.

The local press showed a keen interest in the asylum's performance in its early years. There was a lot of curiosity about this new institution with its palace-like appearance. Initially, it was seen as a bit of a success story. By contrast, reports about the Brighton Workhouse by Brighton newspapers were much more subdued. In 1859, 701 inmates had a Christmas lunch there but the occasion was only given a brief mention in the local press and was described as a rather Spartan affair. It is also possible that, initially, Robertson was quite good at cultivating the support of local journalists.

The Annual Report included reports by the Lunacy Commissioners, the Committee of Visitors, the medical superintendent, the chaplain, the Farm and Garden Committee and finally statistical information. The commissioners' report was usually the most critical one and it was regarded with a mixture of irritation and respect by the Visitors' Committee. By their vigilance, the commissioners ensured that the insane paupers in asylums had a better standard of living than the sane paupers in workhouses – who were monitored by the Central Poor Law Board. They also had the power to visit insane paupers kept in workhouses and their presence was often a source of unease to workhouse authorities. Instead, there was a strong element of public relations in both Robertson's and the Visitors' Committee's reports; although the former became quite adept at using the commissioners' recommendations to reinforce his own demands to the committee.

All the reports on the Sussex Lunatic Asylum's first five months were extremely positive. Despite falling off his horse – which resulted in him having two weeks off work in November – Robertson was full of enthusiasm. Despite the high staff turnover – which wasn't mentioned in his report – he was justly proud that "no accident, or injury to a patient, or escape has occurred".[30] Routine work, a stable diet and organised activities were producing good results even if the improvement in some of the patients was due to their transfer from far worse institutions. Robertson was also setting basic care standards and had refused to keep quiet about patient neglect and abuse at the Brighton Workhouse. Overall, the first few months of the asylum's existence must be regarded as a remarkable achievement, not just by one man, but by the great Victorian reforming energy which he embodied.

Chapter Five

1860
"THE WAY TO CURE LUNATICS"

The peace and calm of the new asylum's short history was rudely shattered by an incident which occurred on the 19th January. The previous November, George Tyron, a criminal lunatic, had arrived from the Kent Asylum. He was thirty years old and had worked as a chemist's assistant until he was twenty-five. His mother had then died and he subsequently had a 'breakdown'. He started to claim that he was a prophet and obliged to obey 'commands' from above. After attacking the husband of a woman whom he was fond of, he was placed in the Kent Asylum. There, he seriously injured one attendant, endangering his life, and was prone to making malicious attacks on the doctors. He also broke 100 squares of glass in a few minutes with his shoe, and without injuring himself. He was then put in seclusion for two years until his transfer to the Sussex Asylum. Kent's Medical Superintendent, James Huxley, sent Robertson a warning note:

> This man has never attacked with his fists in the fair English Fashion; he always resorts to a weapon such as can be used stiletto-wise… This man appears to be an assassin by nature and treacherous. Trust him not![1]

But once at the Sussex Asylum, Tyron appeared calm and collected and completely sane. So much so, that Robertson soon gave him the job of chapel clerk and even wrote to the Lunacy Commissioners on the 6th January, stating that he considered him sane. But it didn't last. On the 18th January, at one of the asylum's weekly balls, Tyron complained to Robertson of feeling unwell. The Doctor placed him in the assistant medical officer's room and gave him some water and whisky. Fifteen minutes later he appeared to be better and was sent to bed. Robertson described what happened the next day as his assistant, Dr

Gwynne, was doing his morning rounds accompanied by two attendants:

> Tyron came up and shook hands with him, as usual, and said he wanted
> to speak to him about some money matters of his own; he then suddenly,
> and without the slightest provocation, attempted with a sharp piece of
> wood he had concealed about him, to destroy Mr Gwynne's eye. The
> blow fortunately glanced off his forehead, but was so severe as to knock
> him down – he attempted to kick and injure him but was speedily
> overpowered.[2]

Tyron was immediately placed in a padded room. An hour later, he told
Robertson quite rationally, that he disliked medical officers, that he wouldn't
injure any of the attendants, and that Gwynne had had a very lucky escape. He
was then put in seclusion and 'personal restraint' – involving his hands being
tied to his belt – was used at the asylum for the first time. Robertson appealed
to the Visitors and the Lunacy Commissioners to remove Tyron to Fisherton
House Asylum in Wiltshire which had specialist accommodation for criminal
lunatics. Whilst waiting for the transfer, Tyron acted like a "wild beast" whenever
Robertson or his assistant came near him but was well-behaved with other staff
and even showed some remorse over his attack on the attendant at the Kent
Asylum. He was finally removed on the 7th February to Fisherton House. Few
would have forecast then that one day he would return again to the Sussex
Asylum.

Tyron's attack illustrated the dangerous nature of work in asylums before
the later use of heavy chemical restraint. It also emphasized the lack of adequate
care facilities for criminal lunatics. Most of them were kept in asylums, prisons
and even workhouses. The only major asylum with specialist facilities was
Bethlem in London. The situation only changed when the Criminal Lunatics
Act of 1860 set up funds for institutions for the criminally insane such as
Broadmoor.

On 18th April, Thomas Gwynne, the Assistant Medical Officer, finally
resigned.[3] A number of incidents seem to have triggered this decision: Tyron's
attack, his small wage increase, and finally arguments with the House Steward,
Mr Samuel Mortlake, which proved to be the last straw. Robertson recorded that
"a most undesirable feeling of jealousy has existed between Gwynne and the
steward in the discharge of their duties".[4] But he lay the blame elsewhere:

> I very much blame the steward's wife for all this discord. She is no help
> in her husband's work but is always giving opinions. She is a dissatisfied
> unsatisfactory person to deal with. In exchange for board and lodging she
> should have supervised the singing group of attendants but refused to
> because a "common man", the painter, was the best singer. She seems to

be a constant source of irritation and discord and having nothing to do is always about the house and stores… Every discord in an asylum reacts unfavourably on the patients and they are my first and chief care and all other arrangements must be made subordinate to their welfare. The attendants and even officers returning to their duty heated from their constant altercations in the Steward's stores – chiefly at the interference of the Steward's wife – are not in a frame of mind rightly to discharge their obligations to the patients… This exerts an injurious influence on my patients, patients so entirely dependent on me in their great affliction for the smallest want and for their every comfort.[5]

Robertson recommended to the committee that the steward and his wife be obliged to live outside the asylum at an increased salary. Instead, the committee merely warned them about their future conduct. Three months later, Robertson was writing that "now a much more satisfactory feeling exists throughout the house" [6] but he still had strong feelings about the steward's wife:

As a guide to any successor of mine who may have to deal with Mr. Mortlock, keep Mrs. Mortlock out of the office of housekeeper if he values his comfort and independence! I have a very strong opinion on this point.[7]

Mrs Mortlock died a few months later whilst her husband continued to work at the asylum until 1901. Robertson perceived staff disputes, however trivial, to be a real threat to the harmony of the asylum. They also took up his time, so much so that on 24th March the Visitors' Committee decided to relieve him from the supervision and management of the garden and farm. A committee was appointed instead. Three weeks later, the arrival of a patient, John Mockford, a 26-year-old married painter from the Brighton Workhouse, would occupy a lot more of his time. It would also lead to the tensions existing between Robertson and the Brighton Guardians breaking out into a bitter public dispute.

THE JOHN MOCKFORD CASE

On Mockford's admission on 13th April, Gwynne (five days before resigning) certified that "he was in a very reduced condition of health apparently from confinement and want of proper management and his person was marked with blows and bruises of recent occurrence".[8] Robertson immediately wrote an angry letter to Mr W. Hollis (one of the Brighton magistrates on the Visitors' Committee) complaining about Mockford's condition and sent a copy of it to the Lunacy Commission:

My dear Sir,

     I think it right to acquaint you that a patient has this day been admitted from the Brighton Workhouse in a shameful state, his limbs and shoulders marked with bruises from blows and the lower part of his back excoriated from being allowed to lie in urine unchanged. The man is quiet – in a state of chronic mania. His name is John Mockford, a house painter and decorator... Serious fault in my opinion lies on the authorities at the Workhouse to permit an unfortunate lunatic to be so abused; the blows and injuries are of recent state, I should say within a week. The excoriation may be of a fortnight or three weeks' standing.[9]

John Mockford died on the 17th April; the same day that the Lunacy Commissioners had written the following letter to the Brighton Guardians:

Sir,

     The Commissioners in Lunacy observing, by the statement of the Medical Superintendent of the Sussex Asylum, that John Mockford, a pauper patient recently admitted therein from the Brighton Workhouse, is alleged to be "reduced from confinement and ill-treatment, and marked with blows and bruises on the limbs", would be obliged by your informing them how long the patient was in the Workhouse before his removal to the asylum, and what his bodily condition was upon entering the Workhouse and leaving it.

Your obedient servant

John Forster,

Secretary.[10]

The Brighton Guardians had already been tipped off about Robertson's letter by Mr. Hollis and had launched their own enquiry, sending a deputation to the asylum on 18th April, the day after Mockford had died. On 20th April, Richard Rugg, the House Surgeon to the Workhouse, replied to the Commissioners:

65, Middle Street, Brighton

Dear Sir,

... I beg to state that he [Mockford] was admitted into the Brighton Infirmary last July as a person of weak intellect only. He remained in that state until about a week previous to his admittance into the asylum, when he was attacked with a violent fit of mania, which is supposed to have been brought on by his mother's not calling to take him out for a day, as she usually did once a month. The excitement gradually increased upon him until he was obliged to be under restraint, which was ordered for him about three or four days before he was sent to the asylum. His bodily health was in other respects good, and had been so from the day of his admission to the day of his departure from our infirmary. There were no more bruises upon his body than what might naturally be expected under the circumstances. I am confident that no blows were inflicted or unnecessary handling resorted to. The Guardians, in company with myself and the Overseer have examined his body, and quite concur with me that the Superintendent has grossly exaggerated the facts of the case.

I am Sir,

Your obedient servant,

R. Rugg.[11]

The Brighton Guardians amassed evidence to support their case. Mrs Willis, the head nurse at the Workhouse Infirmary, stated that:

> Mockford had a change of linen and sheeting every day, that he was very violent, that there were times when the wardmen were compelled to restrain him; but that no unnecessary force was used; but he never complained to her of any ill-usage, that she had no reason to suppose any one ever struck him; and that, if she had heard of his being struck, she would have reported it.[12]

A Workhouse porter claimed that when he took Mockford before the Magistrate:

> … in order to obtain the order for his removal to the asylum, he threw himself down three times, and that the bruises were no doubt, caused by his falling; that he was obliged to carry him from the fly [a horse-drawn light carriage] to the railway carriage, as he would not walk.[13]

Lastly, the Workhouse Infirmary wardsmen stated that:

> … he was in the ward nine days and was carefully watched; that he tried several times to run away, and when prevented he threw himself on the floor violently; that he was washed daily with warm water, and his linen changed every day; that no more force was used in restraining him than was absolutely necessary; and that he bruised himself chiefly by his own violence; that when having his haircut he slipped about and got out of his chair a dozen times; that it took five men to hold him; that he had to be forcibly put to bed sometimes and that he was the most violent case they had ever seen.[14]

The Lunacy Committee of the Workhouse produced a report of their visit, of 18th April, to the asylum. It repeated Mr Rugg's assertions: that Mockford's body only had bruises of a "trifling nature" on his admission to the asylum; that they were chiefly self-inflicted and that Robertson had exaggerated his condition. Furthermore, they claimed that in twenty years of sending their (Brighton's) patients to the London asylums, they had not received one complaint about the state of the patients when delivered. Yet since the opening of the Sussex Asylum, complaints had been frequent. They also pointed out that

Robertson had refused to see them at the asylum and that he was hostile to the Parish of Brighton.

At a noisy meeting of the Brighton Guardians on Tuesday 24th April, several highly critical speeches were made of Robertson. A motion supporting the above report was proposed by William Marchant who claimed that the asylum:

> … is now part and parcel of our business to attend, to superintend it occasionally, to see that our poor there are properly and carefully treated, and that the place is properly conducted. ("Hear, hear")… Where a Parish like Brighton contributes so large an amount to the building and maintenance (£3,000 a year, one fourth of the total cost) of an asylum, this amount forms a most important item in our expenditure, and ought to be watched over narrowly. ("Hear, hear").[15]

William Lucas, seconded the motion, adding that bruises usually discolour more in death but that on Mockford's body there had only been "surface bruises". He added that Robertson's refusal to meet their investigating committee was a "decided insult to the town".[16]

Other speakers agreed and queued up to complain about Robertson's "unjustifiable attack on the officers of this parish" and his discourtesy towards the Brighton Lunacy Committee on several occasions. The motion that "their report be printed, and copies thereof be transmitted to the Home Secretary, to the Committee of Visitors of the Sussex Lunatic Asylum"[17] was passed unanimously.

Robertson had made a mistake in not demanding an inquest and received a mild reprimand in a letter from the Lunacy Commissioners on 27th April. They concluded that:

> … they were of the opinion that assuming the injuries to have proceeded from ill-treatment, it was in the highest degree expedient that an inquest should have been held and they begged that, on the recurrence of any such case, he would not fail to direct that notice be given to the Coroner.[18]

Robertson replied firmly to the Guardian's allegations and defended his own conduct. He reiterated his central claim – backed up by Gwynne's evidence – that Mockford had arrived from the Brighton Workhouse in an appalling condition and had obviously suffered great abuse:

> … that so evident had the patient been subject to blows that when spoken to or approached he always held up his arm to protect himself and shrank back. He had a worn emaciated aspect and was quite unable to swallow any solid food during the few days he survived his removal.[19]

In his systematic reply, reproduced in full in Appendix 1, Robertson more than answered the Brighton Guardians' allegations. He also challenged their claim that they had a right to supervise the asylum:

> The Lunacy Act… does not in any way authorise their official examination of the asylum or of its management.[20]

The Visitors' Committee tried to play down the affair. At their meeting of 19th May, they issued a letter to Robertson and the Brighton Guardians:

> The Visitors regret that any such communication as has taken place should have been deemed necessary on the subject of the deceased patient, John Mockford. They do not consider it within their duty to express an opinion beyond the walls of this asylum on the merits of this case and they trust that the Brighton Guardians will agree with them in the necessity of the Visitors as such adhering to this course.[21]

But for some of the Guardians, the letter didn't go far enough. At their meeting of 26th May, Mr Marchant declared that "the Board was not left entirely in doubt as to whether the Visiting Justices approved or disapproved of Dr Robertson's conduct in this matter".[22] A week later they received a verbal apology from the Visitors.

The Brighton Guardians had got the public vindication – though not in writing – that they had wanted. And Robertson was not given the support from his employers which he was entitled to expect. It was clear that in any further altercations with the Brighton Workhouse, he would be on his own. Not surprisingly, no mention of the Mockford case is made by either the Visitors or Robertson in the 1860 Sussex Lunatic Asylum Annual Report.

What had happened to Mockford? It seems odd that a seemingly harmless idiot, who worked in the workhouse garden, could turn into the "most violent man" whom the staff claimed to have ever seen. The Workhouse Committee stated that it was his mother's failure to visit him which caused Mockford's behaviour to change. Unfortunately, because there was no inquest, we are not able to hear the views of his mother or his wife. In subsequent cases of alleged abuse involving the asylum and the Brighton Workhouse – where public inquests were held – the testimony of the victim's family would be of crucial importance. It is also odd that once Mockford was transferred to the asylum, he suddenly stopped being violent and instead became very subdued. It is not possible to be certain about what had happened to Mockford but it is very likely that Robertson's allegations were justified. Firstly, Robertson was a highly experienced asylum doctor. He could surely distinguish between trivial bruising and bruising resulting from brutal treatment. If the bruising had been minor, Robertson was taking a huge risk that an independent examination of the body – which in the event didn't happen – would not discover this. Secondly, it would have been easier for Robertson to say nothing about Mockford. By alleging Workhouse abuse he was making the asylum vulnerable to the charge that the mis-treatment had taken place there. Unless he was absolutely certain, he was also risking having to publicly apologise to the Brighton Guardians – something he had already done before over another complaint about Workhouse treatment.

The Brighton Guardians, aggrieved at their under-representation on the asylum's management committee, continually criticized Robertson and the asylum in its early years. Their statement that in twenty years of sending their pauper lunatics to London asylums they had not received one complaint, Robertson would challenge later. By not complaining to the Brighton Guardians directly – which he was not obliged to do – Robertson had demonstrated the irrelevance of their authority to the asylum. This seems to have offended them as much as the actual allegations of mis-treatment. At best their reaction to these allegations was defensive, at worst it was an over-reaction which was, in many ways, more incriminating. Conditions in the Brighton Workhouse were at the very least, inadequate. A fact confirmed later on in the year when Mr Lutridge – a Lunacy Commissioner – described the Workhouse Infirmary as presenting "an aspect of discomfort".[23]

The over-reaction of the Guardians was not surprising in the light of recent workhouse history. The Brighton Workhouse had opened in 1822 with 95 inmates. By 1860 there were more than seven hundred. In the previous ten years, three of the four governors had been sacked – the last one in 1859 for misconduct after a series of scandalous events. Many people blamed the Brighton Guardians for paying their Governors such poor wages – £80-£90 per annum as opposed to Robertson's £400 – which had attracted low quality applicants:

> The class of persons from whom Governors are chosen is limited and utterly worthless. Men that have failed in every other pursuit are thought good enough to be Governors of a Workhouse; and accordingly duties demanding the soundest judgement and great energy and intelligence are, in nine cases out of ten, committed in cold blood to insolvent tradesmen and broken down schoolmasters.[24]

This dispute also illustrated the contrasting ethos of asylum and workhouse. The New Poor Law of 1834 had made workhouses institutions of last resort. Under the act the able-bodied poor could obtain assistance only by staying at workhouses, where conditions were made as uncomfortable as possible and families were split up with the view to discouraging all but the really needy. So quite apart from any psychiatric disorder, a large proportion of people coming from workhouses were suffering from serious physical illness or neglect. On the other hand, the new county asylum administrators believed that good conditions in their asylums would increase the possibility of cure thereby saving money in the long term. To many workhouse authorities asylums were extravagant and costly; to asylum superintendents like Robertson, workhouses were an obstacle to therapeutic success.

A recent book, *Insanity, Institutions and Society,* edited by J. Melling and B. Forsythe, has highlighted the way in which county asylums were dependent on Poor Law bureaucracy and inextricably linked to the workhouse system. As we have seen at the Sussex Asylum, the admission of patients was in the hands of workhouse guardians and local magistrates, usually lay people who had little medical knowledge. Robertson had no say in the matter. And although he did try and control the discharge of patients, he could only make recommendations to his Visiting Committee who held the legal responsibility for that decision. Obviously, this lack of jurisdiction, especially over the admission of pauper lunatics, was not a situation that many medical superintendents were happy about.

Apart from the dispute about Mockford's condition, there appears to have been genuine personal animosity between Robertson and some of the Brighton Guardians. No doubt the Guardians, mainly tradesmen who had worked their way up, resented Robertson's wealthy and privileged background. That he showed them little respect added to their grievances against him and his asylum. This whole episode shows Robertson as a man who was not afraid to speak out against abuses even if it meant upsetting powerful bodies such as the Brighton Guardians. Four years later the Brighton Guardians would retaliate with some allegations of their own.

ROBERTSON AND THE LUNACY COMMISSIONERS

If Robertson felt that the Brighton Guardians were the enemy, he saw the Lunacy Commission very much as his ally. It had been established in 1845 when it consisted of six full-time professionals (three medical and three legal) and a group of lay members. Since that date its commissioners had travelled all over the country visiting pauper lunatics in public and private asylums and workhouses. They saw every patient and checked on their health, diet, work and environment. But none of its early medical commissioners had any experience as asylum superintendents and the commission was often regarded by the medical profession as a group of evangelical reformers who had little idea about mental illness or its treatment. They were often accused of being interfering, power hungry, and of recommending unnecessary expense. But not by Robertson. He repeatedly used the commission to pressurize his own committee into agreeing with his requests. That year he wrote:

> The Lunacy Commission advised more objects of interest for the patients and an increase for the library. I entirely concur in the importance in a curative point of view which the Commission attach to these recommendations – I have already asked the Committee twice.[25]

The commission sometimes criticized Robertson but he still wrote a powerful letter in their defence to *The Lancet* six years later (9/6/1866).

> … I am old enough to recall the asylums, public and private of twenty years ago… The public asylums then were little more than dismal houses of detention. The comforts of the patients were few, the means of curative treatment less; the medical officers were ill paid and slightly esteemed, and their authority subordinate or divided with other officials. Of the private asylums the less said the better. The pauper licensed houses of twenty years ago were mysteries of abomination. Even the first-class private asylums were mean and miserable to a degree… How the Commissioners have fought step by step, the upward battle of reform.

Robertson then wrote about the commission's support of the medical officers and its relationship with the (often complaining) Visiting Committees:

> The unvarying tradition of the Lunacy Board has been to bring into prominence and in every way to exalt the position of the medical superintendent; and it is to these efforts that our position of independent authority in the asylum and of influence with the Committee of Visitors is mainly due. I am sure that every county medical superintendent will endorse this opinion. Then, as to the tyranny of the Commissioners over the Committee of Visitors, the thing is a stupid fiction, which no one acquainted with the independent character of the English magistracy will accept. The influence of the Commissioners on the counsels of the Visitors is due alone to the value of their suggestions, the acceptance of which, indeed, is solely at the pleasure of the justices, who are therein much influenced by the opinions of the medical superintendent. To him the suggestions of the Commissioners are a source of strength and aid.

Robertson was right. The constant criticisms of the Lunacy Commissioners were improving asylums and their regimes. And they often used their annual reports to shame institutions into making improvements. The commission was not a great innovator in terms of treatment but it was the single most powerful force in reducing restraint and seclusion in public and private asylums and did try to set basic humane standards of care.

ASYLUM NEWS AND EVENTS IN 1860

Robertson showed a degree of flexibility in his policy of releasing patients which often antagonised the local authorities who were paying the maintenance fees. On 10th March, he recorded that a 21-year-old patient, Sarah Ann White, was discharged but wanted to stay a bit longer:

> The delay arose from her own wish to be employed about the house for a few weeks as housemaid to give her confidence in herself before going into the world… Her writing and reading have improved.[26]

She was discharged on 24th March and was "very warm in the expression of her gratitude for the care she had received here".[27] It was the policy of the Visitors' Committee to see each patient on discharge and to ask about their treatment. Often patients' comments were artificially complimentary – they were reluctant to say anything that might jeopardize their discharge or future treatment – but Sarah White's comments, directed at Robertson, may have been more genuine.

Robertson was quietly pleased with the progress the asylum was making and by the end of April wrote:

> Of the asylum and of the improved and improving conditions of the patients I can hardly be deemed an impartial judge and therefore not venture to speak.[28]

But as the asylum increased in size – especially on the female side – examples of staff abuse of patients came to the surface. Robertson's order book on 19th May recorded that he had:

> carefully investigated a complaint of Mrs. Ware (in No. 5 Ward) that she had been struck by the night attendant on the 16th. He is of the opinion that Mr. George did lose his temper and strike the patient in question. This is the first occasion since the opening of the asylum that a case of wilful injury to a patient by an attendant has occurred… because a good worker, I will overlook this one offence but express my disapproval.[29]

"An act of violence to patients brought to the attention of the medical superintendent required his immediate investigation and for serious breaches leading to dismissal the Lunacy Commissioners kept a register of staff sacked for ill-treatment to prevent them obtaining jobs in other asylums".[30] Robertson was relatively severe about staff abuses but could be tolerant. He understood the difficult nature of asylum work and often gave staff second chances. It seems that patients and their relatives were not afraid to complain about asylum violence and in some cases went over Robertson's head. On 12th December, the following was recorded in the Visitors' minute book:

A letter from the Commissioners in Lunacy, dated 3rd December, was read together with a copy letter from the Medical Superintendent to them respecting an unfounded report of ill usage upon William Curties, a patient, by one of the keepers. The Committee had spoken to Dr. Robertson on the subject who in his report to them distinctly disclaims any intention of discourtesy to the Commissioners in his reply.[31]

On 16th June, the asylum cemetery was consecrated. Previously, burials had taken place outside the asylum grounds but this had proved to be expensive and had taken attendants away from the asylum for several hours. The *Brighton Herald* reported the event:

The conduct of the lunatics throughout the service was quiet, orderly, and decorous: the congregation were not disturbed by any unwanted sound or movement. A procession left the building for the chapel, consisting of one hundred of the lunatics, male and female, the former clothed in unobtrusive grey, and the latter wearing dark dresses, light shawls, and straw bonnets, trimmed with white. In a quiet and orderly manner they entered the chapel, and took the seats provided for them, the men on one side and the women on the other; separated, but not any distance apart. The inmates acted as the choir and in this, as in other musical portions of the service, the inmates kept good time, and appearing many of them to have very fair voices.

There was an increasing separation of the sexes in patient activity and in 1860 the education classes, run by the Chaplain, were no longer mixed. Victorian morality apart, as numbers grew, sexual segregation became a practical consideration.

Press interest in the asylum continued apace with regular reports on cricket matches between the male wards during the summer. The sides usually consisted of nine patients and two attendants. On 30th June, James Wheatley reported on a match between the asylum and the parish of Wivelsfield for the *Brighton Herald*. But it was a report with a difference for Wheatley was himself a patient at the Sussex Lunatic Asylum. Below is an abridged version of his report:

At ten o'clock in the morning many might have seen the patients (those selected to play and the other few to whom the day's holiday was extended), accompanied by the attendants issuing from the interior of the building to a small circle or plot of grass… Here they were marshalled in proper order and rank by the Head Attendant Mr. Knox, and then to those selected to play blue caps were given. These latter, with the band belonging to the establishment preceding them then fell into order, and after them the other patients, as spectators or umpires followed.

Out the provisions came – ham, cheese, bread and beer – and with an order to strike up the music, off started the little happy party, prepared for the events of the day, – success attending them all through. We say happy party; by which we mean the satisfaction which must necessarily ensue to themselves from following the dictates of simple reasonable men, by taking care of themselves by good behaviour in their different positions, both as regards patients, simply as such, and those whose duty it is to watch over them. So, then, with three huzzas, the gates were opened, and on they went to play a game of cricket. A ball – a cricket ball – was to be the winning party's acquisition. With respect to the play we offer no fuller comment than this – that they – all did their very best. An adjoining parish to the asylum kindly gave them the use of the ground to play on; and it was a very fine day. The Wivelsfield parish won the ball, and the asylum pleased to think that one of their party was in excess of runs at one innings, he scored 17. Thus the day passed; and, as the clock was striking seven, the little party again returned – not dispirited: for thus the men played cheerfully, went out cheerfully, and returned cheerfully: This is the way to cure lunatics.

The ground was graced by the presence of the steward's wife Mrs. Mortlock, and others attended. Thus far the narrative of the day ends. But the writer (who, although a patient, was admitted to be a spectator) acted in conjunction with those whose duty it was to record the result of the score. He sat in the waggon with the scorers, partook of their refreshment, and joined them with an amicable spirit, trusting to the ultimate result of the first effort made by the asylum, which is at present in its infancy, to effect a recovery.

"God Save the Queen"

Signed – James Wheatley.

Asylum advocates strongly believed that the 'way to cure lunatics' was to involve them in as many 'normal' activities as possible. Robertson encouraged patient participation and even allowed ex-patients to return to entertain their former fellow patients:

> On the 15th October, I had a comic performance in the Recreation Hall in the afternoon by Joseph Stevens, a patient discharged at the last meeting and which afforded the patients great amusement.[32]

On 25th July 1860, the asylum celebrated the first year of its existence with a holiday. The day's events started with a rather moralistic sermon from the Rev. Arthur Garfit, the Curate of Richmond, London, which was followed by a public dinner in the Recreation Hall, games on the lawn and finally a dance in the evening. Most of the patients were reported to have taken part in the festivities. Again, newspaper reports were optimistic about the progress of the new institution and even the Brighton Guardians' Lunacy Committee was beginning to make flattering remarks.[33]

Robertson was compelled to apply for leave for the month of September due to "repeated and latterly severe attacks of sciatica with feverish symptoms"[34]. The Visitors' Committee accepted his request and placed his new assistant, Valentine Browne, in temporary charge of the asylum. Whilst Robertson was away, the first successful escape occurred. Thomas Clapson, a 28-year-old labourer, escaped whilst in a working party in the kitchen garden. On the excuse that he had to answer a 'call of nature', he disappeared behind a hedge and never returned:

> The patient subsequently was heard of as an inmate of Oxford Castle, whither he had been committed as a vagrant. He is now at large. It was a case, the leading feature of which was the delusion that the sun had got into his throat, and that an operation was necessary for its removal. On other subjects he was tolerably sane, and the authorities at the Oxford Gaol do not appear to have discovered the existence of his mental illness.[35]

By law, if a patient remained uncaptured for fourteen days or more, he could not be returned to an asylum and was considered free until he was certified again. Staff were often fined if patients in their charge escaped but no fine is recorded in this case. On 7th April, one patient escaped with a wheelbarrow but only got as far as Ditchling – about seven miles away – before being discovered and brought back. Another inmate, Thomas Arnold, escaped on 3rd November but was recaptured at his home on the same evening. Meanwhile, some of the neighbours were complaining about the patients being 'walked out' on the weekends. But not all of the neighbours were hostile. On 27th October, Robertson wrote :

> As a contrast to the objections which have been raised against the patients walking out by the neighbours, I may mention that Mr. Humphreys late a master in chancery… at a visit here on business this week expressed his unqualified gratification at seeing so many orderly and well conducted lunatics pass his door on their walks.[36]

Despite this testimony the Visitors' Committee Minute book records on the same day that "complaint was made against the practice of a large number of lunatic patients being allowed to walk on the public roads although under the control of keepers". And they recommended that "such exercise be omitted on Sundays for the present"[37] and that it should take place on a weekday instead. Local reaction to the asylum's inmates does seem to have been mixed and some even claimed that walking and talking with the lunatics was often more agreeable than being in the company of their neighbours.

Robertson continued to show flexibility in his release of patients back into the community. On 8th December, he recorded that "Ellen Gray whose discharge was authorised at the last meeting has not yet left. She was so upset at finding a small sum of pounds which she expected to have lying at the Lewes bank detained by the Parish that I have not felt justified in discharging her. At present I fear a relapse of her symptoms".[38] Two weeks later he gave her a two-monthly discharge with a weekly allowance of 10s. Robertson had allowed her to stay extra time even though as early as May 19th, he had spoken about the steady augmentation of female patients in every new asylum. On 28th July, he asked his Committee for an additional dormitory on the female side for twenty-five patients. He described it as an 'urgent want'. By 11th October, with the asylum barely fourteen months old, he was recording that:

> I consider the female staff side of the house full and that every patient now added is for a deterioration of the sanitary condition and curative arrangements of the house.[39]

Six months after the asylum's opening, the wisdom of the Visitors' Committee in choosing the lowest tenders for the building and architectural work began to look increasingly suspect. More defects became apparent and on 28th January, the clerk to the Visitors, Mr Begg, was ordered to write to the architect, Mr Kendall:

> … informing him of the still existing defects on the baths leaking and threatening to bring down the ceiling in the Number One female ward and of 1500 slates broken in various parts of the roof and the danger of fireplaces with other matters and requesting his attendance at the next meeting of the Committee of Visitors.[40]

Robertson was particularly dissatisfied with the large open fires. They were uneconomical, difficult to control and could be dangerous. On 19th May, a patient called Mary Jacks put her feet into one of them and burnt herself badly. He was also against them for another reason:

> The patients on the convalescent ward could work but instead of this are sitting in a listless state before the fire scorching their clothes, a practice which is objectionable.[41]

By May, the Committee decided to call in an independent architect, Mr Shaw, to decide whether Kendall and the builder, Ayers, had materially departed from their contracts. After seeing the toilets, Shaw claimed that "he never saw such flimsy work in all his life".[42] The Committee decided to retain the balance of Kendall's commission until the defects were rectified; Kendall claimed the work was completed. A long legal wrangle ensued for the next couple of years and the matter was never fully resolved to either parties' satisfaction.

Financially, the asylum was becoming more self-sufficient. Patients were making all the staff uniforms and the tailor's shop and the shoemaker's shop were

TABLE V.

TAILOR'S SHOP.   *Account of Patients' Work and Earnings for the Year* 1860.

CLOTHING MADE UP.		Number of Articles.	Price of making per Article.		Value of Work.			REMARKS.
			s.	d.	£	s.	d.	
Patients'	Coats and Jackets (Cloth)	63	2	6	7	17	6	
,,	Trousers (Fustian and Cord)..	106	2	9	14	11	6	
,,	Waistcoats (Cloth)	13	1	3	0	16	3	
,,	Ticken Dresses	—	2	6	—			
,,	Rugs	8	8	0	3	4	0	
Attendants'	Uniform Coats	8	10	6	4	4	0	
,,	Trousers	12	4	6	2	14	0	
,,	Waistcoats	6	4	0	1	4	0	
,,	Caps	9	2	0	0	18	0	
REPAIRS—								
Patients'	Coats	284	0	8	9	9	4	
,,	Trousers	673	0	8	22	8	8	
,,	Waistcoats	165	0	4	2	15	0	
,,	Ticken Dresses	17	0	6	0	8	6	
					70	10	9	
Deduct Master Tailor's Wages					54	12	0	
Total...................					£15	18	9	

Figure four: Sussex Lunatic Asylum Annual Report 1860

TABLE VI.

SHOEMAKER'S SHOP.   *Amount of Patients' Work and Earnings for the Year* 1860.

ARTICLES MADE UP.	Number of Articles.	Price of work per Article.		Value of the Work.			REMARKS.
		s.	d.	£	s.	d.	
Mens' Leather Shoes.......................	180	3	0	27	0	0	
Women's Leather Boots....................	180	2	0	18	0	0	
,, ,, Shoes	15	1	9	1	6	3	
Cloth and Canvas Boots	2	1	6	0	3	0	
Mens' Leather Boots (Nailed)	27	4	0	5	8	0	
REPAIRS—							
Boots and Shoes repaired	371½	0	8	12	7	8	
,, ,, soled and welted....	572	1	6	42	18	0	
,, locked and strapped	19	0	2	0	3	2	
				107	6	1	
Deduct, Master Shoemaker's Wages				54	12	0	
Total				£52	14	1	

Figure five: Sussex Lunatic Asylum Annual Report 1860

TABLE IV.

Average number of Patients employed daily in the year 1860, *and the estimated value of the labour.*

OCCUPATION OR TRADE.	Daily Average Number of Patients	Rate per Day.	Estimated Yearly Average Value of Patients' Labour.			REMARKS.
		d.	£	s.	d.	
MALE PATIENTS.						
Farm and Garden Labourers	30	4	155	0	0	
With the Painter, Glazier and Plumber	3	6	23	5	0	
„ Carpenter................	4	12	62	0	0	
„ Bricklayer	1	4	5	3	4	
„ Tailor	9	0	70	10	9	See Table V. p. 36
„ Shoemaker	10	0	107	6	1	See Table VI. p. 37
„ Matmaker	7	4	36	3	4	
„ Engineer	3	8	31	0	0	
„ Baker	1	6	7	15	0	
„ Brewer.................	2	6	15	10	0	
„ House Porter	1	6	7	15	0	
In the Stores (including Coal Porters)	5	6	38	15	0	
„ Kitchen	1	6	7	15	0	
„ Laundry	1	6	7	15	0	
Cleaning in the Wards	35	3	135	12	6	
„ in the Corridors and centre Buildings .... }	5	3	19	7	6	
FEMALE PATIENTS.						
In Laundry and Wash-house	35	6	271	5	0	
„ Kitchen	12	4	62	0	0	
„ Needlework in the Wards	65	4	335	16	8	
„ Household Work, Cleaning, Wards, &c. .... }	40	3	135	0	0	
Total	..	..	1,534	15	2	

Figure six: Sussex Lunatic Asylum Annual Report 1860

already sources of profit.[43] The Brighton Guardians bought ten dozen shoes from the latter. The farm was also slowly developing:

> The farm, during the past year, only shows a small profit after paying rates and taxes; but it has been of great service to the Lunatic inmates, by affording them healthy labour; and the Farm Committee look with confidence to obtaining much more favourable results in the future.[44]

The average number of patients employed daily in the asylum in 1860 was 270 (152 females and 118 males) out of an average resident population of 357 patients. But whilst men were mainly employed outdoors on the farm or in the garden or learning a trade in the workshops, the majority of women were employed in household chores. Clearly, some work was healthier than others. In 1860, patient labour was estimated to be worth £1,534 15s. 2d.[45]

One of the trends that developed in public asylums in the latter part of the nineteenth century was the obsession of their administrators to keep the maintenance rate as low as possible. This led to the importance of cure often being compromised by a shortage of money. Inevitably, this also happened at the Sussex Asylum. It may only be symbolic, but in the first years its annual reports began with information about the condition of the patients and the asylum. After a couple of years, the reports began with economic information about the farm and the workshops and their products. Medical superintendents found themselves in a difficult position. They were expected to keep the maintenance rates low and the cure rates high – objectives that were opposed to each other.

1860 CONCLUDED

Reviewing the year's patient statistics, thirty of the discharged were described as 'recovered', six were transferred to other asylums, one escaped, one was in prison, and one was removed into the care of friends. Nearly half those 'cured' had been at the asylum for less than three months. In his 1860 Annual Report, Robertson wrote:

> It will be seen that the recoveries, with few exceptions have occurred in cases submitted early to treatment in the Asylum… Parochial authorities must send their patients quickly to the Asylum for a chance of ultimate recovery.[47]

Of the 34 deaths that year, most had occurred in the winter months; only three died in the summer. [48] Fifteen were 'transfers from other asylums', two were 'sent in to die', two were private patients, one died only nine hours after admission, and one death was 'accelerated by removal'. As Robertson had warned, many of the deaths had been those of men transferred from the London asylums. They had "died during the winter from slow decay"[49], not helped by the inadequate heating system of open fires. Seven had died within a month of being admitted; six within three months.

1860[46]	M	F
Patients	172	227
Discharged	19	20
Deaths	25	9
Average age	45	54

Robertson claimed that past experience showed that the early history of an asylum was marked by a small percentage of recovery and a high rate of mortality. But once good treatment practices were established recoveries could be expected to rise and deaths diminish. Admitting patients as soon as symptoms were recognized and removing unsuitable patients from the asylum were vital to this hoped-for trend. The latter was easier to do if the lunatic in question came from another county. On 22nd December, Robertson persuaded the Visitors' Committee to give one week's notice to the Canterbury Guardians to remove George Campbell, 'a dangerous maniac'.

The reports for 1860 by the Visitors' Committee, the Lunacy Commissioners and Robertson were very positive ones. The reduction of the maintenance rate from 13s. per week to 10s. 6d. – it was 14s. for out-of-county patients and 16s. for private patients – was heralded by the Visitors as a great triumph and was due, in their opinion, to the "improved working of the asylum". But it was also helped by their penny pinching – they had refused Robertson £3 to buy a set of bagpipes for the asylum band. The commissioners made only minor suggestions about improved facilities for the patients. Robertson complained about the parishes not sending their patients to the asylum soon enough but was generally optimistic. Indeed, there were some grounds for believing that the asylum system was working and flattering reports in the local press reflected this feeling.

But 1860 was also the year that the hard reality of running an asylum came home to Robertson. Staff indiscipline – half the staff who left that year (15 out of 30) were sacked, patient abuse, inmate escapes and the Mockford episode had rather soured things. But the most ominous development had been the large increase in patient numbers – from 285 at Christmas 1859, to 399 twelve months later – especially the rise in the number of female patients. So, already, after only a short history, the asylum was virtually full.

Chapter Six

1861
"SWEET BELLS JANGLED OUT OF TUNE"

The year started well with Robertson being pleased to announce that "during all this cold weather I have not had one serious case of cold or bronchitis to treat. The fires have been well kept up and the patients have gone but, little out, and that in the sunshine".[1] Then he received a complimentary report from an unexpected quarter. The Lunacy Committee from Brighton – including William Marchant – visited the asylum on 3rd January. The *Brighton Herald* reported that:

> … they found everything in the most admirable order and condition. Thirty-three males and fifty-two females individually seen and examined – in excellent health and extremely quiet (for the most part); the admirable system adopted in the asylum having apparently had the happiest effect upon them.

But violence and the threat of violence within the asylum was always near. In January, Mr Carter – a patient who was usually well-behaved and harmless and worked in the tailor's shop – violently attacked one of the attendants who was cutting his hair. The Head Attendant, Mr. Knox rescued the attendant but only after having his coat torn to shreds. Meanwhile, George Campbell (a dangerous lunatic whom Robertson had requested to be transferred on the 22nd December 1859) was still there. The Lunacy Commission had refused to move him claiming that the establishment ought to have arrangements for meeting such cases. But clearly it did not. Campbell had arrived from Portland prison the previous October and was decidedly dangerous. There, under the sudden delusion that he was in a house where men were made into mincemeat for the navy, he had killed an unoffending fellow-prisoner. Robertson objected to Campbell's presence in the asylum:

I adhere to my opinion that a homicidal lunatic who has already killed one victim is an unfit inmate of a county Asylum and requires an amount of liberty inconsistent with the curative treatment of the other patients. I had to employ a third attendant for the Refractory Ward in order to watch Campbell and implements have been found in his bed… Should some frightful tragedy result from Campbell's continuous detention the Visitors will have to bear in mind how decidedly I have counselled his removal. The new criminal lunatic asylum (Broadmoor) is a place where such cases can with safety be detained.[2]

Two months later Campbell was still there and despite showing signs of a marked improvement Robertson still wanted him transferred:

He [Campbell] states that he is visited nightly by a voice urging him to good behaviour, while formerly the voice urged him to deeds of violence. I know of no more dangerous form of homicidal mania, or more difficult to guard against its results.[3]

Campbell was finally transferred to Broadmoor in March. Another violent patient, William Greenaway, was admitted after murdering his wife the previous December. Unfortunately, she had strongly pressed for his discharge from Bethlem Asylum and not long after his release he had killed her. Robertson believed "his history is an awful warning of the necessity of refusing the frequent solicitations for the discharge of partially cured patients made by the Guardians or relatives". Greenaway proved to be very dangerous and made two murderous assaults on other patients before eventually being removed to Bethlem Asylum several months later on 31st August by order of the Secretary of State.

Ellen Gray – the patient whom Robertson had allowed to remain at the asylum after her 'official release' before Christmas – came back of her own free will after two weeks in the community:

Although apparently sane when under the influences of the asylum, her morbid self-esteem would appear to unfit her for contact with the world. She expresses a wish to remain for the present in the asylum and I think that's the best course for her.[5]

She was eventually released again on 13th July for a two month trial period with a weekly allowance of 10s. The month before, Robertson had discharged Mary Ann Parker. "How far she may be able to stand the wear of life outside is a question which experience alone can solve".[6] His fears could only have reinforced his opinion that a form of half-way house was needed for some released patients. As long ago as 14th February 1857, he had written a letter to *The Lancet* in support of the Devon Asylum's medical superintendent's idea of hiring a house (accommodating forty patients) at the seaside at Exmouth in order to provide a probationary system for patients who were convalescing. He always considered that asylums should be temporary places of cure rather than long term places of confinement.

On 27th April, a forty-five year old patient, Harriet Simmonds, accidentally died. According to Robertson, she had had a habit of putting stones into her mouth and unfortunately had swallowed a large one which had killed her. But Robertson did not request a coroner's inquest and received a reprimand from the Visitors' Committee who claimed that he had "lost sight of the resolution of the Committee that in all cases of death by accident in the asylum notice should be given to the Coroner".[7] He justified his decision:

> I did not deem it a case requiring of the coroner – a proceeding always to be avoided in an asylum, in consequence of the ignorant rumours of mistreatment and cruelty which such enquiries were apt to cause in the neighbourhood.[8]

In fact, allegations of cruelty seemed to be increasing. As early as January, Mary Ann Beech's husband had complained about her treatment. Her Union – Westhampnett – came to investigate and found that the complaints were groundless. But there undoubtedly was some mistreatment going on in the asylum. In November, Robertson sacked Fred Harper – for the second time – for "unkind treatment of a patient".[9]

PATIENT ROUTINE, ACTIVITIES AND TREATMENT

Most of the patients came from workhouses and would arrive at the asylum accompanied by workhouse staff. Otherwise, patients were usually brought there by their friends or relatives. They came by horse-drawn fly or by train. Arrival by train entailed a mile and a half uphill walk from Haywards Heath station to the asylum. Few patients attempted to escape during this walk but one female patient, in March 1885, managed to escape from her 'guards' and locked herself in the station toilet. It took staff thirty minutes to unhinge the door and recapture her. Patients arriving at the asylum for the first time must have found its size both ominous and impressive. They would have cast their eyes on a large building built of yellow brick with polychrome dressings of red and blue bricks – materials that still retain their original freshness today.

First impressions of the asylum, even today, depend very much on the weather. On a bright sunny day it can look palatial and on its south side offers a panoramic view of beautiful countryside; a view that induces tranquillity. But on a dark cold winter's night the asylum building presents a picture of gloom.

Once at the asylum, patients were examined by the head attendant and by the medical superintendent. On the basis of their case notes and physical condition the latter would then decide whether any medicine or special diet was required and then allocate them to wards according to their illness, capabilities and behaviour. The case notes were fairly brief giving basic personal information about their identity. They would also usually contain comments from a doctor about the nature and history of the illness and would be signed by two magistrates. In theory, accurate notes on cases were very important for future reference for the classification, diagnosis and treatment of the disease. In practice, with the hustle and bustle of asylum life, the admission procedures were likely to have been rather hurried. On a few occasions a patient would arrive without any notes and indeed even without a name. The asylum clerk would then embark on lengthy correspondence with a variety of people to discover this information. On one occasion, he wrote to the Baskerville family (of Sherlock Holmes fame) in Somerset to try to identify a patient.

After their meeting with Dr Robertson and Mr Knox, the new patients would be bathed and then provided with simple, functional clothing to wear – grey tweed suits for the men and blue-checked dresses for the women. In the winter, woollen dresses were worn by the women which were more fire-proof than dresses made of cotton. And the most violent female patients were obliged to wear extra-strong dresses made of calico. Asylum clothing was normal for everyday wear but it seems that patients could wear what they liked on special occasions. The clothing was certainly of a better quality than that provided by many of the workhouses. In 1883, thirty-three paupers in Cuckfield Workhouse were sent to prison for tearing up their clothes. And in the same year, Thomas Morris, a patient at the asylum, refused to be discharged unless the Rye Guardians provided him with a decent set of clothes. He claimed that theirs were of an inferior quality to those of the asylum. All patients were bathed, clothed and had their bed linen changed twice a week.

After travelling down one of the long corridors, the new patients would soon find themselves in a crowded ward containing as many as 40 patients. Almost a hundred years later, some of these wards would contain more than twice this number. From all accounts, in the early days, cleanliness was scrupulously enforced at the asylum and a local newspaper reporter compared its wards to a top Brighton store's (Hanningtons) shop-window. How much the wards were spruced up for special visits, it is difficult to tell. In 1861, the wards were still fairly dull. The following year Robertson described them as "hardly up to standard" and obtained £600 from the Committee to improve them. With the extra money they were soon adorned with more blinds, pictures, plants, wire baskets of flowers and simple ornaments. Robertson reasoned that a pleasantly decorated ward was of great therapeutic value and, not for the first time, quoted the Lunacy Commissioners in support of his argument:

> It was necessary to surround the patients in their wards with small comforts of domestic furniture, making their dormitories more homelike by a trifling outlay on carpeting and curtains, and putting into their Galleries and Day-rooms pictures and objects of ornament of an inexpensive kind, which may serve to engage their attention, occupy their thoughts, and exercise them in habits of care and self-control.

> The reasoning that would prescribe and justify in this respect, a total absence of everything not strictly necessary is now very little used. We have much less frequently to reply to the argument, that the poor have not curtains and carpets in their homes. It is precisely because their homes too frequently are wanting in them, as well in sufficiency of food, that, hardly less than the better and more ample diet, these trifling luxuries are wanted in asylums. This is our conclusion after many years of incessant observation at all the asylums in the country.[10]

Canaries were also kept in the wards and dogs (for a time) were allowed to roam there as well although it seems that most of them were owned by the artisans. We know that dogs were still on the wards in 1863 as Robertson was complaining:

> … that the passages in the centre of the house are very dirty from the dogs that are allowed to run about there. I would be unwilling to deprive the patients of the amusements the dogs afford them. They are now banned from the passages. The patients must teach the dogs in the wards to be clean.[11]

On weekdays, patients were woken up between 6 and 6.30 am and immediately taken to the toilet. At 6.30 or 7 am – according to the season – the working patients were then sent to their various scenes of labour. Males were mainly occupied on the farm or in the gardens. Others were sent to the shops of the carpenter, tailor, shoemaker, etc. For these lucky few there was the strong possibility of learning a trade that could prove invaluable to them when they left the asylum. There were sixteen trades on offer for male patients and six for women. Many female patients remained in their wards doing needlework. Others went to work in the laundry, kitchen or needle-room. Almost three-quarters of the patients were employed around the asylum and, apart from the profits they made, Robertson believed that work had a "priceless value in the moral treatment of the patients".[12] Those who could not work, according to Henry Hawkins, "merely vegetated day after day in vacancy of mind".[13]

The working patients returned to their wards for breakfast at 8 am. Afterwards, the ringing of a clear-toned bell summoned all to a daily service held in the chapel which was about 50 yards from the main asylum building. As the working patients had to return to work at 8.30 am, few of them attended the weekday services. In fact, many more patients attended the services held on Sunday.

Life for patients who did not work was fairly monotonous, especially in the winter. After breakfast, the sick patients remaining in the wards were given a medical inspection by the assistant medical officer. Non-working patients were usually allowed to walk regularly around the small asylum courtyards. Other than that, they could play games or read newspapers in the wards. The weekly routine of patients was only interrupted by visits from Workhouse Guardians, the Visitors' Committee; and by visits from their friends and relatives on Wednesdays.

Summer was obviously a better time for asylum patients. Apart from outside games and sport, they could look forward to long walks and picnics. In June 1861, on two occasions, over a hundred walked the six miles to Ditchling Common to have a picnic. Robertson recorded that there were no mishaps on either occasion. Patients capable of going to picnics went at least once a month in the summer. The outings were described rather poetically by the loquacious Henry Hawkins:

> It is a long day's pleasure with banquet, not "in the distant woods", which would afford opportunity of escape, but on a wide stretching common which inspires something of the sense of freedom and of liberty. Soon after chapel, the commissariat cart is brought round and loaded with ample provisions for the day's campaign. Not trifling is the consumption of bread, cheese, meat, and beer, by that monster picnic party, with appetites sharpened by exercise and by bracing country air.

> Sometimes preceded by a brass band, the patients, in two detachments, pass by orchards, corn-fields, heaths, on to an extended moor, admirably suited for such a gathering. Arrived at their destinations, the holiday-makers give themselves up to the "abandon" of the day. Wickets are pitched; the football is kicked about: a dance is got up, or "kiss-in-the ring" is voted for. Presently a very substantial dinner is served. Then amusements are resumed. Many of the women prefer to pass the day seated on the grass, some in vacancy of mind, other poor things, thinking about home and dear ones there; others with thoughts disordered, "like sweet bells jangled" out of tune.

> Towards early evening a camp fire is lighted, gypsy fashion and tea prepared; at length, with the lengthening shadows, the whole party, a

little wearied, but all the better for the day's excursion, return to the asylum. Thus, in healthful work, relieved by occasional but not too frequent recreation, asylum life passes away.[14]

One imagines that some of the patients (not always in the best of physical condition) must have been pretty exhausted after the six mile trek back to the asylum. The weekly Sunday walks were also an important feature of asylum life and Robertson noted that "the orderly behaviour of patients when out is an example worthy of imitation by the labouring population around".[15]

Hawkins, the chaplain, ran twice-weekly education classes for the male and female patients and taught subjects such as the "History of England" and "Common Objects of the County". They were attended by an average of more than twenty patients of each sex. He also established evening classes for the nurses and attendants which he saw as a way of getting to know the staff rather than as a method of direct instruction. The services in the chapel were also a dominant feature of asylum life. In 1863, on average, 380 patients attended the Sunday services and 180 the weekday ones. The chapel was kept beautifully clean and polished and, like the asylum, "was very remarkable for its profusion of flowers" (*Asylums of the World,* H. C. Burnett, 1891). Hawkins praised the orderly and devotional behaviour of the large body of patients who attended his services and recorded that:

> Many join in the responses, chants and hymns and follow the readings of the lessons in the Bible and that they often make remarks to him about the sermons during the week.[16]

Throughout the year, especially during the winter, various groups of people from the entertainment world came to perform at the asylum. One of the most remarkable visitors was Mrs Macready, an American lady from Boston. She apparently had a deep interest in the pauper insane and had reputedly visited every asylum in her own

Wagons such as this were used to take the more infirm patients for picnics on Ditchling Common

country. Robertson invited her to give dramatic readings and recitals to the patients in February 1862. She asked for no fee; performed without the aid of a book; and recited Sheridan's 'School for Scandal' (amongst other plays) from memory. Other entertainers, like Mrs Prosser, a Shakespearean dramatist, frequently came to the asylum and only charged expenses.

But apart from "healthful work, relieved by not too frequent recreation" and the balanced diet, what treatment, if any, did the patients receive? From the asylum's beginning, Robertson experimented with a number of different treatments. In February 1860, he described to the readers of *The Lancet*, how a 'lamp bath' worked:

> The sweating process can, with perfect safety and cleanliness, be induced by a spirit lamp placed below a wooden chair, the patient being enveloped in half a dozen blankets, covered externally with a sheet to retain the heat. This process produces profuse perspiration in about half an hour. It is assisted by the drinking of cold water and followed by cold effusion – a dripping sheet or two pails of cold water (over the patient)… A brisk walk before and after the bath is of service.[17]

But Robertson's favourite treatment was his 'vapour' or Roman bath (Turkish) which he had ordered in January 1860. It became the first one installed in an English asylum. Robertson enthusiastically declared it a great success and claimed that patients often requested the treatment. He found a striking improvement in patients who used the bath as little as twice a week for twenty minutes. In July 1861, he was writing in the *Journal of Mental Science* that:

> Its best success has been with cases of melancholia with great depression and refusal of food. Cases of maniacal excitement, on the other hand, have not usually benefited by the treatment.

Years later he wrote that he preferred to spend money on Roman baths rather than on drugs. Robertson was also a great believer in the benefits of cold water. On 4th April 1861, for the first time, he spoke at a meeting of the Brighton Medico-Chirurgical Society of which he had been a member since his arrival in Haywards Heath in 1858. He presented a paper entitled "Cold water as a Remedy in Mental Distress". In it he outlined some of the treatment employed at the asylum:

— warm baths and a stimulating diet to treat melancholia.

— $\frac{1}{2}$ fluid ounces of turpentine and castor oil to treat mania.

— a plunge bath as a stimulant.

— continual cold baths as a powerful sedative.

But Robertson's paper mainly concentrated on the use of wet-treatment which he used as a sedative on his most violent and excitable patients. He explained how it worked:

> A piece of macintosh is laid over a mattress, and a folded blanket laid over that. An ordinary sheet is then wrung out of cold water and laid on the blanket. The patient is laid on his back, and the sheet is rapidly wound round him so as to include the arms in its folds. The blanket is tucked over, then three or more blankets. There is a little shivering at first. After 1-1½ hours the patient must stand in a shallow bath, well rubbed with a wet sheet, and then placed in another one. After each sheet treatment two pails of water are then poured over the patient standing in an empty bath.

Robertson admitted that the wet sheet had often produced boils about the body but he saw these as critical, since the patient's recovery often dated from their appearance. He claimed that the treatment was good for sedation and sleeplessness and that violent patients often fell asleep in the sheet.

It was certainly a controversial treatment and one that drew a mixed reception from the other doctors at the meeting. One in particular, Dr Turner, said that he believed Robertson laid too much stress on cold water as a remedy to the exclusion of other ordinary measures such as the regime of the asylum. He accused Robertson of "riding his hobby too far". Robertson countered that it was effective if used on certain patients for short periods. In fact, in 1861, he fined staff for using it on a patient in a state of epilepsy and told them that the asylum was lucky not to have faced a manslaughter charge. At that time there was still no effective medicine for the treatment of epilepsy. Remedies used such as nitrite of amyl and bromide of potassium were unreliable and had unpleasant side effects.

By 1863, apart from the Devon Asylum, the Sussex Asylum was still the only one using a Roman bath. That year, in his Annual Report, Robertson gave an account of a patient's miraculous recovery after having the bath treatment. The patient – a 50-year-old coachmaker from Brighton – had been ill for about twelve months and was described as suicidal. He was admitted on 23rd February. Physically, he was very weak and restless and had the "tremors". Mentally, he was quite confused and unable to understand or answer questions or even say his name. In his habits he was destructive and dirty. Below is Robertson's record of his treatment:

> *25th February* – No sleep, very restless, pulse rate feeble, pupils contracted. Whisky given at bedtime. Packed in wet sheet for two hours; restless; two cold pails afterwards.

2nd March – Better, still incoherent, restless and dirty.

18th March – Worse, incoherent, restless and noisy. Packing and cold pails were omitted. Sedative at bed time. Whisky, extra diet (chops) and occasional warm baths for half an hour at bedtime.

10th May – Noisy, feebler – he has lost ground – He was rambling in his conversation; he spoke of his strength and ability and told me that he would build me a carriage and provide four horses for it. Roman baths every day at 150°. He was so feeble that he had to be carried to the bath.

21st May – Two baths a day at 170°.

17th June – In every way better. His conversation was more rational. He was ordered to continue Roman baths twice a week and to go to the carpenter's shop.

5th October – Mind clear and rational – Worked about the premises alone.

30th November – Discharged on trial for a month. During the month he came to the Asylum to ask for a Roman bath.

30th December – Discharged cured. Now worked at the Brighton Railway Company for 35s. per week.

Robertson wrote "I have little doubt that the Roman bath saved the patient's life and restored him to reason".[18]

A less popular form of treatment was the use of digitalis – a drug prepared from the dried leaves of foxgloves. Robertson used it to sedate excitable patients. Large doses of digitalis could give the patient nausea and diarrhoea and make him vomit. These had been, historically, the classical aims of anti-maniacal treatment but by the 1860s Robertson appears to have been the only medical superintendent still using it – though he claimed that it was used at the Stafford County Asylum. It was highly toxic and Robertson described its use in 1863:

With a wholesome fear of a coroner's inquest, I have not ventured on $\frac{1}{2}$ ounce (4 drachms) doses… It does not make an insane man sane but made a house quiet.[19]

Robertson's use of digitalis and the wet sheet would be seriously undermined by a scandal that hit the asylum in 1864.

Not all of Robertson's methods were approved by the Lunacy Commissioners and one year they objected to the practice of the cutting short of many of the female patients' hair. Robertson tried to justify it:

> In cases of acute mania and in epilepsy with excitement I consider it an important point in the treatment to keep the head cool and I certainly feel surprised at the objection. It does not look well I admit.[20]

In the nineteenth century, some psychiatrists believed that people with certain colour hair were more prone to certain forms of insanity than others. Black-haired people were thought to be more liable to melancholia than light-haired people whilst the latter were thought to be more subject to attacks of mania. However, there is no evidence to suggest that Robertson shared these beliefs.

A MODEL ASYLUM

Despite "rumours of mistreatment" positive publicity about the asylum (throughout its 136 year old history) probably reached its zenith during 1861. Favourable reports from the Lunacy Commissioners and the Brighton Guardians were followed up by complimentary newspaper reports about the Sussex Asylum's second anniversary celebrations held on 25th July. Perhaps in a spirit of reconciliation, Robertson made a special effort to invite the Brighton Guardians to the event and seven of them came accompanied by their own Workhouse Juvenile Band. After giving a performance on the platform of Brighton station whilst waiting for the 10.15 train to Haywards Heath, the fifteen-strong band in neat blouses and caps, and their masters (which included a Mr Thunder), arrived at the asylum just in time to catch the sermon preached in the chapel by the Venerable Archdeacon Otter of Lewes.

As the rain poured down outside and gusts of wind encircled the chapel, those inside must have been slightly bemused by a rather long sermon entitled "She hath done what she could". Only at the end when Otter quoted the lines "My God, my God, why hast *Thou* forsaken me" must the two hundred patients present have felt it had some relevance to their situation. Afterwards, the patients had dinner in their ward dining rooms whilst the fifty visitors, with Robertson at their head, had lunch in the Recreation Hall which was decorated with flowers and evergreens.

After lunch, attempts to play outdoor games had to be abandoned due to the heavy rain. In the afternoon, Robertson's assistant, Valentine Browne, led a party on a conducted tour of the asylum. The journalist from the *Brighton Herald* was very impressed and started his report of 27th July with the words:

> Among the County institutions of which a Sussex man may be justly proud, the Lunatic Asylum of Haywards Heath holds a prominent position. As a structure it is palatial; and everything connected with it is

on a scale eminently creditable to the wisdom and humanity of those who planned it, and those entrusted with its management.

But the journalist admitted that:

> … over the wards of some of these might indeed be written the words of the great Florentine "All hope abandon ye who enter here" – mentally diseased beyond all chance of recovery, nothing can be done for them beyond attending to their physical wants and preventing their harming either themselves or others.

The reporter also confirmed what his newspaper had reported at the Christmas Ball in 1859: that the insane danced in almost total silence and that "the dancers seemed to concentrate all their energies on the dance, and either to have nothing to say or no inclination to converse with one another". But in contrast to 1859, when patients could only dance with staff, now they were sometimes dancing together. Perhaps this change was due to the patient population rising from 285 to 402 during this period, whilst the staff numbers remained virtually the same.

The reporter from the *Brighton Gazette* (1/8/1861) went into more detail:

> First we were shown through the women's wards. Here were some employing themselves in needlework, some reading, some singing, and most of them cheerful. Curious were the questions put to us – "How fares it with the Christian world?" and the like. In passing through, many was the obeisance respectfully given, frequent the smile and occasional the holding out of hand to grasp our own. What could not fail to strike us with wonder and admiration was that, combined with the absence of restraint, there appeared to exist the most perfect control in each ward, by the solitary, highly respectable young wards-women presiding over each. We visited the dormitories, all airy rooms, well lighted, and most beautifully clean. We were shown the kitchen wherein the cookery of the establishment is carried on partly by the sane and partly by the insane, large, lofty, capacious and fitted with every requisite… We then proceeded through the men's wards all of which bore marks of equal cleanliness and attention to the comfort of the inmates. Herein we were asked a few questions, showing dissatisfaction, such as "Can you tell me where I am to find a Magistrate?" "How long am I to be kept in this horrid place ?" and the like; but those were exceptions – the rule was cheerfulness and happiness. Many was the passing bow, many the hands put forward, and the request to be allowed to shake hands. Some we found employing themselves in reading, some in cheerful conversation, some playing bagatelle, others cards; others again were indulging in "the fragrant weed" (tobacco), and most thoroughly did they seem to enjoy it.

> One small door was unlocked, and we looked in, not upon a patient, but

upon an empty room, a room such as we had heard of as a part of such a building, – the padded room, – thickly covered all around and on the floor with padded cloth, a sure preventative of self-mischief from even the most violent. And this was untenanted, and more than this it was seldom used we were told.

The visitors, on the advice of Browne, decided not to visit the men's refractory ward where Greenaway, the patient who had murdered his wife, was held. It was thought that their presence might provoke him. The tour continued:

> There was one ward the visit to which was far from agreeable – the ward for the demented, the hopelessly idiotic. Here we saw poor humanity in its most stricken form, that of hopelessness and incurability. All that here can be done is done in the way of kindness and of ministering to the wants of the poor afflicted ones. Notwithstanding all the kindness we here saw exhibited, notwithstanding all the comforts, cleanliness, and attention we must confess that we closed our inspection of the wards under feelings of a painful depression, an indescribable feeling of pity for the unhappy inmates, and for poor human reason, even at the best. We were gratified at the opportunity given us for the inspection, but we closed the same with a feeling of relief. Our conductor, Dr Browne, is a supporter of the cheering, the enlivening, the elevating system; he seems somewhat sanguine, for we understood him to express his belief that, under the treatment adopted at the Asylum, four out of every five patients sent there within three months of insanity making its first appearance, might be taken as the average of curable cases. May he be correct, and may the system adopted at Haywards Heath prove it.

Neither of the above reports attempted to 'whitewash' the asylum and showed both sides of asylum life. Cheerfulness, comfort and cleanliness on the one side; and sadness, social control and unhappiness on the other.

By July, the asylum population had only increased by three – to 402 – and this must have encouraged a more stable environment. Was the Sussex Asylum really a 'model' institution? The *Brighton Herald* certainly believed so and in an article published on 28th September compared it to a model social colony based on true social principles in which "a few intelligent sane men bear rule and sway over an insane community". It is a community where "there is peace, there is plenty, there is uniformity in food, in clothes, in worship, in amusement, in everything; in short, that pertains to daily and yearly life". And the article concluded by saying that "from the evidence before us we see everything to approve of and nothing to condemn in the present condition of the County Lunatic Asylum, Haywards Heath". In its early years, according to the Lunacy Commissioners, the Sussex Asylum was one of the best in the country.

Compared to other institutions of the day, the asylum did appear to be a model community despite the problems we have already seen in its short history. Workhouses were a far worse option. On the same day that the article above was published, Stephen Trowbridge arrived at the asylum from the Westhampnett Workhouse. He had been confined there for a week in a strait-jacket and had been tied to his bed. Robertson was angry that he had not been immediately sent to the asylum:

> The delay imperils the chance of recovery. It appears to me, much to be regretted that the Guardians should thus entrust the case of a patient in such a critical state, his reason for life hanging loosely in the balance, to the management of the Workhouse Authorities.[21]

Robertson did send a letter of complaint to the Guardians of Westhampnett but it was by no means an isolated case. Later in the year, another patient, Fred Williams – who came from the Chichester Workhouse – arrived in a strait-jacket, locked up and bruised.

ASYLUM NEWS IN 1861

It was the large increase in female patients which concerned Robertson most. At the beginning of the year he decided to admit no more private ones and asked for the out-of-county females from Kent to be removed. On February 23rd, he wrote that "any further crowding in the female wing would be prejudicial to the general health of the house".[22]

There were two inquests on patients during the year and the coroner returned verdicts of "death from epilepsy" and of "natural death" on them. The imbalance of female and male patients was almost corrected in August when 40 'naval lunatics' were admitted as private patients at a cost of 16s. per week. They were in "good bodily condition but a most dangerous and refractory party".[23] Robertson mixed them up throughout the house and soon claimed that they were more orderly and disciplined. But they were all chronic cases and few of them were discharged 'cured' during their stay. Their presence although financially advantageous, had a negative effect on the asylum's cure rate.

A lot of Robertson's time was spent in replying to relatives' requests for the release of patients. In September, the wife of David Elphick, a patient from the Eastbourne Union, applied for charge of him. Robertson replies:

> He is better since admission but he is an old man occasionally depressed and with a suicidal tendency which if discharged I think would more likely than not result in suicide.[24]

Letters asking for patients to be released also came from the parishes who were keen to cut down on their expenditure. Patients were also sometimes re-admitted:

> Mrs French, one of our earlier cases discharged on 26th November 1859, has returned with another attack of melancholia caused by the shameful desertion of her husband who has left the country with her children and another woman.[25]

And unsuitable cases were still arriving. Alice Ramsey, a nine-year-old child, arrived from the Parish of Crawley. "She would be much better cared for in the union house. Its own mother would be the proper person to care for it".[26]

As the year progressed escape attempts increased. One of the naval lunatics escaped and when he was recaptured, claimed that he was trying to walk to Ireland. On November 22nd, a Mr Baldock escaped, followed by a Mrs Taylor four days later. Both were recaptured within a few days.

Eighteen sixty-one was the year that three trains were involved in a terrible crash in the Clayton tunnel, near Brighton. Most of the casualties – 23 dead and 200 injured – were on a Sunday excursion train from Brighton. One or two of the survivors subsequently became patients at the asylum. Also, amongst its intake that year, was a Mrs Agate. The *Brighton Guardian* reported her tragic case on 10th December:

Dreadful Murder and Attempted Suicide at Slaugham

On Thursday morning, a woman named Agate, the wife of Mr. John Agate, a respectable small farmer, residing at Slaugham, a few miles from Haywards Heath, in a state of insane frenzy, murdered her daughter, a child about five years of age, by cutting her throat with a razor, and afterwards made an attempt on her own life in the same manner.

From evidence which was given at an inquest, held on Friday, at the Old White Horse Inn, Slaugham, it appeared that on Thursday morning, a domestic servant, named Emily Downing, in the employ of Mr. Agate, went about nine o'clock, to her mistress's room to call her up, but finding the door fastened, went down again, and waited until her master came in. He went up to Mrs. Agate's room, and called to her, but receiving no answer, burst open the door, and was horrified to find her standing near the door, with her throat apparently cut, and the blood running down her dress, but still more so to find his child lying on the bed, smothered in blood, her head almost severed from her body. Mrs. Agate said, "I did it; I could not help it – I was obliged to do it". A razor, which was, no doubt, the instrument by which the deed was perpetrated, was found in the room.

Mr. Byass, surgeon, who had been sent for, found the deceased, whose death must have been almost instantaneous, lying on the bed, with her throat frightfully cut from ear to ear. On the right side of the neck the whole of the vessels and also the muscles were cut down to the vertebrae, as was also the front part; and on the left the carotid artery had been divided. The wounds must have been repeated.

Mrs. Agate had been for some time past in a low desponding way, for which reason Miss Agate, a cousin of Mr Agate, was staying in the house as a companion to her; but she was always a kind and affectionate mother, and had never been heard to make use of any threats towards the child.

The Coroner thought there could be no doubt that the wounds which caused death were inflicted by the mother while in a fit of frenzy, as the evidence went to show that she was in anything but a sane state of mind; and the jury, being of the same opinion, returned a verdict of "Wilful Murder", committed while under the effects of insanity".

Strangely enough, on the Tuesday before the murder, a cousin of Mr Agate's committed suicide by shooting himself for no apparent reason. He had lived nearby and had been regarded as a successful grocer and draper. No connection seems to have been made between the two events.

1861 CONCLUDED

By the end of the year the asylum's population had increased from 399 to 459 – 228 men and 231 women – and it was now full. Sixty-one patients had been discharged – 29 deemed recovered, 4 relieved and 28 not improved. Many of the latter were probably discharged to make room for the more profitable private naval patients. Robertson calculated that the discharge rate of recovered patients would have been 26% instead of 17% but for the introduction of the naval lunatics. Forty-five patients had died during the year, 10% of the average number of residents. Robertson believed that there were two main reasons for this high figure:

A reference to the Obituary table will show that many cases continue to be sent to the Asylum in a dying state and again that other cases are left so long without the proper treatment which an Asylum alone can furnish, that they die shortly after admission from symptoms which apparently earlier treatment might successfully have combated.[27]

It was a theme that Robertson would return to again and again during his twelve-year rule. Despite this, Robertson was pleased with the year's progress:

I record a favourable report of the general good conduct of the attendants and servants of this establishment – I find a decided improvement since last year and that the year's discipline has not been thrown away on them… The patients, also as a body are quiet, orderly and contented.[28]

And generally it had been a good year, especially financially, with paid labour being successfully replaced by patient labour on the farm which made a profit of £176. Also, the maintenance rate had been further reduced to 10s. 3d. per week. The portrayal of the asylum as a 'model' institution must have been a boost to Robertson's morale. But there were also less positive developments. He now felt obliged to have inquests – even in cases where he did not feel it was necessary – merely to calm public fears about mistreatment. And these public concerns were clearly growing. More dangerous patients were being admitted, and only being transferred with great difficulty, and escape attempts were increasing. Most worryingly, there was no more room for female patients. Despite these problems, the asylum system, as represented by the Sussex Asylum, seemed to be working and providing a superior quality of life for its patients.

Chapter Seven

STAFF PROBLEMS AND PATIENT WORK
IN THE EARLY YEARS

*I*n the early years, the turnover of asylum staff was extremely high with annual sackings frequently in double figures. As, in 1860, when half of the staff who left had been sacked. Although never again were so many dismissed in a single year; many left in the first decade after a comparatively short stay. As we have already seen, a combination of Robertson's discipline and the poor job conditions were largely responsible for this large turnover. He, though, was philosophical about it:

> Many staff changes must be expected in a new asylum. The sudden demand for a large number of attendants brings a lot of useless men to the surface who have already made the rounds of the county asylums and require to be weeded out as the establishment becomes consolidated.[1]

Nurses and attendants were often chosen for their size and strength and received little on-the-job training, unlike staff in general hospitals. Apart from looking after the patients, they were expected to amuse them at all times – very much a key tenet of moral treatment. This included dancing with the patients, playing sport and games with them and acting as escorts on walks, and activities outside the asylum walls. But for the vast majority of the time the nursing was of a custodial nature with the constant counting of patients and the cutlery they used etc., and the prevention of escapes. Much time was also spent in domestic work, making sure the asylum was kept clean. Male staff attended male patients and female staff attended female patients, a state of affairs that did not change until after the Second World War.

The hours were extremely long with thirteen-hour shifts. (Later, despite regulations setting limits on working hours, as recent as the 1930s the nursing staff at the Sussex Asylum were working shifts of similar length.) In the winter, nurses and attendants were expected to be on duty by 6.30 am and in summer by 6.00 am. Throughout the year all staff had to be in bed with their gas lights off by 10.15 pm. And when on leave, they had to be back in the asylum by 10 pm. Contravention of these rules meant fines; persistent contravention led to dismissal.

In some respects, staff experience of asylum life was not greatly different from that of the patients. They ate more or less the same food, drank the same and held their social occasions in the same rooms. They enjoyed organized sports, had their own dances, and attended the entertainment provided for the patients. It has been suggested that some staff and patients, particularly the females, had a much better social life inside the asylum walls than they would have done if they had lived outside. But for others, the lack of amenities in the local area, especially in Haywards Heath, made it difficult to have a normal social life and added to the stress of the job.

The majority of the nursing staff were young, single and lived in the asylum in the early years. Only married staff were allowed to live off the premises. Strict sexual segregation, fairly easy to maintain with the patients, was much more difficult with respect to the staff. Their moral behaviour seems to have given the rather puritanical, unmarried Robertson, particular grief. As early as 24th June 1860, he decided to restrict attendant off-duty time – 8 pm to 10 pm – to alternate nights; male staff one night, female staff the other. He saw the changes "as a matter of precaution not as punishment and that he was fully aware of the anxious and wearying nature of their duties… he regrets leave restrictions".[2] Trying to separate the male and female staff from nightly rendezvous was a constant worry to Robertson. In 1863, he dismissed an attendant, Thomas Hatcher, because:

> he refused to have his leave stopped for continued flirtations with my cook whom he night by night kept out on the Heath till 10 pm in defiance of my rules.[3]

Later on in the decade Robertson ordered that there should be no meetings between male and female staff in the central passages, kitchen or offices between 8 pm and 10 pm. And in 1867, he was protesting that "this house is a hospital for the treatment of disease not a MATRIMONIAL AGENCY office!"[4] From Robertson's journal one gets the impression that he was fighting a losing battle in trying to keep the sexes apart.

On 23rd January 1861, a 26-year-old nurse, Jane Palmer, actually gave birth to a child. She had only started five weeks before but no one had noticed her condition. She was the daughter of a schoolmaster and despite being well-educated and having a good character Robertson believed:

> that the moral influence of such an event was so prejudicial to the discipline of the house that I took responsibility on the 9th day after confinement of removing her to the Chailey Union… Then I wrote to the man who gave her a reference.[5]

The artisans usually lived off the premises. They seemed to have been a boisterous lot and annoyed Robertson with their poor timekeeping and lack of enthusiasm for supervising the patients. When escorting them on a walk it appears that once out of sight of the asylum, the artisans would often sit down and play cards thereby considerably shortening the exercise of the inmates. Robertson was convinced that many of them were just trying to get through their time at the asylum and had little interest in the welfare of the patients. They often came in for his strongest criticisms. On 20th January 1861, he wrote that "artisans mustn't create disorder, they use wards as a thoroughfare and gossip with the patients and attendants".[6] And on 16th July of that year, he complained that "every artisan appears to have a dog about the workshop. No dog in the future will be admitted (there)".[7] They also had a habit of leaving the main asylum gate open – not the best way to discourage patients from escaping – and Robertson decided to fine them 6d. every time they did so. He fined the carpenter and brewer more heavily for coming to blows at the 1862 Christmas Eve Ball in a dispute about their duty. But some of the artisans were hard-working and dedicated. For example, Henry Clarke, the master shoemaker, acted as an organist at the asylum, led the chapel choir and played in the hospital band.

Robertson was equally as strict with his fellow assistant medical officers. Dr Gwynne, on his advice, had already resigned in 1860, and his successor, Valentine Browne, almost followed suit in 1863. On 4th June that year, he admitted a female patient with smallpox into one of the wards. He did not tell Robertson until several hours later and was reprimanded for having "shown the greatest want of judgement and forethought" [8] by not isolating the patient immediately. Browne took it badly and the next day he refused to do his duties. Robertson ordered him to leave the house. Browne only kept his job by apologising afterwards via the chaplain about his "hasty and inconsiderate conduct of yesterday".[9] Fortunately for the asylum, it was accepted. Browne was an exceptionally compassionate man who had served in the Crimean War. His unassuming modesty and kindliness had made him a popular and much loved figure by the patients and staff alike. In a very arduous and demanding job, Browne appears to have been doing extremely well. On 27th June, the Visitors resolved that "no person afflicted with smallpox or malignant fever shall be admitted to this asylum".[10]

Staff drunkenness appears to have been rife in the early 1860s. In January 1860, Robertson sacked his Bailiff, James McCardle, for drinking with Fred Harper (the House Porter whom he had already sacked for being untidy and dirty). And on 25th April 1860, Henry Leach, an attendant, "had to be carried to bed aggravated by introducing spirits into the wards and leading two of the other attendants on to drink".[11] He was dismissed immediately as was the smith, E. Hackham, two months later for being drunk on duty. In June, William Gardiner, the engineer, was admonished – after which he resigned – for bringing beer into the engine room. His successor, Edward Jones was sacked in October, also for being drunk. And it was not only the male staff who drank too much. A nurse, Anne Mackay, who was only appointed in August 1862, was given a month's notice at the end of that year on "account of her intemperate violent demeanour to her fellow servants – a conduct I fear is connected with a tendency to drink".[12]

Beer was produced and kept on the premises as well as being available in the local pubs and beerhouses. The temptation for men working long hours in difficult conditions was obviously great. Although Robertson admitted that the "home-brewed beer of the attendants is the best I've ever tasted in an asylum",[13] he did not like having it on the premises and but for the fear of upsetting the patients, would have preferred to give them water instead (as was the case in prisons). In 1863, almost 26,000 gallons of beer were consumed at the asylum as opposed to only 13,000 gallons of milk. In the same year, one patient escaped in June whilst carrying the lunch beer around. The attendant who was meant to be supervising him was fined 5s. towards the cost of his recapture. Even at the end of the nineteenth century when the temperance movement was at its zenith, at least half the public asylums were still including beer in their weekly diet.

The almost endemic drunkenness at the Sussex Asylum was merely a reflection of a social problem that was on the increase. In 1862, 63,255 people in England were convicted of being drunk and disorderly. It was not only a male problem: 10,000 of those convicted were women. Pubs and beerhouses were open all day (except on Sundays) and the nearest large town to the asylum, Brighton, had at that time almost as many liquor and beer shops as food shops, 480 and 541 respectively.

After drunkenness, theft was the most common reason for dismissal:

> On 1st December (1860), I (Robertson) dismissed Thomas Rowe in charge of a ward, without warning or wages for having appropriated to

his own use a pair of shoes the property of the Asylum… I have for some
time been dissatisfied with Rowe's management of his patients (although)
he came here with a very good character reference from Hanwell Asylum,
Middlesex.[14]

In fact, Robertson usually found staff coming from public asylums, such as
Hanwell, far superior to those arriving from the private asylums. He considered
the worst staff to be ex-military men whom he claimed required "more looking
after than the patients".[15] On the other hand, he believed that farm servants with
some training, made the best attendants. As for the female staff, he thought that
housemaids under twenty had the most potential to make good nurses. Many of
the staff were barely off the streets themselves and as there was no official
training, Robertson usually insisted on trial periods.

Staff caught stealing often faced criminal prosecution. On 1st January
1860, Henry Turner the brewer was caught carrying out of the house a bottle of
whisky, cake and nuts. He was immediately sacked and was given six weeks' hard
labour by the Cuckfield magistrates. On 11th November, Andrew Bonham the
Baker, "was detected stealing by the aid of his boy some dough from the asylum
Bakehouse".[16] He was subsequently brought before the bench and sentenced to
one month's imprisonment. And in August that year, Thomas Chinnery, the
Bailiff, was sacked by the Visiting Committee for fraud but they declined to
prosecute that time. There does appear to have been a lot of petty theft at the
asylum. It ranged from staff sometimes taking the leftovers of the Visitors'
Committee's meals, to pilfering from the farm and stores.

Robertson also regularly fined staff for negligence, commonly through
allowing a patient to escape. In 1861, Mr Marsh the matmaker was fined 10s.
(a third of his weekly wage) when a patient escaped and John Gaston the
bricklayer was fined 2s. 6d. for giving a patient the use of his key. The following
year the painter was severely reprimanded and fined for leaving two patients
alone for five minutes with the result that one of them received a heavy blow to
the head. Robertson also reprimanded and sometimes sacked staff for speaking
to patients in a derogatory way. It was his insistence on treating lunatics with
dignity and humanity which is so impressive.

At times, Robertson seems to have been completely exasperated by the little
annoyances of asylum life, whether it be the troublemaking of the steward's wife
or the state of the laundry. On 30th October 1860, he was complaining that the
clothing and laundry was never on time and that:

> … the sheets come to the laundry which have been used for any purpose
> except that of sleeping in. Often clothes are used as dusters![17]

The following year he complained again about the disorder in the laundry room caused by the lack of means of drying the clothes. This reduced the patients to having just one clean shirt and one clean pair of socks per week "an allowance sadly inefficient for health".[18] In June, he was protesting that the female attendants and servants kept leaving the taps on which was "past all bearing", and that the former "at present, trust too much to the patients and employ them without sufficient supervision".[19]

In 1862, Robertson's main anger was directed at the incompetence of the bailiff-cum-gardener, Edward Wing. Apart from his poor supervision of working parties (which on one occasion led to a fight between patients involving a shovel and a fork), Wing's lack of gardening knowledge led to the asylum having to buy its own vegetables for the first time since opening in 1859. His carrot crop infuriated Robertson:

> It has never been thinned. The carrots are growing in clumps of $1/2$ dozen just as they were sown and thus deprived of air and space of course they have not grown. With the unlimited supply of home hard labour here the Bailiff has no excuse for such neglect. With reference to his foolish statement that carrots ought not to be thinned and grow best when thus neglected. The annexed extract from Scott Burns 'Outline of Modern Farming' is inserted for the Bailiff's future guidance in the management of carrots![20]

Wing eventually resigned his post in April 1863.

Robertson was constantly concerned about the nursing staff's low pay and the lack of accommodation for married employees. He wrote in 1860 that:

> The whole success of my treatment depends on the quality of staff I manage to attract here; the work itself, as I know from personal experience, is very dull and has few attractions. I am about to lose one of my best ward attendants in the house tempted by higher wages to the London Union. They offer there £30-£35.[21]

Robertson tried to persuade the Visitors' Committee to pay higher wages as "I need scarcely say here that liberal wages to those who are worth them is the best and truest economy".[22] He believed that wages in the county asylums were too low and compared very unfavourably with those of prison warders who earned between £55 and £67 per annum, more than double male attendant wages. In October 1860, he lamented the departure of Thomas Paine the painter. "He was a good musician and a fair tradesman" who left for a similar job at Bedford Asylum, "but with a cottage provided as all their artisans have… This want of decent house accommodation is a constant difficulty with the married artisans and attendants".[23] Local rents were high – 4s. per week – and there was

Sussex Lunatic Asylum.

THE ESTABLISHMENT.

OFFICERS.

Medical Superintendent £450		Furnished Apartments, Coals, Gas, Vegetables, and Washing.
Chaplain 200		
Clerk to Visitors 100		
Assistant Medical Officer 100		Furnished Apartments, Board, Lodging, and Attendance.
Clerk and Steward............... 100		ditto
Housekeeper 50		ditto
Head Attendant (Male Department) 50		ditto
ditto (Female ditto) .. 31		ditto

ATTENDANTS AND SERVANTS.

14 Male Attendants .... £28 to £30	0	0	(at discretion of Medical Sup.); Board, Lodging, & Washing.
16 Female ,, ... 15 to 20	0	0	ditto
House Porter 30	0	0	Board, Lodging, and Washing.
Head Laundry Maid 24	0	0	ditto
4 Laundry Maids 18	0	0	ditto
Cook 24	0	0	ditto
Dairy Maid 16	0	0	ditto
Kitchen Maid 12	0	0	ditto
2 House Maids 12	0	0	ditto
Engineer 1	15	0	per Week; House, Coals, & Gas.
Bailiff and Gardener 1	1	0	,, House, Coals, & Vege-
Assistant Gardener 0	17	0	,, ditto [tables.
Farm Attendant 1	0	0	,,
Tailor.................... 1	1	0	,,
Shoemaker 1	1	0	,,
Mat Maker, &c. 1	1	0	,,
Baker 1	5	0	,,
Brewer and Store Porter ... 1	5	0	,,
Carpenter 1	10	0	,,
Bricklayer............... 1	5	0	,,
Painter and Glazier 1	5	0	,,
Blacksmith 1	5	0	,,
Stoker 1	1	0	,,
Ditto 0	18	0	,,
Gas Man 1	1	0	,,
Cow Man 0	16	0	,,
Cow Boy 0	10	0	,,
Carter 0	16	0	,,

25th December, 1860.

Figure seven: Sussex Lunatic Asylum Annual Report 1860

little suitable accommodation nearby. The issue of low pay and lack of decent accommodation was still a grievance at the asylum when the author worked there (as a student) more than a hundred years later.

A partial solution to the lack of married quarters was at hand. On 11th October 1860, Robertson wrote that a near neighbour, Mr Freeman, "has threatened to commit suicide if we decline again to buy his land and house...

His mind is evidently unhinged".[24] He estimated that three married attendants could be placed in the house. Other nearby cottages were soon bought and in 1862 he experimented by placing six female patients with two of the married attendants and their families. He was confident about the trial:

> Of the benefit which a certain class of patients is likely to derive from this transfer to the healthy influences of homelife from the asylum wards, the Medical Superintendent entertains no manner of doubt.[25]

He believed that by building decent cottages nearby for married staff it would not only help keep staff but it would also provide specialist accommodation for certain patients which would help relieve congestion in an already overcrowded asylum. Those he had in mind were quiet, long-term chronic female patients. In 1862, he recommended that six staff cottages should be built with room for three patients in each. It was not a new idea as J. C. Bucknill, of the Devon Asylum, had already successfully placed patients with trustworthy cottagers and asylum staff.

During 1863, Robertson placed nine female patients with three of the married attendants in nearby cottages but by the end of the year he was forced to give up the experiment for two reasons. Firstly, there was a lot of prejudice in the neighbourhood against it and one of the cottage landlords even refused to let it be used for such a purpose. Secondly, Robertson did not find it easy to find volunteers for the cottages where the turnover was high due to patients frequently wanting to return to the asylum. The reasons for this Robertson alluded to in an article he wrote for the *Journal of Mental Science* on 14th July the following year:

> Curiously enough, the patients preferred the Asylum, principally in consequence of the better diet. In the Asylum the food was carefully distributed, but in the cottages the patients were at the mercy of the attendants; and although he allowed 8s a week for food alone, there were constant complaints on the score of diet. The great value of Asylums, which ought not to be overlooked, was to be found in the power of supervision by the principle officers.

And in 1863, three female patients were removed from one of the artisan cottages after they had complained about their treatment from Mrs Wilkinson, the wife of the painter. The latter was soon dismissed for persistently losing his temper with the patients. So, although this first tentative experiment had apparently failed, Robertson believed that it was too limited a trial by which to draw any conclusions. He recommended that in the future the asylum must buy its own cottages and try the experiment again.

Robertson often supported and passed on staff demands to the Committee of Visitors. On 28th November 1861, he wrote:

> The married artisans and attendants have frequently expressed to me a wish to be permitted to purchase provisions at the asylum stores. It is to the manifest advantage of the patients that their attendants should be satisfied and permanent.[26]

Unfortunately, the Visitors were less sympathetic. On 26th October, they decided that the "application of the servants to be supplied with provisions and other articles out of the stores was considered and withdrawn".[27] The poor working conditions at the asylum made it difficult for Robertson to employ experienced nursing staff. In 1861, he was forced to appoint three new attendants who had never worked in an asylum before – James Morgan (an actor), Thomas Hatcher (a railway porter) and William Iremonger (a carpenter). Both Morgan and Hatcher were sacked within two years and Iremonger was to become a highly controversial figure at the asylum.

In 1861, Robertson introduced a system of night nursing during the first six months of the year. Patients were no longer to be left overnight in wet or soiled sheets. The system entailed incontinent patients being woken up four times a night (at 10 pm, 12 am, 2 am and 4 am) by a newly employed night nurse – one on the female side, one on the male – who would change them and their bedding if necessary. If the night nurse required help, he or she could wake up a member of the day staff who slept in rooms between the dormitories. It was a successful system but it was very difficult finding staff to do the night duty. In 1862, Robertson demanded that the Visitors' Committee raise the night nurses' wages on the female side from £20 to £24 per annum because the "duties were very arduous and it was very hard to get anyone".[28] This was not surprising, when you consider that at night two staff were expected to watch over nearly 500 patients. The committee accepted his demand. The following year he managed to persuade them and the Lunacy Commissioners to allow the nurses and attendants to continue receiving Board Wages (1s. 6d. per day) during their ten days' annual leave. But he had less success in trying to obtain them wage increases.

Two or three of the nursing staff had mental breakdowns themselves in the early 1860s and were admitted as patients. In 1863, for the first time, two attendants were made redundant when the government withdrew its naval lunatics. This laying off of staff when patient numbers declined was a pattern which was to be repeated many times throughout the asylum's history. Although many staff were sacked or left the asylum after a short stay, a large minority of those who remained stayed for the rest of their working lives. Apart from asylum work offering relative job security, it also offered a home, a social life and (just as for the patients), a protective environment. And reading the staff's magazine, *Hospital News*, (produced in the 1960s and 70s), one is again struck by the number of retirement presentations to staff who had worked there 40 years or more. In the nineteenth century, staff did receive pensions after long service but the amount was left to the discretion of the Visitors' Committee. Despite their low wages, there are often examples of staff generosity. For example, in December 1862, Henry Hawkins, the Chaplain, gave a talk to them about the famine in Lancashire caused by the cotton crisis due to the American Civil War. Amazingly, he made a collection of more than £14 from those present and sent it to Blackburn.

The asylum staff in the early years were dominated by Robertson's sense of discipline and his concern that the basis of patient treatment must be kindness. The hard nature of asylum work and its poor conditions, as Robertson himself readily acknowledged, meant that people who were really unsuitable would, on occasion, have to be employed. But Robertson's strict enforcement of the regulations ensured that the staff at the Sussex Asylum were never as bad as at some other asylums; for example, the nurses and attendants at the Kent Asylum at that time were described as "brutish, dirty, ugly and rude".

PATIENTS' WORK AND THE ASYLUM FINANCES

Although Robertson was a passionate believer in the therapeutic benefits of the asylum, he had to keep an eye on the level of the weekly maintenance rate paid by the parishes for their pauper lunatics. He had to strike a balance between providing the patients with a decent quality of life and, at the same time, keeping the rate low. Compared to other asylums, Robertson felt that his had several disadvantages. In May 1860, he made a financial comparison between the Essex Asylum (Brentwood) and the Sussex Asylum. He found that the latter spent more on:

- food, because of the asylum's isolated position and distance from a market town.
- heating, because of the inefficiency of its open fires.
- salaries and wages, because Essex had a hundred more patients but roughly the same number of staff.

Despite these excesses, Robertson believed that the comparison was a favourable one and he was confident that the maintenance rate per patient would eventually fall to 9s. per week – it was 10s. 6d. by the end of 1860:

> Looking then to the fact that our rate is steadily decreasing and that the
> items in which an excess exists are remedial – viz. – that in provisions by
> the better cultivation of the farm: that in the house expenses by the intro-
> duction of some scientific method of warming the wards while the salaries
> and wages will fall with the steady increase of patients to which we are
> subject. I venture to think that the financial condition of the house is
> satisfactory in looking to the short period it has been open.[29]

In fact, Robertson proved to be uncannily accurate in his prediction and
the rate eventually fell to below 9s. per week. Patient labour played an important
part in achieving this goal. We have already seen that in 1860, it was estimated
to be worth more than £1,500 per year. Later on, Robertson hoped that with the
acquisition of adjacent land for cultivation, the rate could eventually be as low
as at the North and East Riding Asylum in Yorkshire where due to the efficient
running of their farm, the rate was only 7s. 4d.

The Sussex Asylum farm, right from the beginning, played a central role in
asylum life. In 1860, sixty-two pigs and four cows were bought for £64 11s. and
£62 14s. respectively. Apart from providing fresh produce the farm also sold its
surplus to local people. In 1861 it made an annual profit of £176. A year later,
this figure had almost doubled to £341. And by 1864 it was self-sufficient in its
meat production. The farm regularly provided employment for 30 to 40 male
patients. And during the hay making period, up to 50 female patients helped in
the fields. Surprisingly, few incidents were recorded of inmates using their agricultural implements on each other or on the staff.

The distribution of the type of work allocated to patients was thought to
be important in the early years:

> It was felt to be therapeutic to vary the experience from previous
> employment. Thus if a farm labourer became a patient, he was put to
> learn a trade like shoemaking; whereas a patient who had been used to the
> sedentary job of tailoring was sent to work in the garden or on the farm.[30]

All the patients were given extra beer for working in or around the asylum
but with the high level of staff drunkenness it is likely that some patients may
have exchanged or "donated" their share to the staff. Significantly, no case of
patient drunkenness was ever recorded whilst beer was part of their diet.

In 1862, all the wards and the chapel were decorated by the patients and
the workshops were becoming increasingly successful. The tailor's shop and the
shoemaker's shop, as well as catering for the needs of the institution, showed
annual profits of £69 and £67 respectively. The employment, for the first time,

of a basket-maker, proved equally successful. His shop made and repaired a wide range of goods, from clothes baskets to linen baskets, from bird cages to dog kennels. That year it sold manufactured goods worth £11 13s. 10d. Robertson recorded that:

> The work thus done under his supervision has commanded a ready sale in the neighbourhood and the Medical Superintendent has thus been enabled to employ several patients whom he could not have entrusted with agricultural implements.[31]

On 2nd May 1863, two Lunacy Commissioners praised the workshops:

> The Workshops appear to be well managed: 11 patients being employed as Tailors, of whom only two were originally of that trade, and the same number working as Shoemakers, of whom, all but three have been taught the business here. So, also, with the Basket and Mat makers. By a very judicious arrangement, all the men so employed In-doors have a weekly half holiday on Saturdays, which is devoted to Out-door exercise and amusements.[32]

Workshop activities had been tightened up by Robertson on 1st May 1861:

> In future the following hours will be adhered to by all the artisans and patients employed with them, with the view of lessening the time frittered away daily under the present arrangements.

> 6 am – The artisans will set up their workshops ready and make up the book of the previous day's work. (They had to arrive by 6.30 am in winter and finished half an hour later.)

> 6.30 am – The patients come to work.

> 8 am – Breakfast.

> 8.30 am – The patients return to work.

> 12.45 – The patients return to the wards (not earlier).

> 2 pm – The patients return to work.

> 5.30 pm – Work will not be discontinued until the clock strikes the half hour.

> The lunch and afternoon beer will be brought to the patients at their work which will not be interrupted. The Head Attendant is required to report to the Medical Superintendent any deviation from this order which may come to his notice.
> Signed Dr Robertson.[33]

The female patients' work for the asylum was particularly impressive. Below is an example of their productivity for just one year:

TABLE VI. *c.*

FEMALE PATIENTS' WORK.

Manufactured and Repaired during the Year 1862.

Name of Articles.	Made.	Repaired.
Sheets	162	582
Pillow Cases	15	2638
Shirts	503	5821
Men's Stockings........... pairs	30	5056
Women's do. .... do.	....	9485
Blankets	....	488
Counterpanes	....	1092
Flannel Jackets	....	1172
Do. Drawers	42	833
Shifts	713	5228
Do. Flannel	9	1266
Gowns	347	3945
Bed-gowns	193	2490
Flannel Petticoats	100	2112
Upper do.	78	2078
Aprons and Pinafores	829	4583
Neckerchiefs	636	1842
Pocket Handkerchiefs	907	601
Men's Day Caps	329	14
Women's do.	436	2333
Do. Nightcaps	288	1784
Towels	347	984
Stays	39	1497
Attendants' Uniform Dresses	36	33
Do. Caps	42	33
Do. Collars and Cuffs	210	21
Do. Aprons	57	5
Hoods	81	26
Bonnets	2	40
Men's Slops	24	62
Women's Capes	38	5
Table Cloths	14	85
Men's Tick Frocks	4	5
Boot Uppers bound .... pairs	86	....
Window Blinds	25	....
Boy's Trousers	4	2
Dusters	427	....
Bonnets trimmed	16	32
Ticken Drawers	4	....
Strong Rugs	....	2
Sundries	42	....

The Sussex Lunatic Asylum Annual Report 1862

It seems quite astonishing that nearly 6,000 shirts were repaired in the course of just one year. How many of them belonged to the patients and staff or to the local community it is difficult to tell. We do know that staff clothing (official and sometimes unofficial) was often repaired by the patients. And later, when the first radio was installed at the asylum in the 1920s, females were often encouraged to do repair work for staff whilst listening to the broadcasts. Some patients certainly did have a tendency to rip their own clothes up. The forty naval patients who had arrived in the autumn of 1861, had been so violent initially and destroyed so many of their own clothes that their maintenance rate (paid for by the government as private patients) had quickly been raised from 14s. to 16s. per week. Only later on in the century would clothing such as quilted bed-gowns made of sail cloth prove to be virtually indestructible.

In 1862, out of an average asylum patient population of 481, almost 60% were employed on a daily basis. But this was down on the 1860 figure of 70%. Robertson believed that this was due to workhouses sending more patients to him who were either old or in a dying state and thus could not work. The largest single group in workhouses was the elderly and so they also became the largest percentage of asylum admissions. As for arriving in a dying state: of the 42 patients who died that year, four died within a week of their arrival, two within a month and six within three months. For these reasons, the highest percentage of patients who worked at the asylum occurred in its first couple of years. By the time the asylum closed in 1995, few patients were working but those who did were paid, unlike their predecessors in the 1860s.

Healthy and interesting work had obvious therapeutic benefits to patients. But much of their employment was of a menial nature and there was often a thin line between therapy and the exploitation of cheap labour. Certainly, staff sometimes delegated their own chores to patients which, though normal practice in workhouses, was banned in county asylums. Nor were families and friends allowed to bring in work or activities for their relatives to do. There is no evidence to suggest that Robertson used work to exploit patients but as the number of patients capable of work gradually declined; those that could may have been taken advantage of. And this decline, most prominent after the asylum's first twenty years, meant that the maintenance rate eventually went on a continuous upward spiral.

Chapter Eight

1862-63

THE ASYLUM FILLS UP AND TENSION WITH BRIGHTON

The first suicide at the asylum occurred on 12th September, over three years after its opening. A 37-year-old widow, Anne Brigden, who had only arrived on 6th September, hanged herself using an apron suspended from a banister. Although there was a coroner's inquest on 15th September, none of the local newspapers reported the death or the result of the inquest. Her case notes described her as "melancholic" and she had apparently made three previous suicide attempts prior to her admission. She had tried to poison herself, attempted to choke herself, and had jumped down a 40-foot well. In fact, she had arrived at the asylum with severe bruising to her knees as a result of the last attempt. Clearly, the asylum was not to blame for her suicide, but Robertson was aware that any suicide reflected badly on his administration.

There had been a gradual increase in the number of suicides in the 42 English county asylums since the Sussex Asylum opened in 1859:

1859 – 7 suicides

1860 – 11 suicides

1861 – 12 suicides.[1]

Robertson concluded that "from these figures it would appear that every fourth year should bring its case of suicide in this Asylum".[2]

The Sussex Asylum continued to be hailed as a success story by the local press. On 2nd August, the *Brighton Guardian*, reported on the year's anniversary celebrations:

About 200, in about equal proportion of both sexes, took part in the summer fete, and after out-of-door sports and amusements, wound up with a dance in the large room of the Asylum, in which a few visitors joined… All seemed to enjoy themselves exceedingly, and conducted themselves with a degree of propriety which, a few years ago, it would have been deemed absurd to expect from such a class of patient. The progress which has been made in the treatment, and, in numerous cases, cure, of the inmates of our public Lunatic Asylums, is one of the most striking signs of an advanced civilization; and it is most satisfactory to have such proofs of it as are afforded in our own County Asylum. In the Asylum, as in the out of door world, it is found that a mingled system of work and recreation is best adopted for the restoration of a sound mind in a sound body.

On 12th October, Baron Mundy visited the asylum on behalf of the Austrian government and considered the arrangements there the best he had seen in England. The Mayor of Hastings on a visit was equally complimentary. During 1862, Robertson allowed more patients out to spend days with relatives and friends. And in an article he wrote in the July edition of the *Journal of Mental Science*, he made an astonishingly accurate prediction about the future care of the insane, a prediction that was to be the basis of Care in the Community more than 130 years later. He declared that in time:

> the asylum itself might become a needless therapeutic agent, and the treatment of mental illness can be treated at home or in a general hospital.[3]

But behind the success story of the asylum, there were some worrying developments. The organization of patient work was becoming a priority, perhaps at the expense of a less institutionalized lifestyle. When Robertson had defended his regime during the Mockford Case in 1860, he had rightly claimed that he allowed visiting Guardians to see their patients in the wards and the workshops instead of the traditional asylum practice of herding them all together in one large hall for inspection. When the Brighton Lunacy Committee visited the asylum on 15th January 1862, to their surprise, they found a new arrangement:

> We did not go through the various wards of the Asylum, as has been the usual practice, but the patients were brought into the recreation room. We saw the males first, and the females after.[4]

Whether this change was brought about because of Robertson's declared resentment against the number of visitors wandering around the asylum or whether it was due to practical considerations, it is difficult to tell. Certainly, Robertson viewed visitors, especially Workhouse Guardians, as a necessary evil who had to be tolerated. And he also showed little sympathy to the relatives and friends of patients who in May 1862, requested to visit the asylum on days other than Wednesdays, the official visiting day:

> The extension of facilities for visiting is I think uncalled for. I never refuse any applicant who comes in ignorance of the visiting day or with a fair excuse while in all cases of sickness friends are admitted at all times. The general visiting day is a day lost for work and one day a week is in my opinion enough to sacrifice.[5]

Henry Hawkins described visiting day:

> The weekly visiting day of the friends of the patients is by many anxiously looked forward to. In the forenoon of that day may be noticed country folk or town people, singly or in small parties wending their way to the Asylum. They seldom go empty-handed. A basket or paper bag, containing some gift for their friend, is a usual accompaniment of visitors. The interviews take place in a large room in which the smock-frock and the homely dress of country people, and the holiday coat and smart dress of the visitors from the towns, may be seen as the various parties sit or stand in groups conversing with parent or child, husband or wife, brother, sister or friend as the case may be. At a fixed hour the room is cleared, the visitors depart, the patients return to their quarters.[6]

Although it was much easier for relatives and friends to visit the Sussex Asylum than it had been for them to go to the private London asylums, there were still difficulties. They could only visit on Wednesdays until 4 pm; not very convenient for those who worked. And in winter, the road between Haywards Heath railway station and the asylum was often muddy and almost impassable for those on foot. For this reason, some families preferred their relatives to be kept in the local workhouse because it made visiting so much easier. In fact, the new workhouse being built in Brighton had specialized accommodation for pauper lunatics.

The emphasis on work eventually made some asylums more like factories than places of cure. At the end of 1862, Robertson was bombarded by requests from Mr Edle, the vicar of Busted, to release a deaf and dumb patient called Richards. The Vicar implied that he was only being kept at the asylum for his work. In Victorian times, unlawful committal was a very sensitive issue but Robertson refused to release him and recorded that "Richards is a dangerous, violent lunatic totally unfit to be at large".[7] A patient's capacity to work was certainly a consideration for Robertson and when the government's 36 naval lunatics were withdrawn from the asylum the following June, he lamented that their withdrawal meant that "the work of the house will suffer".[8]

In the same month that Robertson refused the visiting extension, three escape attempts were recorded but all the patients were quickly recaptured. Amongst the admissions that year was James Chambers, a Canadian. He had already been in four asylums and Robertson believed that he was feigning his symptoms in order to get a free passage to Newfoundland. He thought that Chambers was only there in order to avoid starvation and advised the Lunacy Commissioners to send him to Canada. Initially, they refused, but the following year they sanctioned his journey to Newfoundland. Chambers was given an allowance of 14s. for eight weeks (to be paid for by his borough, Hastings). Sending foreign patients back to their own countries was by no means unusual. In 1862, a 27-year-old patient, a German governess, was accompanied by a German physician and the head attendant as far as Cologne in Germany. There she was to be looked after by her friends.

Immediate families of patients were often expected to contribute money towards their maintenance. An interesting summons for non-maintenance against a labouring man, Henry Bishop, was reported by the *Brighton Herald* on 5th April 1862. Bishop had been paying 3s. 6d. a week towards the maintenance of his wife, Lucy Bishop, from the time she had been admitted into the asylum (2 years before) until 14th August 1861. Since that date he had refused to pay claiming that she was not his legal wife. At the summons, Lucy Bishop insisted that she had lived with him for sixteen years and that they had a family and were considered to be man and wife. She said that she had been married before to a man called Shoulders who had been transported for life. She could not remember whether she had married Bishop within five years of her first husband being sent away. The law was that a woman must not have seen her husband for seven years before re-marrying.

Henry Bishop's defence was that there was no legal proof that Lucy Bishop was his wife. He got little sympathy from the magistrate, Mr Bigge, who had been informed about a rumour that the defendant was to be left a fortune by his uncle in two or three months' time. Bishop claimed that his wages were 15s. a week, out of which he had to pay 3s. a week rent, and to keep himself and one child; and that he was not paid at all during wet weather. Mr Bigge cross-examined him:

Mr Bigge:	How old is the child?
Defendant:	20 or 21, I think. (laughter).
Mr Bigge:	Man or woman?
Defendant:	Woman.
Mr Bigge:	I think you can consider that she is not a babe in arms. (laughter).

Defendant:	She is not able to do anything just now. She had a child a little while ago. (Renewed laughter).
Mr Bigge:	It would not do for the defendant to come and tell them that he had a child to support when that "child" was 21 years of age. I see no reason why you should not continue to support your wife. An order for 3s. a week is made.

Occasionally, families paying maintenance charges would disappear. In these cases, the asylum would ask their parishes for the money. If they refused to pay, it was not unknown for the patient to be returned to their parish workhouse.

The overcrowding of the asylum was becoming a serious problem, particularly on the female side. In 1859, there had been 149 female patients, by 1862 there were 258 and some wards contained as many as 60 patients, 20 more than the official maximum. Female beds were being increasingly placed in areas not designed for them, such as the day rooms. In April 1862, six female patients were removed from the asylum to make room for pauper lunatics. Workhouses were again warned only to send their most urgent female cases. Even the Visitors' Committee admitted that the "Asylum was insufficient for the proper accommodation of the number of lunatics for whom it might be necessary to provide".[9] Accordingly, at the end of the year, the Committee provisionally agreed to spend £5,000 on an extension which would provide an extra 100 beds on the female side.

Robertson was also concerned about the plight of the poorer middle class private patients who were being transferred to make room for pauper lunatics. On 4th December 1862, he presented a paper at the Brighton Medico-Chirurgical Society entitled "The Want of a Middle Class Asylum in Sussex". In it he claimed that he was receiving, on average, two begging letters a week from middle class families requesting places for their relatives. Robertson recommended that a middle class asylum accommodating 100 patients (and privately funded as general hospitals were), should be built near the Sussex Asylum. He suggested that it should receive two classes of patients; one paying £100 per year and the other paying £50. The private asylum should only keep a small percentage of the profits and donate the rest to deserving cases. Robertson estimated that £20,000 would be needed to build it and told the other society members that he would start making plans for it if they gave him support.

As the Sussex Asylum became overcrowded, there was undoubtedly a need for accommodation for those patients who were poor but not poor enough to be considered paupers and therefore not eligible for the county asylum. In Sussex, the only alternative was Ticehurst House, which was for the very wealthy. And although there were eleven middle class asylums in England, there were none in Sussex, Surrey, Essex, Kent or Hertfordshire. There does not appear to have been much practical support for Robertson's suggestion even though one of the doctors at the meeting claimed that one half of all lunatics were from the middle class. Despite advocating separate institutions for this social group, at the Sussex Asylum, he always insisted that private patients be treated the same as pauper lunatics. His plan got no further than the sending out of prospectuses to fellow professionals. A year later, one of them would cause him public embarrassment.

By the end of 1862, the asylum's population had increased from 459 to 500 – 242 men and 258 women – and they were living in a building designed for 400 but only really comfortable with less. Forty-seven patients had been discharged – 30 deemed 'recovered', 7 'relieved' and 10 'not improved' (7 of whom were private patients transferred to make room for pauper lunatics). Although fewer patients had been discharged than in the previous year – 61 – the rate of 'recoveries' had actually gone up from 17% to 22%. Of course, this could be interpreted as a sign that treatment was improving but as the rate was based on admissions, it was often heavily influenced by the condition of the new patients on their arrival. In fact, the rate had gone up in 1862 despite the continued admittance of patients who were old and infirm. Forty-one patients (more than 8% of residents), had died during the year, nine of whom were over 60 and nine over 70 years old. Robertson still maintained that the inadequate heating system in the form of open fires, was responsible for raising the mortality rate by at least one percent.

The overcrowding was also causing Robertson personal discomfort. As his accommodation was right in the centre of the building, the noise levels – day and night – became more intolerable. He suggested to the Visitors' Committee that female patients could be placed in his accommodation and that a separate house should be built nearby for the medical superintendent. Although sympathetic to his request, they were helpless to do anything as it was the Lunacy Commissioners' regulation that the superintendent must live in the main asylum building. The Commissioners argued – with some justification – that the on the spot 24-hour presence of the medical officer was crucial to an asylum's success. This condition, although understandable, was particularly hard on those medical superintendents who had families. Perhaps as compensation for not getting separate accommodation, the unmarried Robertson received a wage increase of £100 and was now earning £550 per annum. Equally, it could have been his reward for further reducing the weekly maintenance rate to 10s. per week. But not all the parishes benefited from this reduction. In May, because the asylum was full, Brighton had been forced to send some of their pauper lunatics to Bethnal Green Asylum, London, where the rate was 14s weekly.

In this period, the overcrowding of institutions was by no means confined to county asylums. On 18th October 1862, the *Brighton Herald* reported that the town's workhouse now contained 750 inmates in a building designed for 200. Their new workhouse would not be open for another five years. So, as county asylums became overcrowded, the dream held by many reformers, that asylums should recreate a homely environment, was quickly evaporating.

The following year, a controversial visit by Lord West, a member of the Visitors' Committee took place, on 30th January. He inspected the female wing and suggested that he could see room for 23 more beds. Robertson reacted angrily to his suggestion and wrote to the whole Committee:

> … I now wish to say to you that I cannot hold myself responsible for the general health of the house if further overcrowding be resorted to… I told Lord West that I believed his plans if carried out would raise the mortality rate by 2%.[10]

West was overruled and the agreed extension of patient accommodation was started in 1863. During the building work some of the female wards had to be closed and female admissions were curtailed. Thirty-six of the government's naval lunatics were discharged and by the end of the year the asylum population had actually fallen by 37 to 463. But this was due more to the disruption caused by the building work than to any decrease in demand for asylum places and was only a temporary halt to the overall pattern of increasing numbers.

There was also an increased segregation of staff and patients at asylum events. Originally, the Christmas dance was held on the same day but in 1862 the patients had theirs on Christmas Eve whilst the staff had theirs on the 31st December. Presumably, this new segregation was due to the increase in the asylum's population. But it was a further step away from the ideology of 'moral treatment' which had placed a strong emphasis on the importance of shared staff-patient activities.

Seventy-seven patients were discharged during 1863 – 32 deemed 'recovered'; 11 'relieved' and 34 'not improved'. This last group mainly consisted of the naval lunatics. The percentage of cures (on admissions) had strikingly gone up from 23% to 39% but Robertson was not fooled by these figures and believed that the reduction of patient admissions – from 129 in 1862 to 81 in

1863 – was chiefly responsible for the improvement. Forty-three patients had died during the year although the number of female deaths had actually fallen from 18 in 1862, to 13 in 1863. Again, Robertson was certain that the overall decline in female numbers (by 15) instead of the usual increase, was largely the cause. He put the statistics into perspective:

> How little value for a comparative judgement such statistics are, unless the detailed history of the Asylum is at the same time considered.[11]

Generally, the last two years had been good ones for the asylum with fewer staff changes, some improvements in patient comfort and a well needed extension of asylum accommodation under way. In his Annual Report for 1863, Robertson recorded that no picture, plant or bird had been injured by the patients during the year and that only three panes of glass had been wilfully broken. And amongst the amusements that year there had even been a firework display for the female patients on one of the terraces. Serious overcrowding had been, albeit temporarily, averted and there had been no major scandals. Even the Annual Report was in heavy demand and Robertson had to order 750 copies to be printed instead of the usual 500.

On a personal note, Robertson's prestige in the profession was no doubt helped by his appointment that year as the co-editor of the *Journal of Mental Science* along with Henry Maudsley. Robertson was undoubtedly the senior partner and all contributions to the magazine had to be sent to the Sussex Asylum. This obviously added to his workload but Robertson still seemed as dedicated as ever to his own job. However, there were developments at the asylum which were causing him some anxiety. Firstly, there was growing concern about the increase in male patients, especially as only female accommodation was being expanded. Secondly, 1863 was the first year that there was very little local newspaper coverage of asylum events, including no reports at all on the Fourth Commemoration Day celebrations. And thirdly, there was a re-opening of the ill-feeling between the Brighton Guardians and Robertson. And it was this last development which probably led to Robertson's worst crisis.

ROBERTSON AND THE BRIGHTON GUARDIANS

His first brush with the Brighton Guardians in 1863 came as early as January when Brighton and two other parishes were accused by the Visitors' Committee of sending patients to the asylum under false pretences. Apparently, seven patients had been sent there as pauper lunatics (maintenance rate 10s. per week) whereas in reality the asylum believed them to be private patients who

SUSSEX LUNATIC ASYLUM,

HAYWARD'S HEATH.

THE FOURTH COMMEMORATION DAY

OF THE OPENING OF THE ASYLUM, IN 1859,

WILL BE HELD

On SATURDAY, JULY 25th, 1863.

ORDER OF THE DAY:—

11. 0 A.M.—MORNING PRAYER, with SERMON.—Preacher, the Rev. W. FITZ HUGH, M.A., Rector of Street.

12.15 P.M.—CRICKET—AUNT SALLY—TRAP, BAT, AND BALL—FOOT BALL, &c., &c.

1.30 „ —PATIENTS' DINNER ON THE GROUNDS—LUNCHEON FOR THE VISITORS.

2.15 „ —JUMPING IN SACKS, and WHEEL-BARROW RACE.

3. 0 „ —GLEES by the SINGING CLASS.

3.30 „ —READINGS in the RECREATION HALL, (by Mrs. PROSSER, of Brighton.)

4.30 „ —DANCING on the LAWN.

5.30 „ —PATIENTS' TEA ON THE GROUNDS—TEA FOR THE VISITORS.

6.30 „ —BALL in the RECREATION HALL.

To CONCLUDE AT EIGHT P.M.

The Asylum String Band will play the Dance Music, and the Asylum Brass Band will play.
numerous Airs during the Day.

THE COMMEMORATION BALL FOR THE HOUSEHOLD

Will be held in the RECREATION HALL, on MONDAY, the 27th JULY,

COMMENCING AT 8.30 P.M.

HAYWARD'S HEATH, JULY 16, 1863.

₊ A Train leaves Brighton at 10.0 a.m., arriving at Hayward's Heath in time for the Chapel Service.
Trains return to Brighton at 7.37, 8.0, 8.10, and 9.12 p.m.

should have been paying 14s. per week. Two of the parishes admitted that they had acted wrongly but Brighton claimed that there had simply been a misunderstanding rather than an attempt at deception. Robertson and his Committee suspected that there had been some connivance between Samuel Thorncroft, Brighton's assistant overseer, and the patients' families.

Samuel Thorncroft was a controversial character who had been the governor of the Brighton Workhouse in 1822 and since 1834 had held his present position. The post was a powerful one as he had a major say in who did and did not deserve poor law relief and who should be admitted to the town's workhouse. Thorncroft was a bullying figure who even his admirers admitted was "uncouth and sharp". The local newspapers of that era are full of disputes between himself and local people. But whatever character defects he may have had, Thorncroft was a hero to many ratepayers as he managed to keep the cost of relief down to a minimum. He was also a bit of a loose cannon to the authorities and in 1865 was reprimanded for making a critical speech about them (when drunk) at the foundation ceremony for the new workhouse. That he and Robertson – opposites in almost every way – would clash, was somewhat inevitable.

As already noted, Robertson had started the practice of grouping together the female patients and the male patients separately for the regular quarterly visits of the Lunacy Committee from Brighton. For practical purposes this required that the Brighton Committee had to notify the asylum beforehand about when they would be coming. Some of the Guardians were unhappy about this new arrangement and Thorncroft claimed that previous visits to private asylums had always been unannounced. Apart from this grievance, Brighton's Committee itself was under attack for having extravagant lunches before and after their asylum visits. On 15th May 1863, the *Brighton Observer* published an anonymous letter entitled "Egregarious Pieces of Humbug":

> I allude to the quarterly visits of some 12 or 14 gentlemen to see that our pauper lunatics are well taken care of… these visits by a numerous body of strangers – for the Directors and Guardians are appointed on the Lunacy Committee, quarterly by turns – are invariably attended by bad effects on the patients. Is it not monstrous, that the parties should go on a party of mischief, and then tax the rate-payers with the expenses attending it, to the tune of £40 to £50 a year. Fresh faces irritate patients, and by all means let those gentlemen feed themselves.
>
> Yours truly
>
> SCRUTATOR

The letter had an effect as the Committee was soon reduced to three members.

Part of Thorncroft's job was to organize the conveyancing of Brighton's pauper lunatics to and from the asylum. In August 1863, Robertson wrote to him recommending that a female patient be allowed out to go and stay with friends in Brighton for three days. He asked Thorncroft to come and collect her. But he didn't come. Three months later, on 13th November, Thorncroft came to the asylum in the company of the three members of Brighton's Committee. During the visit, Thorncroft swore at the patient concerned. She became so angry and agitated that she had to be physically removed from the room. The argumentative overseer was then asked to leave after insulting Robertson and the three members. He left, but not before telling them that his knowledge was equal to that of any medical man.

A few days later, Brighton's Lunacy Committee wrote a report in which they strongly censured Thorncroft's behaviour. And Robertson wrote to the Brighton Guardians reiterating the stress caused to the woman patient who, since August, had daily been expecting to be taken to Brighton to stay with her friends. Thorncroft's manners had also upset Robertson who complained that he had "persisted in wearing his hat in the waiting room, in the presence both of the Guardians and myself. It is not seemly that an uneducated servant of the Board should thus, unreproved, conduct himself towards the head of this establishment".[12]

At the next meeting of the Brighton Guardians, Thorncroft claimed that he had 30 years of unblemished experience dealing with lunatics – more than Robertson and the Committee – and that the whole affair was a conspiracy against him. He explained that he had mistaken the patient for someone else whom he knew to have friends and relatives capable of taking her home themselves. He denied having been rude during the visit and (in words that must have been read with some disbelief by the poorer town folk) claimed that his chief desire was:

> to treat the lunatics kindly, to listen to their fancied or probable grievances, believing that to be my duty, and to reply to them in a consoling manner, always advising them to look up with quiet calmness and obedience to the chief of the institution, the Medical Superintendent.[13]

He then presented two glowing letters of character reference; one from Dr Millar, the Medical Superintendent of Bethnal House Private Asylum, London; and another from Mr Ritchie, an ex-officer there. But Brighton's Lunacy Committee still insisted that he had behaved badly and that "this was not the first, second, or third time that Mr Thorncroft had behaved rudely to persons".[14]

The Brighton Guardians set up a nine-man committee to investigate the matter but it was a committee noticeably lacking in men who had been critical of Thorncroft.

After investigation, the committee suggested that the matter be allowed to drop and their recommendation was unanimously adopted but only after a rather noisy meeting in which one Guardian claimed that "Dr Robertson wanted this committee to pay him homage".[15] In a letter to the Guardians on 10th December, Robertson gave his reaction to their decision:

> I extremely regret the unsatisfactory manner in which the Committee have passed over these justly-founded complaints of their Lunacy Committee and myself. Mr Thorncroft implies that, because Messrs Millar and Ritchie (who gave him glowing references) hasten to speak of his courtesy, civility, and politeness, therefore I am at fault when I complain of his ignorant impertinence and unseemly conduct. I cannot accept this analogy. Mr Thorncroft went to Bethnal Green as a patron, and yearly added to the profits of that miserable speculation in suffering and disease by the Brighton patients whom he sent there. Of course the medical officers of the place had the strongest motives of pecuniary interest to stand well with the Assistant Overseer of so important a parish. I am not so placed, and my theory is, that I from the first gave offence to Mr Thorncroft by markedly declining to consult him in my management of the Brighton patients, a course, however, which I must inform the Directors and Guardians I intend to abide by.[16]

In reply, the Chairman of the Brighton Board, Colonel Moorsom, praised Robertson but declared that "it would be most injudicious on the part of the Board to take any further steps in this matter"[17]. His motion was carried by a large majority. Thorncroft had got off lightly because he was a "valuable" public servant and also because he probably could embarrass the Guardians with some allegations (about them) of his own. And many of the Guardians, although not admirers of Thorncroft, did resent Robertson's lack of deference to their authority. Although the incident was closed, the animosity it had created lingered on and would come to a head the following year.

But it was not quite the end of the affair. One of Thorncroft's referees, Dr Millar, the Medical Superintendent of Bethnal House, wrote a letter to the *Brighton Observer* which was published on Christmas Day 1863:

> That Dr Robertson did not always regard a "speculation in suffering and disease" in the light he now effects, I beg to remind him of a private proof of a prospectus, now before me for a "Medical Asylum for the Insane Company Limited", which he forwarded to me himself, in which the inducement held out to medical men to invest their money is "that the enormous profits which private lay speculation in insanity yields, will,

when thus directed into its true professional channel, ensure an ample return on the capital invested". The failure of this scheme might with greater truth be called a "miserable speculation" than that Successful House to which he so intemperately refers.

The letter obviously embarrassed Robertson especially as its readers would not have known that his attempt to set up a middle class asylum in Sussex a year ago was primarily motivated by the need for such an institution.

Robertson had disputes with other Guardians apart from those for Brighton. In 1863, he complained to the Steyning Board about the rudeness of their relieving officer, Mr George French. How much these disputes were caused by the shortage of places at the asylum, it is difficult to tell. In April, Robertson had written to all the parishes informing them to send their new cases to Peckham House in London which was more expensive. But, generally, disputes with other parish Guardians were rare and those with Brighton dominated the asylum's early years.

In February 1864, as the first snow of winter fell giving the town a wintry aspect, Brighton experienced unrest. The occasion was a hotly disputed local election in which the Tory candidate, Henry Moor, narrowly won by virtue of the divided liberal vote. Out of an electorate of 5,400, he had polled 1,663 votes, just beating the liberal, Mr Fawcett, who had received 1,468 votes. On election day, 20th February, there had been serious rioting in and around the Town Hall. Voters' cabs had been overturned, plastered with mud and pelted with rotten oranges and stale fish. One of the candidates, Mr Dumas, had been so badly attacked by "roughs" on the eve of election day that he had been unable to attend the hustings. Other respectable people had been 'bonnetted' – the knocking off of hats, using a variety of missiles – by boisterous locals. It was amidst this atmosphere that crowds on 25th February 1864, crammed into a Brighton pub, "The Northern Tavern", in order to hear an inquest into the death of a 43-year-old cowkeeper. His name was James Snashall and he had died at the asylum on the day of Moor's victory.

Chapter Nine

1864
"SOMETHING LOOSE IN THE
MANAGEMENT OF THE ASYLUM"

THE CASE OF JAMES SNASHALL

O n Snashall's death, the Coroner for East Sussex, Mr Gell, on being
given to understand that it was a simple case of sudden death,
decided not to hold an inquest. But when the body arrived at
Brighton, the deceased's wife, Sarah, found what she thought were marks of
violence on the body and applied to the local authorities for an inquest which
was granted and carried out by the borough coroner, Mr Black.

As members of the public quickly filled up The Northern Tavern pub, the
Brighton Guardian reported on 2nd March that "considerable interest and no
little excitement were occasioned from the fact, of a rumour having got abroad
that the deceased had been subjected to ill-treatment whilst in the Asylum".
Amongst those inside were several men dressed in the distinctive asylum
uniform of coat, waistcoat and cap. They were accompanied by Robertson and
his head attendant, Mr Knox, who found themselves sitting uncomfortably
close to Samuel Thorncroft and three Brighton Guardians. There was a suspicion, at least in the mind of Robertson, that the Guardians had instigated this
enquiry in order to embarrass him. No official record of the inquest exists but
the dialogues below are based on extensive reports in the local newspapers.[1] The
first witness to be called was Sarah Snashall.

THE EVIDENCE OF SARAH SNASHALL

She told the inquest that her husband had been ill for about a year but that his illness had only exhibited itself at night in the form of restlessness and agitation. Sometimes he would clap his hands and sing all night. Other times he would say that the devil had got him and that he was chained down in hell. These symptoms only occurred at intervals and he managed to work fairly well during the day-time. A month before the inquest his condition had deteriorated and he had become violent and had attacked her brother-in-law. He was then removed to the Workhouse Infirmary. She visited him twice there and said that he had kissed her and appeared to be happy and comfortable.

On 3rd February, on the order of a magistrate, Snashall was transferred to the asylum. Sarah Snashall next saw him at the asylum on 18th February. She was accompanied by her sister, Martha Leury. James Snashall appeared to be very ill and complained of being cold. She saw a bruise on his forehead and he told her he had another bruise on his arm. After rolling up his shirt sleeve she saw a badly inflamed mark extending round the muscle of the upper part of the left arm. It was swollen and about two inches in width. Her husband said that it was the straps that made the wound. This was denied by the attendant standing nearby who told her:

> "I can't think what he means about the straps, because we have no straps here; we are not allowed to use them. I don't know if it was done before he came here."

James also complained to his wife about being hurt in the stomach. She then told the inquest that they were only allowed to stay with him for fifteen minutes. Two days later he died. In answer to further questions she admitted that he had appeared to be more rational and collected at the asylum than when she had seen him at home. The Coroner continued to question her:

Coroner: Did you hear your sister say anything to the attendant?

Sarah: Yes, when James said he had been strapped she said to the attendant: "Oh, do be kind to him; it is evident that he has had the straps". And then James told her that he had been thrown down and jumped on. She then asked the attendant about this who strongly denied the charge.

Coroner: Is it not true that, before he left Brighton, he has frequently said things that were not true, – things which had no existence?

Sarah: Not in the day-time; sometimes in the night.

Coroner: Did he say such things as that he had bought a hundred acres of mangel wurzel, or a hundred cows?

Sarah: Well, not particularly.

Coroner: Now, be careful. You must not let your feelings carry you away. You are sworn to speak the truth.

Sarah: (Crying) And I will as far as I can, sir. He used to say such things in the night time, but not during the day.

Coroner: Is it correct that he said at the Asylum that he was sick after eating?

Sarah: Yes, and I said to the attendant, "Is that true" and he replied, "Yes, he brings his food up after every meal. He was sick before he went there".

Dr Robertson, watching carefully, declined to ask her any questions. The next witness, Martha Leury, Sarah's sister, told the inquest some details about James Snashall's insanity. She said that she had lived in his house for two years. Four months ago her husband had heard Sarah screaming and found James with his arm round her neck. When he asked him what he was doing he replied that he was "warming her". Martha Leury then went on to corroborate her sister's testimony about their visit to the asylum. She added that when she had questioned the attendant about the use of straps and ill-treatment, he had replied "It's no use you taking notice of anything he says". Then James had told her "they will strap me again as soon as you are gone".

THE EVIDENCE OF THE BRIGHTON WORKHOUSE STAFF

The next witness called was William Weller who worked as a warder at the Brighton Workhouse Infirmary. He recalled that after being in the workhouse a week, Snashall had become violent and that they had put him in a straight-jacket for six or seven hours. He was not strapped down and the jacket was not tight. He added that Snashall was a very powerful and violent man:

Coroner: What was his conversation?

Weller: His conversation was very well, but his ways were most disgusting. On one occasion he said he would run me through with a knife but I took no notice of that.

Weller then stated that he washed Snashall all over the morning previous to his going to the asylum and the only mark he found on him was a red spot or bruise on his back. He found nothing the matter with his arms. Weller's assistant, William Parker, supported his testimony. The last workhouse witness was William Smith, who worked as the removal clerk in Thorncroft's office and often visited the workhouse. He had taken Snashall to the asylum. He claimed that Snashall was very quiet on the journey there but that he had become very noisy on arrival. Later on, after Thorncroft had informed him of Snashall's death, Smith went round to see Sarah Snashall who lived nearby. He told the inquest about the conversation he had had with her sister, Martha:

Leury: Do you know that he is a murdered man?

Smith: No, it's not my business to enquire about that, but to enquire about the burial.

Leury: Well, he is, and we shall have enquiries made about it, for the sake of the other poor creatures there.

THE EVIDENCE OF THE ASYLUM STAFF

The first witness called was William Knox, the head attendant at the asylum. Knox was a portly figure who always dressed with soldier-like neatness and spoke with a thick northern accent. He told the inquest that he had examined Snashall on his arrival, on 3rd February, in front of Smith. He found that Snashall had a sore place on his buttocks, as if he had laid or sat in his wet clothes, and informed Robertson of this. He continued:

Knox: I saw Snashall ten or twelve times a day. He constantly walked about in a very incoherent manner and would wander about taking off his clothes. He had very restless nights. I believe he died of restlessness.

Coroner: Was the deceased ever violent?

Knox: Once, on the night of his admission. He was then wrapped in a wet sheet and blanket. The next morning he was much calmer, and seemed refreshed.

Coroner: Are you aware of any violence being used to him, except his being wrapped in a wet sheet?

Knox: I am not aware of anything of the kind; and I don't believe any ill-usage could take place without my knowing it.

Coroner: How do you arrive at that conclusion?

Knox: His attendant was such a kind man that I do not believe it possible he could have suffered the slightest mis-usage. I have observed the bruise on Snashall's arm. It wasn't there when he was admitted.

Coroner: To what do you attribute the bruises you speak of?

Knox: To friction with the sheet.

Coroner: Surely, it was something more severe than that to cause such injury?

Knox:	No, I think not. I ground my opinion on the fact that I have seen similar marks caused by the friction when a patient has been wrapped up in the sheet. I have seen several cases like it.
Coroner:	Do I understand that the sheet is bound tightly round the body?
Knox:	No, beneath the sheet is a towel which pinions the arms by passing over both arms and under the back. It is a common round towel. The sheet is simply wound round the patient; no cords or anything of that kind are used. The patient is self-pinioned; the weight of the body keeping the sheet in its place. The wounds on Snashall's arms were caused by working them up and down in the towel in his endeavours to release himself from the sheet.
Coroner:	Have you any straps at the Asylum?
Knox:	Not in use.
Coroner:	Have you such a thing in existence?
Knox:	No, we have never used them in the Asylum. I have however seen patients brought to the Asylum strapped down by Parish authorities.
Coroner:	Have you ever known any of the patients to be knocked down and trampled upon?
Knox:	No, I never saw the slightest symptoms of harshness used against the deceased. He never complained to me about ill-treatment and said he was very comfortable and happy.

It is interesting to note that Knox failed to fully answer the Coroner's last question. The next witness called was William Iremonger, the attendant referred to by Sarah Snashall and Martha Leury in their evidence.

Iremonger testified that the above women's testimonies were correct except for three points. He denied saying that Snashall's wounds may have been caused before his arrival at the asylum – by implication blaming the Brighton Workhouse – or that he had been sick after every meal. And he claimed that nothing was said to him about Snashall being 'knocked down'. Pressed on this last point by the Coroner, Iremonger insisted that he was "sure of it". Sarah Snashall and Martha Leury were then recalled and swore again that they had asked Iremonger about James being knocked down. Iremonger replied that he did not remember being asked the question. He then said that he knew the injury on Snashall's arm was caused by the sheet but could not explain why he failed to tell the two women this. In reply to further questions, Iremonger told the inquest that he had washed the body after death and had only seen the bruises on his arms and the one on his buttock which had existed before his admission.

Iremonger's rather weak testimony could not have pleased Dr Robertson who was the next witness. Robertson, an upright slim bearded figure, stated that:

> on the evening of Snashall's admission I was called by Mr Knox to see him. I found him in the padded room in a very excited state. I administered one drachm [about 3½ grams] of digitalis on his admission, and ordered half a drachm to be given to him three times in every twenty-four hours. Seeing the medicine had not taken the effect I anticipated, I ordered him to be packed in a wet sheet; the sheet to be changed every two hours until he slept. I visited him the following morning and found that he had passed a violent night, but he was then more quiet. His case was one of paralysis, with mania, and as bad a case as I ever saw. Whenever I visited him I was very particular in making enquiries about whether he had been sick and was only told of his having vomited once. Then I reduced the doses of digitalis. I was not aware of the sores on his arms.

Robertson was then questioned about the course of treatment adopted in the asylum. He explained to the jury that using a wet sheet was particularly mild and soothing to the nervous system and that he had undergone the same treatment himself for six weeks (after falling off his horse and injuring his back). He said that he had asked the deceased repeatedly if he had any sickness and he said 'no' till the day he had mentioned and after that he had discontinued the digitalis. Robertson disagreed with the opinion of his own head attendant:

> I can't believe that any movement with any towel would produce that chafing of the skin (on the arms) which I saw at the post mortem examination… the extreme chafing of the arm was caused in a great measure by the deceased's extreme restlessness; and his habit of continually taking his clothes off.

The coroner then asked Robertson to account for the differences in the testimony of the two women and that of Iremonger. He said that he could not, but, affirmed that "in cross-questioning, people are liable to make mistakes". One of the jury, Mr Burden, then claimed that, like Mrs Snashall, he had only been allowed to stay a short time – 30 minutes – on a recent visit to the asylum although the official time permitted was two hours. Robertson admitted that this was contrary to the rules which hung in the Visitors' Hall. The hours for visiting patients were from ten to twelve and two till four. He finished his testimony by insisting that he had never seen any harsh treatment towards Snashall; nor did he, to his knowledge, ever complain of any.

The last witnesses from the asylum were James Wilson, a night attendant, and Charles Cheshire, an attendant who had occasionally looked after Snashall in the day time. Wilson testified that he was present when the sheet and towel were applied and that the same sheet was kept on all night and that it was not removed every two hours. Wilson was not aware that Dr Robertson had ordered it to be changed. The following morning he saw the injuries on Snashall's arms. Cheshire testified that he had never seen any violence used towards the deceased. Whilst washing him, he had only seen the abrasion on his back which was there on admission. At mid-day on the 20th February, Cheshire had been present when Snashall had died suddenly whilst sitting on a settee.

THE POST MORTEM

When the body of James Snashall had arrived in Brighton, the Brighton Guardians had instructed a local doctor, Mr Sewell, and the parish surgeon, Mr Verral, to conduct a post mortem. At the inquest Mr Sewell presented their findings. He stated that there:

> …were marks on Snashall's arms that could have been caused by straps or ligatures; that there was a bruise on the right side of the forehead and on the left cheek but that there were no external marks of violence on the body; that there was a swollen spot on his back which could have been occasioned by a fall, which appeared like a bruise of many days standing; that there was no trace of injury on the abdomen and that his organs were examined and his chest was found to be perfectly healthy.

Finally, Mr Sewell concluded that the immediate cause of death was a blood clot on the brain and that the bruise on his forehead could not have caused it.

THE CORONER'S SUMMING UP

Mr Black, the coroner, pointed out the discrepancies in the evidence of the attendant Iremonger, and commented on the manner in which he denied having stated that the deceased was sick after each meal when Mrs Snashall and her sister positively declared that he did make such a statement. He said that the jury had seen their demeanour and saw them brought face to face, and it was for them to give credence to whomsoever they chose. He continued:

> It was clear that death was not the result of violence; but they could not disguise the fact – although it was foreign to the enquiry – that there had been neglect on the part of some of the officers at the Asylum. They had it in evidence that Dr Robertson ordered a wet sheet to be put on every two hours on the first night and yet the attendant who watched the deceased, stated that it was not changed all night. Here was a decided dereliction of duty on the part of someone, in not obeying the instruc-

tions of the Medical Superintendent. Then, again, if the deceased was sick repeatedly, as Iremonger told Mrs Snashall, he should then have communicated to that effect to Dr Robertson, who would then have discontinued the doses of so strong a medicine as the tincture of digitalis. However, these facts were not for them to consider – they had simply to ascertain the cause of death, and this, Mr Sewell told them, was apoplexy (a stroke).

The jury, composed of "highly-respectable and intelligent tradesmen selected from the locality",[2] unanimously decided that there had been a great dereliction of duty somewhere at the asylum, and that the wife and sister had been quite right to demand an inquest. A juror asked the Coroner if they could not append to their verdict an opinion to this effect. He replied that it was outside their province and that their duty was simply to enquire into the cause of death. Another juror said that he hoped the press would give the enquiry full publicity as it was the only means by which the public could become cognisant of the facts. The jury then returned a verdict of 'Death from Apoplexy'.

The inquest had lasted upwards of five hours. So long, in fact, that Robertson had actually missed the verdict because he had left the pub early in order to catch the last train to Haywards Heath which left Brighton station at 8.30 pm. As he sat on the train, he must have reflected on the rather hostile atmosphere in The Northern Tavern and on the obvious harm the whole affair had done to his and to the asylum's reputation. He later commented that the hearing had been a fair one but regretted not being present to respond to the criticisms of the jury at the end. Some of the Brighton press gleefully publicized the jurors' opinions and the *Brighton Examiner* talked about the "loose management of the Asylum".[3]

AFTER THE VERDICT

Despite the inquest verdict, the matter did not rest there. At a meeting of the Brighton Guardians, reported in the *Brighton Gazette* on 10th March, one of them, Mr Woollett, declared that:

> … there was something loose in the management of the Asylum, and that the orders of the principle medical man had not been attended to. The evidence of the staff had been very conflicting… Mrs Snashall found her husband very comfortable at the Workhouse Infirmary, but when she saw him at the Asylum he presented a very different picture, bruises etc… It was apparent that Dr Robertson gave an order for certain treatment to be pursued which every one must admit was extreme… He thought that the Board ought not to allow the matter to rest where it was. It was not quite clear to him that death had not either resulted from violence or from some gross neglect on the part of the officers of the Asylum.

Woollett then moved the following motion which was carried unanimously:

> It is resolved that this Board respectfully request the Visitors' Committee to the Asylum to institute a further and searching enquiry into the alleged neglect of the Asylum officers, as stated by the Coroner in his summing up.

At the same time, Mrs Snashall and her brother-in-law wrote to the Lunacy Commissioners alleging that James Snashall had died "covered with bruises from head to foot" and that his death resulted from violence whilst he was in the asylum. The Commissioners then wrote to the Visitors' Committee advising an enquiry. The latter agreed and set up a nine-man committee to investigate the matter. The enquiry was held at the asylum on Saturday 26th March, just over a month after the inquest.

The enquiry turned out to be rather an anti-climax. It had been rumoured that Mrs Snashall was going to produce numerous witnesses; instead she arrived at the enquiry accompanied only by her sister and her local doctor, Mr Moore, whom she had asked to examine her husband's body. Samuel Thorncroft later alleged that her brother-in-law had asked for expenses for witnesses to attend the enquiry but he had refused to pay him any money. Mrs Snashall had also asked Woollett if she could be legally represented but he had told her that he thought it would not be allowed. The enquiry was attended by Thorncroft, several Brighton Guardians (including Woollett), the Brighton doctors who had conducted the post mortem (Sewell and Verral), and also by Robertson and some of his staff.

Mrs Snashall was questioned first. When asked why she had not originally informed the coroner that her husband's body had been "covered with bruises from head to foot", she replied that no one had asked her at the inquest. In her letter to the Commissioners, she had also alleged that his buttock had been cut with a sharp instrument. Dr Moore, her doctor, confirmed this although he admitted that he had only examined the body briefly and under candlelight. At this point, Woollett interrupted to ask if the investigating committee intended to finish the enquiry that day or whether they would be disposed to adjourn it, in order that Mrs Snashall might have the assistance of a legal adviser. The Chairman of the committee, Mr Bigge, replied that they intended to conclude the enquiry that day and that he did not see any necessity for her to have a legal adviser as this was an enquiry not an indictment.

Without a legal adviser, Mrs Snashall had little chance of sustaining any of her allegations before what was, in effect, an internal enquiry. But, more damaging still, was her own revelation about the letter to the Lunacy Commissioners:

> It was sent with my consent. I did not sign the letter, did not authorize my signature to it, and did not know that my name was added to it. The letter was never read to me. I knew that it had been written, but did not know what it contained.[4]

Thorncroft was then questioned about his involvement. He claimed that "he didn't have anything to do with Mrs Snashall" and that he had played no part in advising her to take these proceedings and was merely at the enquiry on behalf of the Brighton Guardians. He could not resist though, asking Robertson whether the "Commissioners in Lunacy would approve of a man being wrapped up like a mummy in a towel and sheet for six or seven hours". Robertson replied that the Commissioners were well aware of this treatment.

Robertson and his staff were questioned next and largely repeated what they had said at the inquest. But Robertson went into more detail. He explained that it had taken four men to apply the wet sheet to Snashall and that the treatment entailed the patient being placed on his back in the wet sheet which was then rapidly wound round him. The sheet had not been changed all night because:

> the difficulty of placing him in the sheet, owing to resistance was so great that the Head Attendant feared to disturb him and again renew the struggle – the more so as he became calmed towards morning.

Robertson maintained that being left in a wet sheet all night was not dangerous and that, in fact, the sheet dried after two hours and then had the effect of the 'Sudorific' method – sweating – which was quite common practice. The wet sheet had been used a hundred times at the asylum "and on no occasion have I seen the slightest injury or suffering to the patient result from it". He added that in only six cases had he been forced to prevent the towel from being removed but that straps were never used and did not exist in the asylum. Robertson claimed that packing in the wet sheet had been very successful in producing sleep in cases where large doses of opiates had failed. He reminded the enquiry that Snashall had only been wet-packed once.

As for Snashall's sickness, this had occurred, according to Robertson, only once after his wife had given him some oranges and cakes to eat. The digitalis had then been discontinued. He strongly defended his use of digitalis and wet-packing and quoted several medical experts who approved of their use. Robertson went on to say that the asylum inmates were very sensitive to any ill-treatment on the part of any of their number, and frequently mentioned things to him during his ward visits. But none of them had complained to him about

Snashall being ill-treated. Robertson finished by saying that "I never felt more satisfied of having treated a patient, according to the measure of my ability, both wisely and well".

The Brighton doctors, Verral and Sewell, were cross-examined next. They both agreed that the mark on Snashall's buttock was probably the result of bed sores and that the allegation that his body had been "covered with bruises from head to foot" was a complete exaggeration. Dr Moore, Mrs Snashall's witness, agreed with this last remark but still insisted that he had found a wound, recently inflicted on the body. and "could not conceive how any one could have examined the body and not seen this wound, if he had his eyes open". Nevertheless, Verral and Sewell repeated their inquest conclusion that James Snashall had not died as a result of violence whilst at the asylum.

The verdict of the enquiry: "that there was no foundation whatsoever for the charges made against the Asylum", was hardly surprising. With no legal representation, no eye-witnesses and with only Moore's candlelit examination to sustain the allegations, the outcome was rather a formality. Thorncroft and the Brighton Guardians declared that they were satisfied with the enquiry although Mr Woollett said that he had some apprehension that Mrs Snashall might not be satisfied because of not having anyone to represent her. Mrs Snashall's reaction to the proceedings was not recorded but she must have felt let down by the Brighton Guardians who had encouraged her to demand the enquiry but had then given her little support on the actual day. Even a member of the enquiry committee, the Rev. J. Goring, announced his surprise at the lack of questions on the part of the Guardians.

THE IMPLICATIONS OF THE SNASHALL CASE

The case hugely embarrassed the asylum and raised serious doubts about its practices. And some sections of the Brighton press seemed to enjoy whipping up feeling against Robertson and his institution. The *Brighton Examiner*, in their editorial of 15th March, had heaped praise on Thorncroft for "battling so manfully" against the asylum authorities in the past and for continuing to do so. But not all the press agreed. The *Sussex Advertiser* talked about certain people needlessly fanning the flame with the effect that "an unjust and undeserved stigma was cast upon the officers of the Asylum". Robertson believed that the Brighton Guardians had used Mrs Snashall in an attempt to undermine him. He was particularly aggrieved that she had not complained directly to him about her husband's condition but instead had gone straight to the Guardians. This prompted him to:

…recommend that a book be placed in the Visiting room for the friends of patients to enter any complaints or observations on patients which they may wish to make in order that I may learn them at the time and enquire into them.[5]

A book already existed at the asylum for visiting lunacy committees, to write down comments about their visits. Indeed, a row was still going on about critical comments written about Thorncroft's behaviour at the asylum the previous year. Robertson's recommendation was accepted but unfortunately no trace of this potentially valuable book exists today.

In the light of the Brighton Guardians' refusal to sanction the examination of any of their patients dying at the asylum, Robertson wrote to the Lunacy Commissioners stating that "in the interest of medical science every patient dying in an asylum should as a matter of course be examined".[6] His request was turned down, probably for ethical and economic reasons. In reality, ordinary people had a great fear of post mortems in Victorian times and only a small proportion of those who died at the Sussex Asylum were buried in its cemetery. Most families preferred to make their own funeral arrangements.

Eleven days after the enquiry, Henry Woollett, (probably Robertson's greatest critic) wrote to the *Sussex Advertiser* on 6th April. His letter claimed that the Guardians had tried to ask questions at the enquiry but had been told that they were irrelevant by the committee. Woollett then demanded an investigation into the use of "that rank poison", digitalis, at the asylum. He ended his letter with this thought:

> **Had** this enquiry been for a **rich** instead of a **poor** widow the arrangements would, I am sure, have been different.

Woollett's letter provoked a strong reprimand from the newspaper's editor who called it "a coarse and gratuitous insult to the Magistrates and the Asylum authorities". Robertson was well aware of the toxic nature of digitalis and its tendency to cause sickness. For this reason he used it sparingly as a sedative. He admitted that it did not "make an insane man sane but made a house quiet".[7] By 1864, it had virtually disappeared from the list of drugs recommended against insanity [8] and only Robertson was using it. The drug is still used today in small quantities, but only to treat heart disease.

So what had happened to Snashall? Reviewing the evidence, it can be seen that when he was admitted, James Snashall was immediately given digitalis to calm him down and he continued to receive it until his wife's visit. He was clearly sick afterwards – probably due to the food she admitted she had brought him – but if he had been frequently sick beforehand, as she alleged Iremonger had told her, none of the four attendants who worked on the ward had reported it. On the night of his admission, the digitalis had not managed to calm Snashall down and so Robertson had ordered the use of the wet-sheet. He firmly believed in its effectiveness as a sedative. In 1862, he had written that "I have again and again seen cases arriving in a state of violent acute mania, actually fall asleep in the first and second application of the wet-sheet".[9] And fifteen years later, Henry Maudsley – the founder of the Maudsley Hospital – was still writing that "without doubt it is a valuable measure in some cases of acute excitement and has a soothing action".[10]

Robertson had ordered Snashall's sheet to be changed every two hours but after the violent struggle to place him in it, the sheet had been left on all night and had not been changed. Had this become normal practice? It was recommended that the wet sheet should not be used for more than three hours, and that it should normally changed after 1½ hours. Significantly, immediately after the inquest, Robertson wrote down a set of rules[11] incorporating this recommendation for the use of "water-treatment" and provided a book in which staff must record every time it was used. Although he had told the inquest that the wet sheet's purpose was medical rather than a form of mechanical restraint, there was a very thin line between the two. Extracts from this book show that the wet sheets were often applied immediately after an act of violence:[12]

Poole –   This patient struck a fellow patient named Brissenden on the nose. Dr Robertson ordered him to be packed in the wet sheet for two hours, renewed every two hours and afterwards to have 2 pails of water, one 70° and one cold which has been done.

19/3/1864.

Philcox – Packed in wet sheet for 1½ hours. Was violent, knocked a fellow patient down named Smith and contused his forehead and left eye.

23/10/1864

The disadvantage of the treatment was that it could only be used on healthy patients. In 1869, a 31-year-old patient, Ellen Wood, died two hours after being packed in a wet sheet on the day of her admission. Robertson had not been aware that she had a weak heart and poor lungs. He was censured by the Lunacy Commissioners for this error. Eventually, Robertson's successor, Dr Williams, came under fire for using it, as the Lunacy Commissioners increasingly considered it to be a form of restraint. The last recorded use of the wet-sheet at the Sussex Asylum was on Richard Simons on 28th March 1887.

Apart from the discrepancies in Iremonger's evidence, the inquest and the

Russell _ (phthisis) _ Roman Bath twice a Week. 21 Feby 1864
Discontinued 15th April /64

Russell _ 2 pails at bed time 70 & Cold (Except on R.B. days) 21 Feby 1864
Discontinued 1 June /64

Piper _ Roman Bath once a Week. 20 Decer 1863
(melancholia with delusions. cured. (to care of his friends) Discontinued 15th April /64

Hartwell _ Roman Bath once a Week. 9th Jany 1864
(melancholia. much improved. Discontinued 7 March 1864

Ford _ 2 pails at bed time 70 & Cold (Except R.B. days) 28 Novr 1863
Discontinued 2 May /64

Ford _ Roman Bath once a Week _ 31 Jany 1864
Discontinued 2 May /64

Fry _ 2 pails at bed time, 70 & Cold (Except R.B. days) 4 Decer 1863
(syphilitic eruptions).
Discontinued 2 May /64

Fry _ Roman Bath once a Week _ 4th Decer 1863
Discontinued 27th Jany 1865

Sawyers _ Roman Bath once a Week _ 25th Sepr 1863
Discontinued 15th April /64

Millar _ 2 pail at bed time, 70 & Cold. 14 Feby 1864
Discontinued 13th March /64

Parsons _ Roman Bath (twice a week at his Own Request.) October 1863
Discontinued March 1865

Baker _ Roman Bath (at his Own Request) once a Week _ July 1863
Discontinued March 1864

Evenden _ Roman Bath once a Week _ 9th Jany 1864
(did no good. Discontinued 14 Feby 1864

× Evenden _ 2 pails at bed time 70 & Cold _ 14 Feby 1864
Discontinued 1st June /64

Two pages from the water treatment book

James Emrey. packed in Wet Sheet for 5 Hours.
(Dr Williams) 8th January 1869.

Charles Stoner. packed in Wet Sheet 1 Hour
Morning & Evening. (DrR.) 22 January 1869.
                    Discontinued 30 Jany 1869.
James Gower. packed in Wet Sheets from
10 am till 7 PM - (Dr Williams) 29 January 1859.

James I Millar. cold pails at FAH - 2 pails
Water at Bed time 86 & Cold (Dr W.) 15 Feby 1869
                    discontinued, 19 Feby 1869.
George Clarke packed in Wet Sheet from
10 a m till 7 PM (DrW.) 17 Feby 1869.

James Mann. packed in Wet Sheet
from 11 am till 6.30 PM. (Dr Williams)
23 Feby 1869.

Noah Smith. 2 pails Water at Bed time 86
    & Cold - (Dr Williams) - 27 Feby 1869.
    discontinued 3 April 1869.
Thomas Clarke - 2 pails Water at Bed time
86 & Cold (Dr Williams) 31 March 1869.
                    discontinued 1 May 1869.
George Rich - packed in Wet Sheet
from 11.3 am till 6.30 PM. 17 Apl 1869.
Was packed in Wet Sheet 1 Hr 30 Mts on
18 April 1869. (Dr Robertson.

enquiry revealed a serious lack of communication between Robertson and his staff which led to his orders being ignored. It also revealed the important role of William Knox, the head attendant on the male side. He was literally the eyes and ears of Robertson who, in reality, had little contact with the patients. Knox even had authorisation to implement wet-treatment if he thought it was necessary. But was he covering up for ill-treatment at the asylum? Knox, on his own admission, saw James Snashall ten or twelve times a day and Robertson obviously relied on him for information about his condition. It is interesting to note that at the inquest Knox's explanation that the bruises on Snashall's arms were caused by the sheet was not shared by Robertson. The Chaplain, Henry Hawkins, later described Knox as being "a just and sympathising overseer"[13] to his attendants but perhaps he was too sympathetic towards them and it is possible he may have occasionally turned a blind eye to patient mis-treatment.

It is quite clear that the attendants had struggled with Snashall when they had tried to put him in the towel, blankets and wet sheet. Apparently, according to Knox's evidence at the enquiry, he had tried to bite staff during this procedure. The bruises on his forehead and cheek (as revealed by the post mortem) were probably inflicted then. The bruises on his arms may have been caused by the too tight application of the wet sheet or even by the six or seven hours spent in a straight-jacket at the Workhouse Infirmary – though no bruises were recorded on his admission to the asylum. Whether Snashall had a wound or a bed sore on his buttock, is unclear. James Snashall obviously had not been "jumped upon" by asylum staff but he had, at the very least, been manhandled violently by the attendants.

The Snashall case left many questions unanswered and caused a huge dent in the reputations of both Robertson and the asylum. The whole affair seems to have demoralized Robertson. It can not be a coincidence that he stopped writing his Asylum Journal (which he had been doing for almost six years) on the 26th February, the day after the inquest at The Northern Tavern. Years later, he still maintained that Snashall had been well-treated. But, it was not the first time that allegations had been made against an institution in which Robertson had worked.

Previously, in 1846, Robertson had been working as a resident physician at a private asylum in Gateshead. That year, an anonymous letter appeared in *The Lancet* on 7th November. It alleged that a patient had been "knocked about" at the asylum. Two weeks later, Robertson wrote a spirited reply to the journal saying that "if the allegations be true of any institution – and I have reason to fear they may be so – none would rejoice more than myself at their exposure and punishment".[14] In 1864, he still held the same sentiments but his position and responsibilities meant that he was under no obligation to see patients on a daily basis and as Henry Hawkins would later write, that as influential as Robertson was, he was rarely seen on the wards. His lack of first-hand knowledge made it more difficult for him to know exactly what was going on in the wards.

After the trauma of recent events Robertson asked for and was given six weeks leave because he had "neuralgia again" and had not had any lengthened leave for eighteen months. He left his assistant, Valentine Browne, in charge and informed the Visitors' Committee that Dr Maudsley (his co-editor of the *Journal of Mental Science* who lived in London) would be on stand-by in case of any emergency. Later on, Browne himself was given six weeks' leave due to illness.

Allegations about the ill-treatment of patients at the asylum again hit the local newspapers later in the year. On 1st September, The *Brighton Gazette* reported on a meeting of the Brighton Guardians which had taken place two days earlier. It quoted fresh allegations from Robertson's old adversary, Samuel Thorncroft:

> Mr Smith called upon him and stated that he had heard, from a female who had visited the Asylum on Monday, that a lunatic named Harvey, was much bruised about the legs, and the female believed that the patient had been knocked about. Harvey had been a patient there five weeks. Another person, named Bell, had a daughter an inmate of the Asylum, for whom he paid 7s. a week. When he came to pay the Assistant-Overseer (Thorncroft) the money, the man informed him that Mrs Bell went to see her daughter on Wednesday, and on her return she informed her husband that the girl had a black eye which she showed her mother and cried, but was too imbecile to explain how it occurred.

It is unclear whether this 'Mr Smith' was Thorncroft's assistant or not. Thorncroft admitted that this was the first time such a complaint had been made to him. The Guardians decided that their Lunacy Committee should immediately investigate the two cases. It met on 31st August, only to be informed that the first case had died on the previous day. But his name was Hargreaves not Harvey. They did investigate though, the case of the girl Bell. After seeing her they reported that:

> It was fully explained that the injury to the eye was caused by a fall, beyond the control of any one, and that it did not occur from falling out of bed but that she had fallen against a table. Your Committee are fully satisfied that it did not arise from a blow inflicted by another person, or from ill-treatment; and are satisfied with the answers given by the officers of the Asylum.[15]

As for the Hargreaves case, Robertson, having seen the allegations of abuse in the local newspapers, immediately applied for a coroner's inquest and it was set for 2nd September.

THE CASE OF THOMAS HARGREAVES

The inquest was held at the asylum before Mr F. G. Gell, who had been the Coroner for East Sussex for 35 years. (Gell was in his eightieth year and would be dead himself two months later.) Several members of the Hargreaves family attended along with Thorncroft, Woollett and several other Brighton Guardians. The jury were taken to see the body and then proceeded to hear the evidence.

Robertson was the first witness called. He described how Hargreaves had arrived on 11th June 1864, accompanied by the following report written by Mr Geere, one of Brighton's parish surgeons:

> Great neglect of his person, his condition being filthy; refuses to answer questions; at one moment listless, at others excited and violent. Has struck at his son with a poker; wanders about; uses violent language.[16]

His family claimed that his first attack of lunacy had occurred only three weeks previously. The cause of it was thought to be mental anxiety arising from depressed circumstances. Browne, Robertson's assistant, wrote a report on Hargreaves admittance:

> His mind appears to be quite confused; he does not know his name; he is unable to answer questions coherently; expression vacant; very dirty in his habits; in a feeble reduced condition of bodily health; can scarcely walk, apparently from general paralysis; has a boil on the lower part of his back, and one on his seat; also a bruise on the front of the right arm, two old bruises on the back of his left hand, and a brown discoloration on the middle of his back; his head swarming with lice.[17]

Robertson wrote to the Lunacy Commissioners informing them that the patient was "in a state of dementia and in a miserably reduced condition".[18] He was very restless at night and fell out of his bed and bruised his head on 17th June. He did the same on 6th July and was then removed to the padded room. Robertson recorded on 7th August that he was:

> another of our most wretched cases; has to sleep in the padded room to prevent him injuring himself; I cannot think that this man has been only three weeks ill on admission. A very heavy handful.[19]

And on 28th August he was:

> failing very rapidly; unable to swallow solids, living on beef tea; a most miserable object; very restless.[20]

Hargreaves died two days later. Robertson wrote that the cause of death was "decay of dementia – admitted in a miserably reduced state". A son of the deceased, being asked if he wished to question Robertson, said he never knew his father to have boils on the back although he had recently changed his shirt for him. Robertson replied that the boils had been discovered on his admission from the Brighton Workhouse (where he had spent two days) by Dr Browne and had been pointed out to him four hours later.

Next, Ann Baker, the wife of Hargreaves' illegitimate son, said that she saw him in the asylum about seven weeks ago. He had a wound, apparently a severe one, strapped up with plaster; also some scratches:

Coroner: Such as might be produced by falling out of bed?

Baker: I think not. There was also a bruise behind his left ear, where the blood had trickled down. I did not examine either minutely, and he was unable to give any account of them. I thought the bruise might have been inflicted with a stick rather than a fist. The second time I came was Wednesday fortnight, when I found him with his left hand cut and strapped up. He was unable to give an account of anything, and I thought him more fit to be in bed than sitting in a chair. There was another cut on the same hand, not strapped up. I looked at his head, and there was a cut, but it was getting well. My husband and myself feeling uncomfortable about it, he stripped the deceased's trousers up, and there he saw other bruises and cuts. I cannot call them scratches. My husband turned back the collar of his waistcoat, and found something crawling [a body louse] and I killed it on the boards with the toe of my shoe. There was only one and in other respects he was clean.[21]

In reply to further questions from the Coroner, Mrs Baker insisted that the bruises she saw on her second visit were fresh ones.

William Iremonger, the attendant whose testimony in the Snashall case had been suspect, was then called as a witness. He corroborated Robertson's evidence and said that it was not an unusual occurrence for Hargreaves to fall about. Mrs Baker claimed that she saw blue marks about the hollow of his neck after he had died. But Iremonger disagreed with her:

Iremonger: I was with him when he died, and assisted in laying him out, and I saw nothing of the kind.

Coroner: Now has any cruelty or ill-treatment been practised towards him?

Iremonger: None whatever.

> Coroner: Because they talk of blows and bruises, and I don't know what.
>
> Iremonger: No, I have seen him daily. He has had proper food. I have given him beef-tea and other things myself. I never struck him. When he fell out of bed and cut his head he was placed in the padded room, not by way of punishment, but for his own security. He was alone in the room; but he was visited every two hours.[22]

Hargreaves' son then said that he could not understand how it was that his father, so low and helpless when he saw him, should be restless and fall out of bed. Iremonger replied that the insane "always got restless at night".

Before the inquest finished, Thorncroft received permission from the coroner to present evidence from parish staff to show the jury that the workhouse was not responsible for the condition of the deceased on his admission to the asylum. George Geere, the parish surgeon, had found Hargreaves fastened in a room at home and on a bed in a filthy state, with the women of the house afraid to go near him. Thomas Barber, a visitor of out-door poor, found him in a room, empty but for "a very little bit of straw bed in the corner" and that "there was a great want of necessaries"[23] in his house. Finally, Samuel Hammond, a chief ward nurse at the workhouse, claimed that Hargreaves, on admittance, had a severe bruise on the muscle of his right arm and another on the small of his back.

At the end of the inquest the Coroner said that it was most desirable that the public should be satisfied about the cause of his death, and that the relations should also be satisfied; and at the same time allowance should be made for feelings of irritation existing among them. The jury returned a verdict of "death from natural causes and not through any violence, neglect, want of proper care, or nourishment, nor from ill treatment".[24]

AFTER THE VERDICT

This time the jury (not from Brighton but local people) added no hostile remarks to the verdict. And at this inquest, Thorncroft and the Brighton Guardians had been put on the defensive by the innuendo that perhaps Hargreaves had been abused at the Workhouse. They quickly laid the blame for his poor condition at the door of his family. It is not clear what had happened at the workhouse; but was it just a coincidence that at the asylum, Iremonger had been involved again? His explanation that Hargreaves' injuries had been caused by him "falling out of bed" did little to quell rumours of asylum violence circulating around Brighton. Henry Woollett, the Brighton Guardian, claimed that physical abuse was common at the asylum. Robertson publicly criticized him over this allegation. At a meeting of the Brighton Guardians held on 6th September, Woollett continued the feud:

> What he [Woollett] had said was substantially true. If Dr Robertson wished he could let that gentleman know of statements which had been frequently made to him in his shop. [Woollett owned the biggest iron-monger's in Brighton]. He could refer him to one case in which an inmate was sent home, most unjustifiably, in such a state as must reflect disgrace upon any public asylum. He could tell the Doctor of complaints which had been made to him, – of statements which made his heart ache; and he should have no objection whatever to furnish particulars of names, although he would not give them at the present time. He was not a medical man, it was true; but with reference to the case of Hargreaves there was one point which certainly struck him as being strange: though Hargreaves was not fit to be left by himself, yet they found that patient sentenced by the Doctor to what might be termed seven weeks' solitary confinement. In a common sense view of the case this did not appear to be proper treatment towards a man deprived of intellect.

Woollett went on to repeat old complaints about Robertson's discourtesy towards the Brighton Guardians and about their lack of representation on the Visitors' Committee. He ended his speech:

> From what he knew of Dr Robertson he could say that, should he [Mr Woollett] ever be so unfortunate as to lose his intellect, he only hoped he might never be placed under that gentleman.[25]

The allegation that Robertson sent patients home in a deplorable state would seem out of character. If anything, he was often accused of not sending patients home early enough and of being over-cautious about their release. His flexibility over releasing patients was demonstrated again that year:

> The Guardians of Horsham ask that Marshall be sent out on trial. The patient is desirous to be allowed to wait till spring as he thinks that he could then get work.[26]

He allowed Marshall to stay on even though he was well enough to leave the asylum. This understanding approach often infuriated parish authorities who believed that they were paying maintenance charges on unnecessary cases. And in 1864, Robertson was still refusing to sanction the release of Richards despite the pleas of a local vicar:

> Further application has been made for the discharge of Richards whose case has been repeatedly before the Committee. He's no better and hardly a month passes without attacks of violence and excitement.[27]

Robertson was so incensed by Woollett's latest personal attack that he refused to meet the Brighton Lunacy Committee when they visited the asylum on 22nd September. He explained his reasons in the *Brighton Guardian* on 5th October:

> He felt a disinclination to meet them owing to the many hard things which had been said of him at the Board meetings, and of which he felt he was undeserving, and that it was impolite and ungenerous to make such frequent and harsh attacks on him and his management, causing to himself great annoyance, and inducing the friends of patients and others to have very unfair and unfounded prejudices against him. Dr Robertson further said that he desired much that a cordial understanding should be established between himself and the Brighton Board.

The Brighton Guardians saw Robertson's last words as an act of reconciliation and one member "felt sure that there was every disposition for peace on the part of Dr Robertson".[28] Even Henry Woollett accepted the statement without comment. From now on, there was to be an uneasy peace between the two sides; perhaps a grudging acceptance that they had to get on.

Not everyone blamed either the asylum or the Brighton Workhouse for the deaths of Snashall and Hargreaves. The letter below appeared in the *Brighton Herald* on 10th September 1864:

> Another investigation into a case of alleged ill-treatment of a patient (Hargreaves) in the County Lunatic Asylum has, like the former one, proved that charge was entirely and utterly groundless. Might not our Brighton authorities exercise more discretion, in future, in listening to such charges?…
>
> Recipients of charity are notoriously difficult to please, and require but little encouragement to induce them to prefer unfounded and vexatious charges against officials. Should any future occasion arise, it would be well for the Lunacy Committee to ascertain the state the patient was in whilst under the care of these anxious and affectionate relatives. In the two cases which have been subject of inquests it will be found that the friends of the lunatic, whose sensibilities were so wounded by the appearance of a bruise, had shut their eyes whilst the patient was under their own care to sores, bruises, and, in the last case, to filth inexpressible, which existed on the bodies of these poor creatures on their admission to the Asylum.
>
> I am your obedient servant,
>
> Common Sense.

This rather unsympathetic letter did inadvertently highlight a major problem which many families of pauper lunatics faced. Namely: how could they be expected to care for a severely deranged person in the impoverished circumstances in which most found themselves? Whatever the disadvantages of life at the Sussex Asylum, the Mockford and Hargreaves cases illustrated that the alternatives were often worse.

1864 CONCLUDED

The two inquests during the year overshadowed important building alterations. The Infirmary was remodelled and now had twenty-six beds including five single rooms. It was warmed by hot water pipes and two open fires and "will now bear comparison with the wards in any of the London General Hospitals".[29] And the new building built to expand female accommodation contained one ward of 25 beds, two of 45 beds, eight single rooms and five nurses' rooms. It opened in August. Due to the building work, forty female patients had had to sleep in the Recreation Hall and Robertson was pleased to report that "no accident, injury or escape had occurred during this period". But, as previously noted, the expansion did not increase male accommodation and the asylum could now accommodate 355 females but only 235 males. Nor did it take into account the asylum reformer John Conolly's recommendation that two thirds of asylum accommodation should consist of single rooms. At Sussex, only one seventh of the rooms were single.

The asylum, apart from being hit by two inquests, was also, rather symbolically, hit by two earthquakes which shook Sussex on 30th April and 20th August. The centre of the last one was near Lewes; only six miles away from the asylum.

Twenty-eight staff left that year; a high number when the full staff complement (including Robertson and Browne) was only 52. Nine staff came and left during 1864 and some were obviously on trial. Nevertheless, it was still a very high turnover which could not have been conducive to the stability of the asylum.

By 31st December 1864, the asylum's population had increased from 463 to 501 and the male side was almost full. Thirty-nine patients had been discharged – 24 deemed 'recovered'; 7 'relieved' and 8 'not improved'. The recovery rate had gone down from 39% in 1863, to barely 18% in 1864. Robertson attributed this to an almost doubling of the admissions during the year. Fifty-seven patients died in 1864 – the highest annual figure yet. Six had died within a week of arriving and eight within forty days. Little was known about three of the dead as there was "no information" about their ages, previous jobs or family circumstances.

It was in this year that the thousandth case was admitted into the asylum since its opening five and a half years before. Of these, 230 patients had died; many within the first few months of their arrival, confirming Robertson's contention that some patients had been "sent in to die". The asylum population was certainly becoming more elderly, so much so, that Robertson decided to order a bathchair that year for the increasing number of paralytic and helpless patients. On a more positive note, the weekly maintenance rate had gone down to 9s. 9d. during the last quarter. And even the Brighton Guardians declared that they were very happy with what they saw when they visited the asylum on 22nd November.

It had been a momentous year for the asylum and it could be said that 1864 was a turning point in its fortunes. Up to then, the Sussex Asylum had only received favourable publicity from the local newspapers. But now, the term "allegations of ill-treatment" began to be associated as much with the County Asylum as with other more notorious public institutions. Of course, the asylum was legally cleared of any wrongdoing but it was also apparent that practices very alien to the principles of moral treatment were surfacing there. The question was: could Robertson and the asylum recover from the negative publicity of 1864?

Chapter Ten

1865-6

"A CREDIT TO THE COUNTY AND A
PATTERN TO THE COUNTRY?"

By 1865, there seemed to be two opposing perceptions about the Sussex Asylum. The first saw it as a great success story; as an enlightened, progressive and efficient institution run by a passionate administrator. It not only had a good name nationally but was becoming famous internationally. The second perception was that behind the backs of the medical officers, violence against patients was common place and that in some respects the asylum was little better than a workhouse. This opinion was undoubtedly encouraged by influential men like Henry Woollett, Robertson's implacable enemy of the previous year. Both perceptions were, to some degree, accurate.

The first perception was one that was shared by many who visited the asylum in those early years. On 18th May 1865, the *Sussex Agricultural Express* reprinted an article by two French psychologists who had been there. The article was sent in by Mr Hollis, one of the Brighton members of the Visitors' Committee, perhaps in an attempt to counteract the adverse publicity of 1864:

> The Asylum at Haywards Heath, in the county of Sussex, recently erected, is an elegant structure, and contains about 500 patients of both sexes. It is governed with the most striking ability, by Doctor Lockhart Robertson, particularly, as regards the perfect discipline which he has introduced amongst the attendants, and which has made the Asylum a model, even in England, where the attendants are of a higher class than in France, and by which means in their Asylums the non-restraint system is carried out undeviatingly, although in France it is still deemed to be impracticable. M. Morel and I [M. Fairet] visited last summer this

beautiful Asylum of Sussex, and we had thus an opportunity of personally admiring the faultless order which the able and zealous efforts of Doctor Robertson have impressed on that Asylum, where no means of restraint are employed, however severe the form of mental disease may be.

(*Annales Medico-psychologiques*, March 1865).

As we have seen, the 'perfect discipline' at the Sussex Asylum was instilled at a price, as the high annual staff turnover confirmed. The question of restraint at the asylum was a more difficult one to answer. Officially, there was none and no one was in a strait-jacket or tied to a bed. But the application of the wet sheet was later classified by the Lunacy Commissioners as a form of restraint. And, arguably, at a time when there were no powerful drugs available with which to restrain patients, using no methods of physical restraint was impracticable. Robertson was strongly opposed to the use of restraint and later on that year witnessed for himself its full horrors when he visited France in August. In a letter to *The Lancet* (30/12/1865), he enclosed some rough notes about his tour of two French asylums:

Aug. 7th – Went at 8 am to St Yon. 1000 patients; twenty in restraint; two in seclusion (nymphomania) for two years! A filthy, miserable old place, built in squares. No workhouse lunatic wards in England worse. Patients noisy; the demented unemployed.

Aug. 8th – Quatres-Mares. Fifteen in seclusion; ten in restraint. Brick floors. Fifty dirty beds. Total, 665. Seats fixed. No recreation hall or amusements. Baths only used three or four times a year for ablution purposes. A thread of water dripping on the head one or two hours for treatment (patient the while fixed in the warm bath by a wooden guillotine like cover). Straw beds in wooden boxes (many). Men in restraint five months at a time. No wine for paupers; water and cider.

I would only add one illustration from memory of this picture; the recollection of a harmless idiot we found tied up and fastened by the camisole to a bench because he tore up the grass, and whom we induced the attendant to release, and who quietly and helplessly lay down on the grass. Nor can I easily forget the complaints of a man restrained for five months to his bed; and his sufferings from the flies on his face all the hot summer through, and which he had no means to drive away.

Robertson finished his letter by attacking the restraint system employed in Europe where there were an estimated 2,000 strait-jackets in use.

There was no better illustration of the positive perception of the asylum than by a report which appeared in the *Brighton Gazette*, on 4th October 1866. The reporter vividly describes not only the asylum facilities but also some of the patients from Brighton. At the asylum he was met by the head attendant,

Mr Knox, who was holding a bright bunch of keys, and who then took him on a tour of the building through a maze of corridors, stairs and rooms. Below is an abridged version of his report:

"A Visit to the Sussex County Lunatic Asylum"

I know not where to particularly praise; throughout the building every-where is cleanliness displayed, such cleanliness as would put to shame many householders, windows in every dormitory open, blankets, counterpanes, etc., after careful attention piled in each room ready for use, strips of carpet near to each bed with scarcely a stray thread, and the few necessary articles of furniture bright and becoming, engravings framed, lending a cheerful appearance. The bath rooms, used twice a week were clean to a nicety. Flowers and vases with flowers, caged birds in the corridors we noticed, and even a small terrier and a cat, both great pets. In the dining rooms the numerous tables gladdened one, and under the careful supervision of the many attendants a repast was then (and is daily) provided, sufficient to satisfy the requirements of all. Order reigned, there was not any stint, and grace said at the conclusion of the meal, every recipient quietly betook himself or herself to his or her accustomed quarter.

These dining rooms at other times afford amusement. Dominoes, draughts, cards, etc., are allowed and it was pleasing to witness a party engaged at a game of cribbage and another assembled round a bagatelle board. A friend (one of the party) taking up the cue and failing to make a score was greeted with much glee by Johnny H. accompanied with the remark, "He don't know how to play". Poor Johnny, the asylum I am afraid will be his only home, unless when the new Brighton workhouse is completed, he becomes an occupant of the lunatic portion. Happy enough he seemed, always laughing. I may be pardoned here for asking assistance from many who can give it. Upon the tables were copies of the "Illustrated News", "Leisure Hour", "Sunday at Home", "British Workman", etc., but thumbworn and torn, clearly showing that their contents had over and over again been enjoyed. Could any of your readers leave picture papers at your office I feel sure you would take charge of them and thereby diffuse much happiness.

One inmate who, for the time, appeared quite rational and recognised me, said, "they are all Liberals here, but I should like a Brighton Gazette." Having a copy in my pocket I gave it to him, and, upon returning through one of the corridors, I perceived him intent upon its contents, and enjoying also at the same time a meerschaum[1], which, from its deep colour, had evidently seen good service. Another (H. B.), admitted November, 1865, immediately afterwards addressed me, "I am glad to see *you*, I am quite comfortable; but it is an imposition upon the Brighton ratepayers to keep me here, when I am quite well. Do what you can to get me home." Poor fellow, I knew him as a steady, industrious man, working for an auctioneer in Brighton, and having a wife and family, and a member of the Manchester Unity. His case is a sad one as regards his family. He was a passenger in the train which came to grief in the Clayton Tunnel. He did not think himself injured, but after a little time he was obliged to lay up. He rallied, but became worse. Had the man not met with the accident he would have improved his position and been enabled to look to and provide for his growing family. Should he die, and his former employer withdraw his generous support, the wife and family would be left almost destitute. His is a religious mania.

Another inmate (C. C.), about forty years of age, admitted in 1865, I found stouter than when I knew him in Brighton as a smart dashing young fellow. His father was an old Brighton coachmaker. A few remarks and I found he knew me. He said "I keep racehorses now, I have won the Two Thousand, Derby, and Leger this year." His case is hopeless. Another was full of talk with a Bible under his arm. He had attacked a warder at Hastings and believed himself "The King of England".

Another (H. F. W.) was about the most favourable case I met with. He has only been nine months an inmate, is employed at tailoring, and expressed himself most thankful for the kind treatment he experienced. I was informed that he was generally quiet, but under the impression that he could not sleep in any room twice, and to humour him, he was constantly shifted. Another (W. P.) admitted 1859, could do nothing but point to the walls of the room and remark that "it is just the same paper".

Another (J. W.) admitted 1860, was anxious only for something to aid him in his kite-flying. Sixpence given delighted him. Another (C. P.) admitted 1861, seemed rational. He jumped down the deep Brighton Workhouse well without injuring himself. He is very industrious, but fancies every one is robbing him, and is watched, fearing suicide. W. D., nearly 50 years of age, an old pie-man, looked well, and, in the New Workhouse, will probably end his days. B. B., admitted 1861, was another case of religious mania. He was anxious to leave, but only upon the condition that he was treated as a gentleman. A youth (J. R.) only four weeks an inmate, 18 years of age, from his feeble appearance, surprised me upon being informed, that six men were not more than enough to restrain him in his worse attacks.

H. F. (whose father with difficulty has recently been compelled by the Assistant-Overseer and authorities to contribute 5s. weekly towards his maintenance) looks wretched. On his wife visiting him a few days ago he did not know her. When excited, his language is dreadfully bad. Two men were pointed out as very bad tempered – savage in fact; but the keepers moved about without the slightest hesitation or fear. "Alfred" and "Spencer", addressing them, immediately came forward, and retired when told "That will do". On the conversation turning upon the treatment of such cases, a friend was at his request shown the "padded room", happily seldom needed, where harm could not ensue, with which he expressed himself pleased.

Many were the cases, I am sorry to say, arising from excessive drinking, and, though appearing rational, in the words of Mr Knox, the attendant, "They will only be right whilst kept from it." Several presented a pitiable appearance – idiots – one, in addition, deaf and dumb, but all I could see were cared for, well and warmly clothed, and under complete control. From Brighton I ascertained there were 47 male inmates: one (H. S.) was the worst – dementia and epilepsy, and unable to leave his bed. He looked ghastly, and will never mend. All the males, having conversational powers, stated that they were comfortable, and, in contrast to the females, few asked to be removed. Dismissing the male inmates, I must repeat that the attendants are assiduously attentive, and that kind treatment, and not harsh conduct, is invariably exercised. Their situations are arduous ones, being called upon night and day, and they are deserving of the consideration and respect of their employers.

Of the females, 62 in number, chargeable to Brighton, I was particularly struck on their being made known to me, with their loquacity and vituperativeness, and I am under the belief that there were more bad cases than with the males. One, P. F. (of foreign parents, sometime since in business in Brighton, and for years in the Asylum), was a pitiable case, mind completely gone. Others, – A. W., said she had 35 caskets of jewels buried at Arundel Castle in 1817; S. P. had money in the Brighton Savings Bank; S. F. believed her son was confined in the Asylum cellars; E. B. had bought a husband and wished to leave at once; J. N. (admitted in 1851), had been discharged in 1862; S. R. (daughter of a solicitor formerly of Brighton), immensely stout, had not a word to say; M. M. had (as I was told) her usual accounts made up for work done, leaving a considerable balance due to her; J. C. had killed her husband in 1833; the rest not being bad cases, when spoken to said they were quite well and anxious to leave.

Having another engagement, I could not go over the extensive grounds and workshops, and the recreation hall, where many are employed, and bidding farewell to the attendants, of whose kindness to the patients under their care I felt convinced, I had but time in company with Dr Robertson, the esteemed medical officer of the Asylum, who sometime previously had joined us, to visit the chapel opposite, which is a very handsome one holding about 250, with clock tower, side aisles and low stained wood benches. Upon inquiry on leaving, Dr Robertson, whose professional skill has deservedly been widely made known, and who was particularly courteous and attentive, directed attention to a new dining room, etc., in course of erection. I returned to Brighton deploring the sad affliction of the inmates, but pleased beyond expression with the comfortable home, in every respect, provided for them.

Since writing the above, I notice that the Lunacy Committee of the Directors and Guardians of Brighton speak in high terms of the management and good treatment of their lunatic poor therein.

This article must have gone some way to restoring Robertson and the asylum's reputation after the scandals of 1864. The reporter's observation that he found the female patients abusive, talkative, and wanting to go home; whilst the male patients were relatively relaxed, was an interesting one. We can only speculate about the contrast in behaviour. Perhaps, because women were more vulnerable to asylum incarceration (for economic reasons) than men; they were more bitter about being locked up and away from their families. Also, the asylum offered female inmates far fewer activities and less diversity of work than was provided for their male counterparts. In fact, a couple of years earlier the Lunacy Commissioners had complained about the lack of indoor games for female patients.

Henry Maudsley had also visited the asylum that year (8/3/1866) and reported that "the Asylum is in excellent order and no patient is in seclusion".[2] But what is interesting to us is, was this a true reflection of what the asylum was like, or had the visit been engineered? Obviously, the asylum was well-prepared for these pre-arranged visits. Since its opening it had consistently been praised for its cleanliness and orderliness. But the reporter's contention that the "attendants are assiduously attentive, and that kind treatment, and not harsh conduct, is invariably exercised", must be thrown into doubt by the growing evidence of ill-treatment at the asylum. Apart from the allegations of asylum brutality encouraged by some of the Brighton Guardians (who had an obvious axe to grind), the second perception – that patients were physically abused – was often backed up by eye-witness accounts from members of the public.

On June 10th 1865, W. Purvey and his son were working in fields near the asylum when they came across an attendant, George Aldridge, who told them he was looking for a patient called Henry Best whom he had lost in the woods. Purvey then describes what happened next:

I found him in a ditch. I hollowed to Aldridge the attendant and told him I had found him. He said hold the B_____ and don't let him go. When he arrived he then hit him on the back part of his head and then twice with his fist in his face. Henry Best then sat down and cried mercy; then Aldridge put his hand on the back part of his neck and tried to punch his head down between his legs and said he would break his bloody neck and then he let go of him and kicked him several times on the lower part of his back. I then walked away to my work and turned round again and saw him kick him several times on his stern.[3]

The Purveys made their complaint to the Cuckfield Union, who paid Best's maintenance. The Visitors' Committee investigated the matter and cautioned Aldridge as to his future conduct. Rather strangely, Robertson recorded in his 'Order Book' that the Visitors had not believed the evidence and had entirely acquitted Aldridge. Robertson, (in words very similar to those he had used about the Gateshead allegations in 1846) wrote that "if he believed there had been the slightest evidence, he would have taken legal proceedings himself".[4] Soon after the incident, poor Henry Best died of smallpox. Aldridge left the asylum six months later. Unfortunately, the fining of staff for letting patients escape inadvertently encouraged them sometimes to take revenge on recaptured patients.

The following year, there was another eye witness account of staff violence:

> James Shaw of 5 Cheltenham Place, Brighton, a carpenter employed by the contractors, has stated to Doctor Robertson that on Thursday 23rd September, or one day that week, that he saw Robert Plow, an outdoor attendant, twice strike Stephen Marchant, a patient employed under him on the ground weeding. Robert Plow strongly denies the charge. Dr Robertson feels it his duty to suspend Plow from his duties until the next meeting of the Visitors on 29th September when the accusation will be fully investigated.[5]

At the meeting, the charges were not proven but Robertson advised Plow to resign (which he did) and to seek employment elsewhere. Robertson believed that staff should avoid even the appearance of violence towards any patient and that "insanity is a disease and in all cases of difficulty medical aid (not force) is to be sought".[6]

Plow had got away relatively lightly. One month later, two powerful warders were sentenced to two months hard labour for beating up a patient at the Surrey Asylum even though they had been attacked first. They were convicted on the evidence of three workmen temporarily employed at the asylum. During the trial the prosecution counsel pinpointed the major problem encountered in the prosecution of violent asylum staff: "A great difficulty would be thrown in the way of establishing the charge by the fact that the person who was alleged to have been assaulted was not in such a state of mind as to admit of his being called a witness".[7]

For the medical officers, trying to distinguish between self-inflicted injuries; injuries inflicted by fellow patients; and injuries inflicted by staff, was almost an impossible task. But in October 1865, Robertson decided to ask his assistant medical officer to record on a daily basis, amongst other things, any serious injury or accident to a patient. A book soon began to record a litany of incidents:

> October 24th – Henry Fuller cut his hand by breaking a pane of glass. Robert Black had a black eye self-inflicted.
>
> October 28th – Liz Taylor fell this morning against the wall and cut her forehead slightly.
>
> October 29th – Thomas Vents fell in a fit this morning and striking his left temple against a corner, received a long deep wound.
>
> November 3rd – Caroline Emery fell in a fit and received a contusion around the right eye.
>
> November 11th – James Agate was found by the night attendant at 1 am with a wound round on his forehead right above the nose from which a considerable quantity of blood had flowed – supposed to have been inflicted by one of the patients.
>
> November 20th – Mrs Dickinson having got possession of a knife attempted to cut her throat. The wound is trifling and superficial.[8]

Robertson accused the nurses of neglect for the last incident and removed Ann Wilson from being in charge of the ward and gave another nurse, E. Vinnell, one month's notice. The incident concerning James Agate illustrates the point that it was easy for staff to blame patients for any violence that occurred. On the other hand, it may be presumptuous to assume that most injuries were caused by violence on the part of another person. As the notes above show, epileptic patients often had a tendency to hurt themselves and as Robertson had frequently admitted, medicine could do little to control epilepsy. On 10th December 1865, the assistant medical officer wrote:

> I directed Robertson's attention to Mrs Bartlett of No. 6 ward who complained to the Head Attendant of rough usage from Mary Anne King temporarily in charge of the ward. The patient bit the nurse and the nurse hit back. Dr Robertson informed Mary Anne King that he feared she had not shown sufficient forbearing in the performance of her duties – she will be suspended next time. She had shown great want of judgement and temper. He'd tell the Visitors the next time he saw them. The patient's mental state of varied delusions made it extremely difficult to arrive at the truth.[9]

King resigned of her own volition a few days later. Robertson had to deal with an increasing number of complaints from relatives and friends about ill-treatment, the lack of communication and unnecessary detention. On 1st May 1865, he received a letter from the Guardians of New Shoreham concerning a patient, William Brazier, who had died on 27th March:

His friends are very much dissatisfied with the appearance of the body – many abrasions caused by undue violence on the part of the attendants. Abrasions occurred a short time before death.[10]

No investigation was recorded. The following year there were at least five complaints from relatives and friends about staff violence. But the most serious complaint came from the wife of a 58-year-old patient, John Payne, who had died at the asylum. During the inquest held on 4th September, she accused the asylum of ill-treatment. Perhaps because Payne was not from Brighton, only the *Sussex Agricultural Express* gave a full report (7/4/1866) of the proceedings. This is an abridged version:

An Important Inquest at the Lunatic Asylum – Alleged ill-treatment

Mary Anne Payne deposed that her husband was removed to the Asylum 29th November 1865, and that before this time he was not violent. She had seen him eleven times since he had been in the Asylum. She saw him on Sunday week. He was sensible, and lying on a water bed. He asked if she had anything for him, and she offered him an orange but the attendant would not let her give it to him. On the previous Wednesday, she saw him in the visiting room, where he was led in by an attendant. He complained of his treatment, that he had not had enough to eat, and was knocked about with a bat. She turned up his clothes above his knees and observed bruises on both legs just above his knees. She told the attendant that he was not kindly treated, but he did not answer her. She brought some food for her husband to eat, and gave him a little piece of ham, but he could not take it. He was so exhausted that he wanted to go and lay down. The attendant said that he now and again gave him a piece of bread, but the deceased contradicted him. The deceased told her, in the presence of the attendant, that the bruises on the knee were caused by his being beaten about with a bat, but he did not say who knocked him about. When she saw him on Sunday week, his left leg was very much swollen and bruised below the knee. He said that the mark was where they hit him. He did not say why they hit him. He could not get out of bed without help, in consequence of being so weak. He asked for some water and the attendant said he was to wait, and he would bring him some beef tea or whisky. She stayed ten minutes afterwards, but during that time no beef tea or whisky was given to the deceased. She saw her husband on Wednesday last; he was then in a dying state, but she was not allowed to stay with him. Mr Lewin, the assistant medical officer would not let her stay, but ordered her out and told her that she might come again tomorrow if she liked. Her husband asked her what was the matter, as she was crying; he said he was very well. She went away and did not see him again alive.

On that Wednesday she saw some fresh bruises on the lower part of his body. Mr Lewin was present and turned deceased over or else she would not have seen them. About a fortnight after he came to the asylum she noticed that he had a cut over the eye, and the attendant told her that one of the patients had struck him. About a fortnight ago she complained to Mr Cooke, the relieving officer at Lewes, of the way in which her husband was treated. On Sunday week she saw Mr Lewin in the visiting room, and told him that the deceased was not kindly treated, and she wanted him home. He made no answer. Previously to Wednesday Mr Lewin always behaved very kindly. She was not violent in her conduct and did not threaten the attendants.

The next witness was William Iremonger; the same attendant who had been involved in the two well-publicized inquests of 1864. Iremonger had been in charge of Payne. He claimed that up to ten days before his death, Payne had slept in a normal dormitory, but due to his wanderings during the night had been transferred to a single room. Iremonger said that Payne's left leg had been bad on admission. He then described Payne's diet:

> He had breakfast at 8 o'clock – beef tea and bread; at half past ten he had some beef tea and half a glass of whisky; at one he had the ordinary dinner; except that for him the meat was minced to prevent him choking himself. He would usually have beer to drink, but lately he had half a glass of whisky. At 6 o'clock, for supper he had beef tea and half a glass of whisky, and bread crumbled in; or if he could eat it the bread would not be crumbled in. Between dinner and supper, about 4 o'clock, he had sometimes bread and milk, sometimes beef tea, and sometimes arrowroot. He ate his meals heartily. Witness served out two glasses of brandy to the night attendant to give him during the night. From the time he was removed to a separate room he was unable to feed himself, and was fed by the attendant. Witness had himself fed him twice a day since his removal. A day before his death he refused some of his food because he was too weak to take it.

Iremonger went on to describe Payne as a:

> … troublesome patient, very restless, and his habits were very filthy. He would tear his clothes and blankets, and try to eat them. The paralysed patients mostly are filthy and tear their clothes to pieces but deceased was worse than any other. He remembered that a patient struck deceased over the eye and caused a cut; the deceased tried to take something belonging to the other. At night he would walk about between the beds in the dormitory. He had seen him fall about in the day time.

Mrs Payne was then recalled and admitted that her husband was restless and sleepless at home recently and that he wouldn't go to bed. But she claimed that his habits were very clean. The next witness was Thomas Watkins, the night attendant who confirmed that Payne frequently got out of bed, sometimes a dozen times in one night "but was never punished for doing so that the witness was aware of ". He claimed that every night he administered to him half an ounce of bread with beef tea each two hours.

The assistant medical officer, Fred Lewin, was called next. He explained that he was in sole charge of the asylum at the moment as Dr Robertson was away. He said that:

> … the deceased was in a fair condition when he was admitted, but his health was not good. Since the beginning of March he had general paralysis of the insane. He died from that cause on 29th March. On the previous day the witness told the deceased's wife to go away in consequence of complaints that she was insolent to the attendants. The marks on the deceased's left leg were occasioned by an old ulcer or injury. The swelling was caused by languid circulation; he had scarcely any circulation at all.

At the end of the inquest, the jury decided that the deceased had died from the "general paralysis of the insane" and that he had not been ill-treated at the asylum. General Paralysis was thought to have been a disease of the brain caused by over-work, over-worry, sexual excesses or over-drinking. It was not then recognized that it was, in fact, the advanced stage of syphilis.

The jury's verdict was not surprising as Mrs Payne had brought no witnesses to substantiate her allegations. The case showed how patients were probably more vulnerable to staff abuse during the night time. And given the record of staff drunkenness, one wonders whether Payne ever received the two glasses of brandy from the night attendant. Mrs Payne's alleged rudeness to staff was by no means an isolated case. One week after the inquest a female visitor was thrown out of the asylum on visiting day for bringing wine to her relative and for being rude to the staff; telling them amongst other things, that she "could do what she liked". And later on that year, the assistant medical officer refused to see a patient's relative who had been rude to him.

Legally, the asylum and its staff had yet again been cleared of any wrong-doing. But these inquests were only interested in whether death was caused by ill-treatment rather than whether ill-treatment went on in the asylum. The readers of the *Sussex Agricultural Express* could hardly fail to notice the discrepancies between Mrs Payne's testimony and that of the asylum staff. And in the long run, it would be the verdict of public opinion that would count much more than the verdicts of public inquests in formulating perceptions about large public asylums.

The relationship between the families and friends of the patients, and the asylum authorities was often a difficult one. Patients were encouraged to write letters to their families and the parish Guardians were often "overloaded with letters to bring home".[11] But "many patients expressed great disappointment at not being oftener visited or written to by their friends".[12] On 3rd January 1865, the Brighton Lunacy Committee felt:

> … bound to urge on persons who have relations or friends in this insti-
> tution, frequently to communicate with them by letter, message, or inter-
> view, as such attentions are highly esteemed by the poor unfortunates,
> and it is believed go far to effect recovery, whilst neglect sorely exasperates
> the mental state of those who are so wretched as to require thus to be
> restrained.[13]

Relatives and friends of patients from Brighton did find it difficult to visit the asylum on Wednesdays and many wanted their insane to be kept in the workhouse where they would be able to see them more often. Robertson and the Brighton Guardians, for different reasons, both believed that 20 or 30 of the parish's patients could eventually be transferred there.

Sometimes there was an embarrassing lack of communication on the part of the asylum. In June 1865, a young patient named Pilbeam died:

> The parents of the young man had called upon him more than once and
> seemed much distressed that they had not received notice in time to be
> present at either the death or the burial of their son. He died on a
> Saturday, but no notice of his death reached them till the following
> Monday afternoon. They went to the Asylum next day, when they were
> informed that the inquest was held the previous evening and that their
> son was buried.

> One of the officials told them that if they had arrived the day before, they
> would not have been permitted to have seen their son. Having subse-
> quently seen an old man who had been on the jury, they were informed
> by him that he was too deaf to hear anything that took place at the
> inquest; and the parents were so distressed, that they wished an enquiry
> to be instituted into this matter.[14]

Brighton's Lunacy Committee conducted an investigation and cleared the asylum of any misdemeanour. The family said they were satisfied with the enquiry.

A continuous dispute between Robertson and the patients' relatives was over the question of whether or not a patient was well enough to be released. Robertson was bombarded with letters and requests over this very question. On their visit of 29th March 1865, the Brighton Lunacy Committee asked for the release on trial of several of their patients and:

… recommended the discharge of Esther Flowers whose services were required by her husband and family. Her husband had frequently applied for her discharge. She was most indignant at being left there.[15]

Robertson turned down all their requests. The Brighton Guardians then passed a motion to employ two independent doctors to visit the asylum and to give their opinion about the cases concerned. But nothing seems to have come of the idea and probably the Lunacy Commissioners (apart from the asylum authorities) would not have allowed it.

If families failed to obtain the release of their relatives through letters, they sometimes turned to illegitimate means. On 25th October 1865, Robertson received a letter from Thomas Polhill requesting the release of his son, Edward. Robertson replied that it was imprudent to discharge him. On 23rd December, Edward made his escape whilst returning from the farm. Robertson believed that "there can be little doubt but that his escape was planned by his friends".[16] Polhill was not recaptured. Soon after, Robertson received the following letter:

> I write to inform you that I shall send the (Asylum) clothes back I have by rail to Haywards Heath and pay the carriage. I should thank you to write to my father and let him know when you have received it. I am thankful to say I am quite well, and have been for 16 months, only have not been sent home. Nor do not know when I shall get home. Sir, you need not send any one after me. I am quite well and able to keep my wife and family and you need not be in any trouble about them.
>
> I am Sir,
>
> Your Humble Servant, Edward Polhill.[17]

It spoils a good story, but sad to say, Edward Polhill was admitted to the Sussex Asylum again several years later.

There were at least six other escape attempts during that year but all were recaptured. Most of them occurred during the walks or on returning from the farm. A common ploy appears to have been requesting to answer a call of nature and then not coming back. Without help, most patients were recaptured within a few hours. In October, two female patients escaped due "to the careless, negligent manner of the female attendants"[18] who apparently spent too much time gossiping to each other. In this case, they had failed even to notice that anyone was missing until several hours later. Robertson fined four nurses 1s. each and complained that "the patients might as well have walked out unattended".[19]

Robertson also received letters which were complimentary:

Wadhurst, Sussex.

Dear Sir,

From a deep sense of gratitude to yourself, and all who had the charge of my late husband. I beg to say in the name of his poor widow and self, that we heard and saw last Saturday quite enough to make us <u>very thankful</u> for what had been done for him, to beg to offer our warmest thanks.

With great respect

Yours obediently

Stephania Springett.[20]

It is difficult to know how many appreciative letters Robertson received as only a few of them have survived. But they illustrate that the asylum did offer its patients kindness as well as the alleged ill-treatment.

OTHER ASYLUM NEWS 1865-66

On 21st April 1865, the asylum suffered its second suicide when Elizabeth Merriott, a 51-year-old patient, drowned herself in the cold rinsing tank in the laundry. She worked there and had never shown any suicidal tendencies. The asylum's second suicide had come a year earlier than Robertson had predicted, but he knew that there was little one could do to stop a really determined person from taking their own life. He did though, insist on the staff taking precautions such as the counting of cutlery etc. and putting away any potential weapon. In fact, most of the successful suicides in the asylum's history were achieved by hanging. Although attempted suicide was a criminal offence in Victorian England, the local newspapers were full of stories of people trying to do just that, perhaps an indication of the desperate conditions which many found themselves in.

On 2nd May 1865, William Hayward, a pauper lunatic, arrived at the asylum from Hastings. Unbeknown to anyone, he had smallpox. The disease quickly spread amongst the male patients and by 23rd June, 32 had caught it. The asylum had no separate accommodation for patients with contagious diseases and so 24 male inmates were placed in farm buildings converted into a temporary hospital. Eventually, four male patients and one member of staff, George Marsh the matmaker, died of the disease.

The smallpox did not reach the female wing of the asylum until 21st June and by then nearly all the female patients had been vaccinated. Only 30 had refused to be, probably because of the vaccination's tendency to produce a fever itself. Sixteen females caught the disease but were fortunate enough to be placed in the recently built female infirmary. As it was virtually isolated, all of them recovered quite quickly. And by 7th August 1865, Robertson could declare that the asylum was free from smallpox.

Contagious diseases, such as smallpox, still spread tremendous fear amongst communities in that period. Little more than twenty years before, 86 people in Brighton had died of the disease in one outbreak. The swiftness with which it had spread throughout the asylum did reinforce the need to build a separate hospital within the grounds where contagious diseases could be isolated. As smallpox continued to be prevalent in the 1870s, the Visitors' Committee finally agreed to the building of a small detached 20-bed isolation hospital in 1876.

Robertson had been away on leave when the smallpox had struck and things had got worse when his assistant, Valentine Browne, had died of an unre-lated illness – probably a stroke – on 17th May. Temporarily, the asylum had been without any medical officers. Fortunately, Dr Henry Maudsley had come down from London and a Dr Beard from Brighton had assisted him until Robertson's return.

Browne's death was a major blow to the asylum and it shocked and saddened the whole establishment. The Lunacy Commissioners reported that:

> Many of the patients expressed to us their regret at his loss, and said that he had always shown them the greatest kindness.[21]

Browne was only 43 years old and had been a general practitioner before coming to the asylum. In a moving address, Henry Hawkins, the Chaplain, paid tribute to Browne at a memorial service held at the asylum chapel on the Sunday after his death. Below is a short extract:

> His nature was very retiring. In days when self-assertion is considered to be a necessary condition of success; when, if a person wishes to get on in the world, as it is called, it is thought that he must have a good opinion of himself and push his way, it is not common to meet with one who spoke so little of himself, and kept so much in the shade. He that is gone, though of mature years and much experience, was unpretending and diffident, almost to a fault.

> A word as to his *kindliness* and *sympathy*. There is probably no one here who came under his charge, who has not received at least a considerate feeling word from the good physician whose place among us knows him no more. And many here have recalled not kind words only, but gentle attention and benevolent deeds at his hands! Much, it may be said, was in the way of his duty; but how much there is in the manner of doing things. Real sympathy is beyond price. He always spoke as one who not

only knew about the cases of the sick and the suffering, but felt for their condition. Even at the last, in intervals of consciousness, he showed that he was not unmindful of others.[22]

Browne was buried at Cwm, a small village in North Wales. It is a mark of the esteem in which he was held, that a mural tablet dedicated to his memory, was erected in the asylum chapel – almost the only member of staff to receive such an honour. The life of an assistant medical officer was not an enviable one as their workload often doubled when the medical superintendent was away. Receiving only a quarter of the latter's salary, they rarely received the esteem and credit that went to their superiors. Browne was replaced by Dr Fred Lewin who by September was already requesting a month's leave and who resigned exactly a year after his appointment.

Lewins was replaced by Dr Samuel Duckworth Williams who would eventually take over from Robertson four years later. Born in 1841, he was the son of William Williams, the medical superintendent of the Gloucester Asylum. He arrived at Sussex from the Northampton General Lunatic Asylum where he had been acting Medical Superintendent. Duckworth Williams was a dynamic but shy man who was described as a crack shot, golfer, fisherman and mountaineer. But the chief joy of his life was music and he and his wife and daughters would be keen participants in future musical events at the asylum. Williams must have known Robertson already as he was a contributor to the *Journal Of Mental Science*. In January 1866, he had written an article on "The Use of Digitalis in the Treatment of Mania". Williams was later described as a man full of kindness and sympathy and proved to be a worthy successor to the dedicated Valentine Browne.

Although Robertson had abandoned the experiment of placing chronic female patients in the homes of attendants, he occasionally resorted to using their homes out of necessity. On 31st March 1865, a five-year-old 'idiot' boy from the Westhampnett Union was admitted to the asylum. Robertson immediately sent him to board with an attendant's family. He agreed with the Lunacy Commission's view that a separate institution was needed for that category of patient, especially for children.

During the year, the chaplain organised five missionary meetings including, in November, 'The Mission of the Kalsapad', (Madras) which delivered an address illustrated by pictures of Indian customs. The audience of staff and patients were said to be deeply interested and at the end donated almost £10 to the Society for the Propagation of the Gospel in Foreign Parts.

During the following year, 1866, there were inquests on three patients who had been found dead in their beds in the morning. In none of these cases was ill-treatment alleged. On 13th April, a patient, Mrs Thorn, tried to commit suicide by jumping off a bridge whilst on a walk. It was the first attempt of its kind and Robertson gave 5s. to the attendant who rescued her. Pauper lunatics were traditionally buried in unmarked graves but in 1866 the asylum authorities decided to allow small iron indicators (with the patient's number on) to be placed in the asylum cemetery. Occasionally, these can still be found today, sometimes turning up in unusual places.[23]

The high staff turnover continued in 1866 with at least 32 leaving, including ten who came and left within the year and who were probably on trial. Robertson was a regular attender of the Medico-Psychological Association annual meetings. The Association was useful for medical superintendents who could discuss ways of improving patient care, treatment and asylum administration with other doctors. But it did little to improve the pay and conditions of ordinary staff which, as has been said, were far inferior to those of prison warders. And, arguably, the Association sometimes made questionable decisions. In July 1864, its asylum superintendents "decided to draw up a series of statistical tables for asylum purposes. With a uniform system, facts of value or treatment can be arrived at".[24] So, from 1865 onwards, patients' personal details at the Sussex Asylum, previously presented on one sheet of paper in the Annual Reports (see Figure 3, Chapter Four) and reasonably easy to understand; were now hidden away in several statistical tables. The new uniform statistical system effectively de-personalised information about county asylum patients.

1865-66 CONCLUDED

Over these two years, Robertson appears to have been particularly busy. In 1865 alone, apart from his trip to France in August, he had attended the Medico-Psychological Association meeting in London (which usually lasted a week) and also the Brighton Medico-Chirurgical Society in November where he had presented a paper on the 'The Therapeutic Value of Digitalis'. He also wrote articles, including two on 'The Means of Extending the Public Asylum System', which appeared in the *Journal of Mental Science* in January and April, a magazine which he was still editing. It is difficult to know to what extent his outside interests affected his asylum duties.

As predicted, the male accommodation in the asylum filled up in this period and in 1866 work was started to provide more. By the end of 1866, the asylum's population had risen to 543 – 240 males and 303 females. Fifty-six patients were discharged that year – 42 deemed 'recovered'; 13 'relieved' and only 1 'not improved'. Seventy patients died – the highest total yet – and

Robertson felt compelled to include in his Annual Report, a list of 25 cases who had died within days and months of their arrival[25]. Most of them had come from the workhouses and were in a miserable state. Robertson contended that they had been "sent in to die" and that they made a significant contribution towards the asylum's death rate.

NOMINAL LIST OF TWENTY-FIVE PATIENTS ADMITTED IN A HOPELESS DYING STATE DURING THE YEAR 1866.

Initials and Union.	Sex.	Age	Date of Admission.	Date of Death.	Cause of Death.	Condition on Admission.
S. B., Brighton......	M.	42	January 5th	January 10th	Decay of Melancholia.	Very feeble and much reduced.
J. B., Westbourne...	M.	42	February 12th	February 17th	Decay of Mania.	Very reduced.
S. W., Ticehurst......	M.	47	January 1st	February 21st	Decay of Melancholia.	Reduced. Bad cut throat, suppurating open wound.
W. H., Cuckfield ...	M.	71	February 17th	March 3rd	Decay of Melancholia.	Reduced. Dying.
R. W., Petworth ...	M.	54	January 26th	March 11th	Hemiplegia.	Very reduced.
C. D., Westhampnett	F.	43	March 19th	April 5th	Decay of Mania.	Reduced.
G. F., Thakeham ...	M.	70	March 27th	April 17th	General Paresis.	Reduced. Last stage of disease.
J. T., Hastings	M.	49	March 26th	April 17th	General Paresis.	Reduced. Ditto.
J. S., Brighton	M.	31	January 26th	April 22nd	Decay of Epilepsy.	Reduced. [dition.
H. W., Cuckfield ...	M.	67	April 16th	April 23rd	Congestion of Brain—Epilepsy.	Very reduced, in a hopeless con-
G. T., Steyning......	M.	36	April 17th	April 29th	Melancholia, Dysentery.	Very reduced. [food.
J. W., Brighton......	M.	37	April 26th	May 1st	Exhaustion from Acute Mania.	Much reduced from refusal of
C. P., Cuckfield......	M.	47	May 17th	June 27th	General Paresis.	Very feeble. Last stage of disease
T. B., Brighton......	M.	41	January 16th	July 12th	General Paresis.	Reduced. Ditto.
A. W., Newhaven...	F.	52	July 13th	August 15th	Acute Melancholia, accelerated by disease of Liver, &c.	Enfeebled.
M. F., Cuckfield ...	F.	74	June 13th	August 31st	Decay of old age.	Very feeble.
S. A., Hailsham ...	F.	79	April 4th	September 24th	Decay of old age.	Very reduced and exhausted.
H. S., Steyning ...	M.	50	May 7th	October 19th	General Paresis.	Feeble. Last stage of disease.
P. H., Lewes	F.	46	April 10th	November 1st	Morbus Addisonii.	Very reduced.
E. B., Ticehurst ..	M.	62	August 4th	November 7th	Decay of Melancholia.	Enfeebled.
E. R., Battle	F.	76	July 19th	November 13th	Decay of old age.	A feeble old man.
C. P., Ticehurst......	M.	56	November 14th	November 27th	Paralysis.	Hemiplegia. Dying.
J. G., Horsham	F.	52	November 1st	December 9th	Paralysis.	Dying.
D. S., Westhampnett	M.	69	December 6th	December 24th	Senile Dementia.	Very feeble—dirty in his habits.
E. B., Brighton......	M.	27	October 27th	December 27th	Phthisis.	Reduced. Phthisis. Last stage.

Figure eight

The two contrasting perceptions about the asylum, mentioned at the beginning of this chapter, probably represent exaggerated views. The truth probably lay somewhere between the two. Suspiciously, William Iremonger had been involved in all three of the major public inquests which alleged ill-treatment. It stretches the imagination to believe that he was completely innocent. But he was not necessarily a typical attendant. It was ironic though, that Iremonger himself would eventually die at the asylum. Since 1864, the asylum did appear to recover some of its good name and it is interesting to note that in this period the word 'asylum' was still used in the true sense of the word – as a place of refuge. New institutions for destitute young women and for the blind in Brighton were respectively known as "The Young Females Asylum" and "The Blind Asylum" even though they had no connection with insanity. As yet, the word 'asylum' had not been stigmatized by its association with mental hospitals.

During the years 1865-66, there was very little news about the asylum in the local press. Perhaps this was a consequence of the saturation coverage given to the scandals there in 1864. Or it may have been because of the greater newspaper coverage given to the proposed new workhouse being built at Elm Grove in Brighton. This new lack of press interest may have been a welcome relief to Robertson and the asylum authorities but may have signified a move in the direction of public indifference. And there had been no more serious clashes with the Brighton Guardians. (They themselves had been strongly reprimanded by the Lunacy Commissioners for repeatedly sending a pauper woman to Lewes prison for sentences of hard labour when she was clearly insane.) But there was a cloud on the horizon. The asylum, which had originally been built for 400 patients, would soon be able to accommodate 700 and it was becoming what the early asylum reformers had always feared: a 'monster' asylum, with little more than a custodial function.

Chapter Eleven

1867-70
"ROBERTSON'S LAST YEARS AT THE SUSSEX ASYLUM"

At the end of its opening year, 1859, there had been 285 patients in the asylum. By December 1867, this number had almost doubled to 567. Two years earlier, the asylum's Committee of Visitors had lamented that:

> … this increase in the number of lunatic patients, which no human being can control, has necessitated a constant addition to most if not all the County Asylums in England.[1]

There was a hint of desperation in suggesting a loss of control. This pattern of expansion was reflected in every public asylum in the country. The number of insane people in England and Wales had increased in the previous 20 years from 18,000 to 43,000. At the same time the number of beds in county asylums had risen from 5,500 to 26,000 and the average number of residents had gone up from under 300 to well over 500. Workhouses were also accommodating more pauper lunatics. Why did the number of pauper lunatics increase so much in the second half of the nineteenth century and how did Robertson react to this trend?

To begin with, the general public and many experts were mystified by this dramatic rise. All sorts of social and cultural developments were blamed: railway travel – at that time an uncomfortable and dangerous mode of transport which resulted in the inclusion of 'railway brain' and 'railway spine' as illnesses in Daniel Tuke's *Dictionary of Psychological Medicine* (1892) – increases in smoking, drinking, immorality, over-indulgence in general, and poverty. Others blamed the pace of life generated by the 'new industrial age' and 'Victorian civilization'.

Page from Tuke's Psychological Dictionary of 1892.
1 Acute mania (a Dutch patient); 2 Chronic mania (Kent Asylum); 3 Acute melancholia (Bedlam Hospital, never speaks); 4 Melancholia (Bedlam); 5 General paralysis; 6 Idiocy; 7 Sporadic cretinism (39 years old)

This was producing a new competitiveness – hinted at in Hawkins' memorial to Browne – which was having an adverse effect on the human nervous system thereby leading to more mental breakdowns. And what has rather a contemporary ring about it: the new age was also blamed for the weakening of parental authority and for the loosening of family ties.

The widespread ignorance about insanity and its causes was never better exemplified than in the opinions of the chairman of the Lunacy Commission, Lord Shaftesbury. He had told a parliamentary enquiry in 1859, that he believed that the main cause of insanity was intemperance – at least 50% – and he forecast that the success of the temperance societies would eventually lead to a fall in the numbers of insanity cases. Of course, he was proved completely wrong. But some eminent psychiatrists agreed with him and "called for government legislation to reduce the number of public houses, shorten their opening hours, and force them to close on Sundays".[2] Other medical men, though, believed that the increase was due to the widening of the classification of insanity. Indeed, many people who had previously been considered troublesome, sinful or just infirm, were now being sent to county asylums by local authorities. This was certainly true in the case of the number of alcoholics who, as confirmed by the local reporter in the previous chapter, were to be found confined in asylums. Although it was a self-fulfilling prophesy – the deduction that because many lunatics in asylums were alcoholics therefore excessive drinking caused insanity – it was an understandable one.

Sometimes lunatics were sent to the asylum who Robertson considered to be sane. On 30th January 1864, he recorded in his Order Book that:

> Alfred Wilding was discharged cured last June and was re-admitted on 20th January. He appears to me to be perfectly sane. I have re-examined him carefully since his admission and I can find no trace of mental illness.

In order to send a patient to an asylum, the signatures of a parish surgeon and two magistrates were required. They did not always agree, as an article entitled "A Curious Case of Alleged Lunacy" which appeared in the *Brighton Herald* showed.[3] Below is an abridged version of the report:

> Reeves, a coachman and gardener, has lived on the most amicable terms with his wife. Three weeks ago Mrs Reeves applied to the Assistant-Overseer (Thorncroft) to have her husband removed to the Workhouse Infirmary, asserting that he was of unsound mind. Today, he was brought before the magistrates.
>
> A parish surgeon, Mr David Richards, said Reeves was of unsound mind, and was suffering from paralysis of the brain, and the limbs generally. He

couldn't use his arms or walk without assistance. He was under the delusion that he was always attired in white clothes. He also complained of people being under his bed in the night-time; and fancied that if he was discharged from the Infirmary, he could get employment at the Railway station. The Chief Warder of the Infirmary corroborated the evidence of Mr Richards.

Reeves complained to the magistrates that he wasn't allowed to speak to anyone in the Infirmary. He was then questioned:

> Mr Bigge: Do you think you can get employment at the Railway station?
>
> Reeves: Yes.
>
> Mr Bigge: What can you do?
>
> Reeves: Oh, anything.

Mr Richards reminded the magistrates that he had hardly any use of his limbs. Reeves (striking his feet on the ground) said "What's that then?". Mrs Reeves was then called. She had been married for four years and although her husband had never been violent towards her he had recently shown signs of an unsound mind and she feared he might be violent. Previous to his removal to the Infirmary, he was quite incapable of doing any work, and was not fit to be left alone.

Reeves called his wife a "liar" and appealed to the Bench to say whether he was of unsound mind? (His violent manner certainly favoured a reply to the question in the affirmative).

His landlady thought Mr Reeves was of unsound mind; but she based her convictions entirely upon two points – that he "looked very strange" and that "sometimes he wouldn't go to bed at 11 pm". She said she had never seen him act at all in a violent manner, but nevertheless, she was afraid that he would do some one some violence "because he looked so strange". She also said that once or twice she stopped up all night to watch him; but she could give no satisfactory reason why she did so, only repeating that "he looked so strange".

The magistrates sent Reeves home because there wasn't enough evidence. The man then left the court, accompanied by his wife, and followed by a large concourse of people.

(We may add that the parochial van was in readiness, outside of the police station, to convey the man to Haywards Heath; but, of course, it was not required).

Robertson and other prominent reformers believed that there had not been an actual increase in the proportion of the populace deemed insane, but that the rise was due to "factors such as the transfer of patients from private dwellings, where their existence was not officially known, to public establishments where they were registered and reported, to population growth, and to the excess of asylum admissions over discharges and deaths." [4] He also maintained that some pauper lunatics were in fact really from lower middle class families but had managed to enter county asylums under false pretences thus making the increase in pauper lunacy seem much higher. At the same time he argued that the number of private patients, which had remained virtually the same over the last 20 years, was proof that insanity was stable and not rising.

Some of Robertson's colleagues at the MPA picked him up on the inconsistency of his argument that middle class insanity was not increasing, which seemed at odds with his statement that some of the increase in pauper lunacy was due to middle class patients being admitted as paupers. They also maintained that some of these were being sent to less expensive asylums abroad thus hiding the real increase in their numbers. For Robertson though, the key to the increase in pauper lunacy was their more accurate registration. If he was right, the number of cases would level off and with effective treatment, would eventually fall.

For this reason, Robertson was optimistic about the future and, in an article in the October 1867 edition of the *Journal of Mental Science*, outlined the prospects for the care of lunacy in Sussex. The *Sussex Advertiser* (23/10/1867), admitting that many of their readers could "hardly see any end to their [the insane poor] increase or to the disposal of them" reprinted parts of Robertson's hopeful article. He started it by declaring that he believed that the number of pauper lunatics in the country in the future would not exceed more than 55,000. This would be commensurate with a ratio of 1 in 400 of the population. Robertson then applied this calculation to Sussex:

> The population of the county, according to the last census, and corrected to July, 1866, is 377, 180. The total number of pauper lunatics on the 1st January, 1867, was 837, or 1 in 450 of the population.

They were thus distributed: –

	Male	Female	Total	Per Cent
In the Sussex Asylum	236	294	530	63. 3
In the Workhouses	76	99	175	21. 0
Living with Friends	51	64	115	13. 7
Boarded out Privately	9	8	17	2. 0
Total	**372**	**465**	**837**	**100. 0**

We shall have at the county asylum about 700 beds when the alterations are completed, and the entire plan for the enlargement of the asylum provides 800 beds, viz., 350 male and 450 female.

If, allowing for increase of population in the next twenty years, we place the inhabitants of the county at 500,000, we should, taking one pauper lunatic and idiot to every 400 of the population, have in this period a total of 1,250 to provide for. On the standard which I have taken, of 60% requiring asylum treatment, 25% workhouse accommodation, and 15% being placed in private dwellings, we shall be able to receive 750 at the county asylum. There can be no great difficulty in finding proper accommodation for 300 in the twenty-five workhouses in the county, and I believe that 250 families may be found, able and willing to undertake the care of their insane relatives.

The *Sussex Advertiser* ended its article by hoping that "we see the beginning of the end, and that Dr. Robertson's thoughtful calculations may prove sufficient to meet the difficulties in view". His forecast about how many patients there would be in the asylum in 20 years time would prove to be more accurate than his forecast about the total number of cases in the country. In the next chapter, we will examine the accuracy of his predictions.

"Anticipating 'community care', Robertson felt sure that future progress in the treatment of the insane lay in the direction of increasing their liberty and home treatment".[5] He hoped that the 15% figure for home care that he then had in mind would increase. Two years earlier he had suggested that chronic lunatics, individually or in fours, should be placed in small licensed houses in their own villages. But he was most concerned that they should be supervised regularly by the Visitors and the medical superintendent as "the present condition, in England of the insane poor boarded in private dwellings, either with relatives or with strangers, is most unsatisfactory".[6] In fact, the history of the care of the insane in the home had been one of "ill-treatment and neglect".[7]

Robertson wanted pauper lunatics boarded in private dwellings to be supervised by the Lunacy Commission rather than by the local Board of Guardians. And for the local county asylum to keep case records of "pauper lunatics in the community" and to monitor them in the same way as they did their own inmates. The asylum could employ a relieving officer to visit the patients regularly. The latter would be given an allowance but it was not to exceed the maintenance rate of the asylum.

The idea of placing 25% of the less serious cases in workhouses was already being partially planned for in Sussex as the new Brighton Workhouse, which opened on 1st September 1867, contained specialist facilities for the insane. By

PROGRAMME.

PART I

Overture. (Pianoforte)	"Tancredi"	Rossini
Recital.	The Church Yard Scene (Hamlet)	Shakespeare
	Mr. D.J. Smithson.	
Recit.	"Angels ever bright and fair"	Handel.
	Miss C. Vandeleur.	
Song.	"Come into the garden Maud	Balfe.
	Signor Julian Masi	
Recital.	"School for Scandal"	Sheridan.
	Act 2nd Scene 1st	
	Sir Peter Teazle . . . . Mr.D.J. Smithson).	
	Lady Teazle . . . . Miss Vandeleur.	
Solo (Pianoforte)	"Grand Fantasia	Benedict
Recital	"The Spanish Champion" Signor Masi	Heemans.
Duet	" Silar Stanchezza ("Il Trovatore") Mr. H. de Ville.	Verdi
	Maurice - - Signor Masi.	
	Anzuchena . . . . . Miss Vandeleur.	

Interval

PART II

Recital	"Misadventures at Margate"	Ingoldsby
	Mr.D.J. Smithson.	
Song	"Within a mile of Edinboro town"	Scotch.
	Miss Vandeleur.	
Song	"Good bye Sweetheart Good bye"	Hatton.
	Signor Masi.	
Recital	"Othello" (Act III Scene 1st)	Shakespeare
	Othello . . . . . Mr D.J. Smithson.	
	Iago . . . . . . Mr. H. de Ville.	
Duet	"Grieve no more"	Hatton.
	Miss Vandeleur & Signor Masi.	

Concert programme for 1868, handwritten by Robertson

183

January 1st, 1867, there were already 10,307 pauper lunatics in 688 workhouses in England and Wales. Robertson believed that they were better off in the small county workhouses rather than in the large urban ones. His experience led him to conclude (rather surprisingly in view of the poor condition so many workhouse patients were in when they arrived at his asylum) that:

> … the aged, imbecile and demented lunatics prefer the workhouse to county asylums, partly from the greater freedom from discipline (from enforced order and cleanliness, baths etc.) which they enjoy, partly from the association with sane patients there instead of the insane, and partly because it is situated nearer their own Parish and family… The truth is that the insane poor who are sufficiently sane to argue the point, are constantly asking to be sent back to the Union [workhouse].[8]

As with patients in private dwellings, he wanted workhouses to use the same case-books and statutory records as the asylums did and to be visited by the local county asylum medical officer at least once a year. He also believed that cottage asylums could be built – planned like a village – to accommodate up to a thousand patients. They could be constructed within the asylum grounds and would be midway, in terms of treatment, between the asylum ward and the private dwelling and combine the advantages of both. The cottage residents would be able to attend the asylum general dining hall for the principle meal thus partially resolving the problem of cottage staff not giving their patients the correct dietary allowance. Robertson was convinced that the asylum would remain the focal point for the treatment of lunacy because, uniquely, it had the capacity to treat all forms of mental disease.

One quarter of all pauper lunatics were classified as idiots and Robertson believed that special asylums should be built for them. He was not in favour of their being placed in families, as was the practice in Scotland. There, they were farmed out for profit in individual cottages. The families were poorly paid with the result that the patients were often unfed and ill-treated. They were also rarely visited by the Scottish Lunacy Commissioners. Idiot patients were extremely vulnerable to mistreatment as they often lacked the capacity to complain about abuses.

In 1847, the first public asylum for idiots had been founded at Highgate, in London. It was moved to Earlswood, Surrey, in 1855 and took patients from all over the country. Relying heavily on public donations, it was already full in 1867 with 438 patients. That autumn there were 223 cases for admission but only thirty places available. Like the Sussex Asylum, it had plans to accommodate 800 patients eventually. Public meetings were regularly held in Brighton to raise money for Earlswood and local newspapers made frequent appeals for donations. In one such appeal, the *Brighton Gazette* on 2nd October 1867, declared that:

> To "educate" idiots may to some persons appear an unpromising and hopeless task. Experience has, however, shown otherwise. Many who are termed idiots, – and properly so, – possess in some matters very acute mental powers which, if rightly developed, may be turned to profitable account. Those who have paid a visit to the Earlswood Asylum have been surprised at the musical, mechanical, and other abilities manifested by the inmates.

Probably, there were several reasons for the large increase in pauper lunacy in Queen Victoria's reign. The new classifications of what constituted insanity and who was thus eligible for asylum admission was a major factor. Traditionally, idiots had not been confined; now they were being sent to asylums. And people who had in the past been kept in the workhouse – the elderly, the infirm, epileptics and paralytics – now found themselves classified as 'lunatics' and transferred to asylums. The better care there often meant that patients, especially female ones, lived longer. This lowered the death rate, but also lowered the cure rate as the asylums soon filled up with chronic long-term cases who had little hope of being discharged. And finally, as pauper lunatics were not entitled to any relief once they left the asylum, some may have been reluctant to leave. As we have seen, Robertson often allowed cured patients to stay on for short periods before discharging them into the outside world.

In 1867, patients were still arriving from workhouses and private asylums in what was described as a feeble state, and sometimes worse. On 29th October, Henry Reed, a patient chargeable to Brighton, arrived from Bethnal Green private asylum. "He was much bruised" [9] and he had a fractured rib. He died on 2nd November. Dr Williams conducted a post mortem in the presence of Robertson. It showed that Reed had died from a brain haemorrhage but confirmed that he had a broken rib and a bad bruise on his right arm. Although these injuries had not caused his death, an inquest was hastily arranged by the coroner for Monday, 4th November at 9 pm, to be held at the Sussex Asylum. Dr Millar, the medical officer of Bethnal Green, (and the same doctor who had clashed with Robertson about care in private asylums in 1863), sent this explanation of Reed's condition:

> It appears that the evening before Henry Reed was removed he had a scuffle with a fellow-patient in the Infirmary, and it is not unlikely that the rib was broken at the time he received the bruise on his arm. [10]

At the inquest, Dr Williams said that he thought the broken rib "must have occurred about two weeks before the patient's removal and the bruise about a

Staff notice relating to the patients' Wednesday Balls, signed by Robertson.

week, neither of which had anything to do with the cause of death, and that his death was not in any way the result of violence".[11] After an enquiry of about two hours, the jury returned a verdict of "death by natural causes" but appended a note saying there was an "extensive bruise on the right arm and one fractured rib".[12] Though unlikely in this case, it was not unusual for patients to arrive at the asylum with bruises after a long journey. Some were obviously reluctant to come. Williams recorded in July 1867, that one woman patient was so violent that they "had to hire men on the road to bring her from Bethnal Green Asylum, London".[13]

After the inquest, the discrepancy about *when* the injuries had occurred was not taken up by any of the local newspapers – only one, the *Brighton Gazette*, had reported the inquest but had made no comment about the verdict. Even the

Brighton Guardians decided that no discussion was necessary. Robertson informed the Lunacy Commissioners about the circumstances – as he was required to do by law – but didn't pursue the matter further. Incidents such as this, whether occurring in private or public asylums, did little to reassure the public. It is also unclear why Robertson and Williams ignored the coroner's advice of the previous year that "in future the post mortem examinations should be performed by a medical man not connected with the asylum".[14] Later on in the year there was an inquest on a patient called Stringer but none of the newspapers reported it. The bruising and fracturing of patients' ribs in all types of asylums was to become a major public national issue which even the local papers could not ignore.

Robertson's health continued to cause him problems and the Minute Book of the Committee of Visitors recorded on 23rd February that he was on "leave of absence again for ill health".[15] He was also away on 12th October, when four nurses attacked a patient called Browne for allegedly refusing to change her dress. Williams punished the offenders:

> Dr. Williams acting for the Medical Superintendent feels it's his duty to stop the leave of Hillier, Midhurst, Mitchell and Bartlett for the remainder of this month as a mark of his extreme disapprobation of the disgraceful proceedings respecting the patient Browne on Saturday evening – As Midhurst appears to have been the most to blame it will be a matter for further consideration on Dr. Robertson's return whether she shall be reduced to the rank and wages of a third nurse.[16]

It is not recorded whether or not Midhurst was punished further but Hillier left six months later to become the head female attendant at the Epsom Asylum. Williams continued to record everyday events in his daily notes:

> May 6th – Dinners on the female side not properly cooked and the meat somewhat tainted… Patients were kept waiting an hour for their dinner consequently.
>
> June 26th – Saw the husband of Elizabeth Best and told him hers is a hopeless case.
>
> July 2nd – John Harry Evans refused to leave the tea table this evening with the other patients and when the attendant tried to remove him he became violent and in the scuffle fell down.
>
> July 6th – Evans squared up to two or three patients. He claimed I only listened to the attendant's complaints and not to his.
>
> July 24th – Frances Andrews is much bruised owing to the necessity for two nurses constantly to restrain her.
>
> Aug. 19th – Showed Dr. Holdz from Russia around the Asylum.
>
> Dec. 14th – Harriet Arthur – bruised after striking herself.[17]

Three patient escapes were recorded during 1867. On 31st July, Joseph Friend escaped. As he was a hawker by trade, an attendant was sent to Lewes races to look for him. A week later he was found at Brighton by an attendant who brought him back. On 4th August, George Bryant escaped whilst going to chapel but was brought back immediately. On 8th November, George Baltmore got away from the gardener. He was not recaptured within fourteen days and was therefore discharged.

Staff turnover continued to be high with 20 staff going, two of whom were sacked. On 1st March, Williams recorded of one of them:

> William Kitchenbaum the florist, who is under notice to leave, obtained leave of absence for today under the ostensible reason of seeking a place – when returned he was the worse for liquor and had a slight black eye – Shall send him notice to leave immediately as besides this instance, his conduct has been generally unsatisfactory.[18]

It was not only Robertson whose health suffered whilst working at the asylum. Kate Brooks, a female attendant, had a nervous breakdown after six months and was re-admitted as a patient. And in September, Miss Buckle, the female head attendant, who had been at the asylum since 1859, was given three months' leave to rest. The danger of asylum work was emphasized in May when Robertson decided to ban all razors from the wards. From then on, attendants could only shave at home with a heavy fine for disobeying this order. During 1867, two patients gave birth which up to then seemed to have been a rare occurrence. The end of the year saw the return of George Tyron, the criminal lunatic, who had almost blinded the then assistant medical officer, Mr Gwynne, in 1860. He arrived from Fisherton House Asylum and was apparently much improved.

By December 1867, a new wing for male patients had been added. This extra space would have a positive effect on the death rate over the next few years although that year a record 72 patients had died, fourteen within a month of admission. Two new dining halls were also completed, one for females and one for males, each seating 350. The dining areas in the wards were converted into sitting rooms. The ward bathrooms were also expanded. The new dining halls eliminated the use of dishes, plates, and the smell of food in the wards and day rooms (except for the bed-ridden patients). But they also made the asylum less homely and increased the institutionalisation of the inmates. Robertson admitted in his Annual Report that the change of meal-time routine had been a difficult one. Hawkins described the new arrangement:

> At the breakfast hour the Male and Female patients assemble in two handsome halls, not unlike College halls, without the high table and the

grave portrait of founders and benefactors. Here they take their various meals, seated, in batches, at what may be termed mess tables. An attendant says grace; various attendants watchfully provide for the wants of those under their respective charge. There is no confusion or disorder – the greatest method and regularity prevail. The chapel service follows breakfast.[19]

The advantage of the new system was in the method and regularity rather than in any therapeutic benefit. No one was allowed to leave the dining halls before all the cutlery had been accounted for. Given the large increase in asylum numbers, the old system of eating in the ward day rooms had probably become impractical. Two years later, the week-day service was also stopped, replaced by a short service in the dining halls after breakfast.

The chaplain, Henry Hawkins, left in 1867 to take up a similar post at the Colney Hatch Asylum, London. It was a much larger institution with over two thousand residents. Hawkins' legacy has been some highly descriptive words on the asylum and its officers. In his article, "Glimpses of Asylum Life", written in 1869, he describes the effect of the surrounding countryside:

> Surely the charm and loveliness of the surrounding scenery must, in many instances, imperceptibly soothe and tranquillise the afflicted mind, and contribute, more even than direct remedies, towards restoring its peace and healthful balance. The very air which nimbly and sweetly recommends itself unto the gentle senses can hardly fail to prove health restoring.[20]

Hawkins, not surprising for a religious man in Victorian Britain, was essentially conservative and not in favour of all the reforms:

> … after the coarse and rough treatment of the insane in past years, a reaction has set in, with a tendency, perhaps towards over-indulgence and ultra refinement in their management.[21]

Nevertheless, Hawkins seems to have dedicated his life to improving the care of pauper lunatics. In 1871, he helped set up 'The Guild of Friends of The Infirm in Mind' which encouraged neighbours of asylums to make personal visits and encouraged ladies to write and send gifts to patients. With the help of Robertson, he also set up in London the first 'After-Care Association' in the country in 1879. It was specifically for women who had just left asylums but who needed a place of convalescence (if they were not to end up in the workhouse) before returning to the community. The Association received lukewarm support from asylum staff and it had little influence but it was a start. Hawkins also wrote numerous articles about getting the local community more involved in asylum life and booklets to assist staff in their demanding work. He recognized that many patients, above all, needed friendship, and he encouraged asylum staff to maintain contact with their former patients once they had left their jobs. He perceptively saw that after-care had no time limit. Hawkins was still writing about the subject in *The Lancet* as late as 12th October, 1901, – an article entitled 'Treatment of the Insane Then and Now'.

Hawkins seems to have been a very popular local figure. Farewell parties for him were arranged in Haywards Heath and at the asylum, where 800 people attended, although strangely, not Robertson. Hawkins obviously had great respect for Robertson although he found that "Robertson's remarks were some-what caustic at times, and inclined to be very aggressive".[22] Hawkins was replaced at the asylum by Thomas Crallan, a passionate meteorologist.

It was during 1867 that Robertson's involvement with asylum affairs seemed to diminish. Joint editor of the *Journal of Mental Science* since 1862; this year he became President of the Medico-Psychological Association and also jointly translated Wilhelm Griesinger's 'Mental Pathology and Therapeutics'. We know that he was away from the asylum for at least three spells, including the annual MPA meeting held in June. Given that his correspondence duties as medical superintendent were already heavy without the above activities, his direct contact with patients must have been very limited, although as Hawkins has written, his influence was still strong even when he was not present.

Robertson received a wage increase of £100 in 1867, giving him an annual salary of £650. Unfortunately though, his health seems to have got worse. The strain of living in the asylum for 24 hours a day affected most medical superin-tendents and led to many having breakdowns including Robertson's assistant, Dr Williams. And as Robertson's outside interests grew, it was Williams who was becoming more and more important to the management of an asylum, which, like a many-headed monster, was growing each year.

For the remainder of Robertson's time at the asylum he was clearly not very well and needed several breaks for his health. During a six week leave of absence in April 1868, he visited the oldest asylum in Europe, 'Hospital de Los Locos' (founded in 1492) in Grenada, Spain. There, he saw patients left naked in straw as part of their treatment. He described the institution as a "monument of igno-rant neglect".[23] And in the following two years he visited asylums in Canada and America. So, although ill, his passion for improving asylums was still there. But his discontent with his own position was gradually becoming more apparent. In 1868, the Lunacy Commissioners once again refused his request for his accom-modation to be placed in a separate building. And for the first time we find a trace of bitterness in his Annual Report:

> The care and anxiety attending the opening of a large Asylum can hardly

be exaggerated, and when the Medical Superintendent adds that, in addition, the buildings of the asylum and the number of patients have been doubled during the period 1859-69, he ventures to think that an expression of thankfulness for the measure of success which has attended his work is not on this occasion misplaced. There are few decades in the life's work of one individual, and the Medical Superintendent can hardly hope to be permitted to record the results of another ten years work in this Asylum.[24]

This hint of discontent followed on his public declaration of June 1868, that if a vacancy arose in the Lunacy Commission; he would apply for the job. Ironically, that year he had been censured by them for accepting a private fee. They wrote to him on 7th March, 1868:

Your proposed disposition of the fee (if any) paid to yourself by the relatives of W. Cotton scarcely acquits you of a violation of the rules of the Sussex Asylum.[25]

There were three public inquests during 1868 but, as in 1867, they were not reported in the local newspapers and all were found to have died from natural causes. The same year, the overcrowding in asylums was partly addressed by an amendment to the Poor Law. Workhouses were now allowed to receive any chronic lunatics from asylums who were deemed suitable by their medical superintendents. This enabled the Workhouse Guardians to save on cheaper accommodation costs and the asylums to have more spare beds. But this amendment gave little hope for those chronic lunatics returned to workhouses. As one of the Visitors' Committee admitted; "there was not one master of a workhouse who was fit to take care of lunatics".[26]

Despite some chronic insane being returned to workhouses and despite the move towards placing some patients back into the community with their family and friends, asylum numbers continued to rise. By the end of 1868, the Sussex Asylum population had gone up to 650. Of the 128 patients admitted that year; 113 had arrived with the cause of their insanity 'not ascertained',[27] a contrast to today's almost obligatory psychiatric label.

A tragic incident involving an ex-asylum patient, a shy, young 26-year-old girl, Jane (not her real name), occurred in July 1869. At the asylum she had cut up her dress and had asked to be put under restraint. After six months she was released 'recovered'. That summer she stayed at Rottingdean, Sussex, with her sister, brother-in-law, and their two-year-old son, Henry. One Sunday morning, she took the child for a walk along the cliffs between Rottingdean and Saltdean. Passers-by saw her carrying the child in her arms on the other side of the road running parallel to the cliffs. Minutes later she called at the house of a coastguard and told his family that she had thrown the child over the cliff. After a frantic dash to the scene by several local people, the little boy was recovered from the beach still breathing, but he died later that evening. After an inquest, Jane was sent to trial for his murder.

Her lawyer, Mr Grantham, tried gallantly to get her acquitted. He pointed out that her grandfather had died insane, that one of her brothers had committed suicide, and that another one had died after being hit by a train. He argued that given her family and personal mental history there was no evidence to show that she had committed the crime apart from her own confession, a confession that she had contradicted on another occasion, and that her nephew could have accidentally fallen over the cliffs. Instead of being acquitted, Jane was found 'not guilty for reasons of insanity' and she was detained indefinitely at Her Majesty's pleasure at Broadmoor Criminal Lunatic Asylum. She remained there until she died in 1917.

It was not the only tragic event of the year involving an ex-asylum patient. In May, James Stubberfield – who had been at the asylum in 1859 – killed his wife whom he had dearly loved, in front of his eight-year-old son. He received the same sentence as Jane. It is interesting to note that in both cases there were no recriminations in the local newspapers against the asylum authorities for releasing 'dangerous' lunatics back into the community. In the case of Jane, there seems to have been widespread sympathy, even from her own sister – the mother of the dead child – who had held her hand constantly during the trial.

Robertson's relationship with the Brighton Guardians appears to have improved during his last couple of years at the Sussex Asylum. In 1868, they consulted him about the windows in their own lunatic wards in the workhouse. They accepted his recommendation that they should replace the iron bars on the windows – which the Lunacy Commissioners would surely object to – with window frames made of iron and wood, a type already fitted in the asylum. In 1869, Robertson asked for and obtained a third medical officer, Alfred Newth, who was a qualified apothecary. Another officer had been badly needed; some other asylums already had three medical officers for far fewer patients. Apart from treating patients and staff for sickness, Robertson and his assistants also had to treat at least a hundred people outside the building: the families of the staff.

The last years of Robertson's time as Medical Superintendent were relatively stable ones without any major scandals. But the complaints of ill-treatment continued until the end. On 3rd February, 1869, some patients complained to him that Rachel Waller was "ill-used in the bath yesterday and then put in cold water".[28] The nurses denied it and he found no bruises on her.

The next day, though, she died, apparently from a chronic disease of the brain. And in August, with echoes of the Snashall case, Emma Hood died two hours after having the wet-sheet treatment. But unlike then, the inquest acquitted the asylum of any blame and Robertson was not criticized in the press.

ROBERTSON RESIGNS

His health – "his neuralgias" – seems to have deteriorated in 1869. In March, he was too ill to read his paper on 'The Alleged Increase in Insanity' to the Brighton Medico-Chirurgical Society. By the end of the year he asked his committee for a two to three months' leave of absence starting from the 1st December which was granted. This meant that for the first three months of 1870, Williams was the only medical officer at the asylum apart from Newth the apothecary. In January 1870, Robertson finally resigned his post, giving two months' notice, and obtained a job as a Visitor in Lunacy, working for the Lord Chancellor in London. In his resignation letter, he was not slow to point out his achievement:

> Knowing as I do that the Haywards Heath Asylum stands second to none, in the estimation of the Commissioners in Lunacy, and of the medical profession, both at home and abroad, I may on this occasion say that already the work which I began here has in my hands greatly prospered.[29]

On his leaving day, Robertson was presented in the Recreation Hall with an illustrated bound testimonial book signed by all the 95 staff. On entering the hall he was enthusiastically cheered by the staff before the Chaplain, Mr Crallan, read the address printed inside the book. Below is a part of it:

> Twelve years have passed away since you were first called to organise and conduct this large establishment, during which you have gained for it a world-wide reputation that renders us proud to have been members of your staff; and now that you are about to leave us, we feel how much we shall miss the master mind that has so long and so skilfully watched over and guided us in our path of daily duty.

> These long years, during which you have presided over us, have been years of almost uninterrupted prosperity to the Sussex Lunatic Asylum and we scarcely dare hope again to find a superintendent who will be at the same time so kind a friend, so indulgent a master, and so skilful a physician.[30]

In a feeling and kind speech Robertson thanked the staff and then spoke of the many little difficulties that arose in the routine of their duty, gave them some advice about the maintenance of conduct, mixed with praise, and then sat down to repeated cheers.

Chapter Twelve

ROBERTSON'S LEGACY

Until 1867, Robertson had still been convinced that a well-run public asylum was the best place for pauper lunatics. In his article 'The Care of Lunacy in Sussex', he had quoted the writer George Paget:

> To my eyes a public lunatic asylum, such as may now be seen in our English counties with its pleasant grounds, its airy and cleanly wards, its many comforts, and wisely and kindly superintendence, provided for those whose lot it is to bear the double burden of poverty and mental derangement – I say this sight is to me the most blessed manifestation of true civilization that the world can present.[1]

Robertson had reluctantly accepted the need to build asylum extensions to cope with the large increase in numbers. Despite this, he had still been confident that moral treatment could work if only curable, and not long-term chronic cases, were admitted. Unfortunately, this had not happened and the Sussex Asylum was filling up quickly with people who were physically incapable of benefiting from asylum treatment. After ten years, Robertson did a statistical review, from July 25th 1859, to December 31st 1868. Out of the 1641 patients admitted to the asylum during that period:

316 had been discharged 'recovered'.

89 had been discharged 'relieved' (better, but not cured).

100 had been discharged 'not improved'.

489 had died, 281 males and 208 females.

So, in approximate terms, of every 100 patients admitted during this ten-year period 20 had been discharged 'recovered', 10 'not improved, 30 had died, and 40 remained under care. According to these figures, once admitted into the asylum, a patient only had a 30% chance of leaving it alive.

Robertson based his rate of cure (recovery) on the number of admissions:[2]

	Numbers admitted	Discharged recovered	Recoveries on admissions
1859	307	6	1.9%
1860	184	30	16.3%
1861	169	29	17.1%
1862	129	30	23.2%
1863	81	32	39.5%
1864	134	24	17.9%
1865	124	33	26.6%
1866	159	42	26.4%
1867	162	42	25.9%
1868	192	48	25.0%

Using this method, when admissions were very low then the percentage of 'recoveries' would be high, as in 1863. Robertson himself was surprisingly sceptical about the value of statistics, especially when used comparatively. He considered that they could only be understood **within** the context of a detailed history of an asylum. Nevertheless, on the surface, the cure rate at the Sussex Asylum seemed reasonably good. But if you based the number of recoveries on the average number of residents, a much lower rate emerges. For example, in 1868 forty-eight patients were discharged from an average number of 616. This made the percentage of recoveries 7.8%. In fact, this was slightly under the national average of 8% which made the asylum's cure rate for 1868 "hardly an impressive record on the criterion of rehabilitation".[3]

More depressing for all the medical superintendents was the thought that twenty years before, the cure rate (based on the number of residents) had been nearer 15%. For Robertson and his colleagues though, it could not have been a coincidence that as the numbers in county asylums had doubled, the cure rates had declined dramatically. He constantly protested about the number of patients who had been "sent in to die" but could do little to stop their admission. He had also failed to dispel old ideas and prejudices about asylums. In fact, the psychiatric profession as a whole had made little impact on the public attitude towards mental illness. The Snashall inquest in 1864 had highlighted the use of digitalis and wet-packing and, allied to allegations of ill-treatment, had tended to confirm public suspicions and had overshadowed the virtues of moral treatment.

Robertson had stoically defended the asylum system and continued to do so despite the doubts he may have had. But he became more and more convinced that chronic cases were better off at home. He confirmed this view in a letter to *The Lancet*, published on 18th September, 1869. The letter also acknowledged the asylum's drift away from a more homely environment:

> The improved treatment of the chronic insane lies in this direction – in removing them, when possible, from the weary imprisonment of asylum surroundings, and in placing them amid the healthier influences of home life.[4]

Robertson believed that at least a quarter of his patients could be returned home. Indeed, he had already started to phase some chronic lunatics back into the community by placing them with their families and friends in 1869. Two years later, Williams was reporting that the scheme had been a success with only two or three re-admissions. Robertson's one reservation about home care – the difficulty of proper supervision – was illustrated in 1869 by the death through ill-treatment of a lunatic who had been living with his sister and brother at Rye.

Robertson was also witness to a sadder, more sub-conscious development occurring in peoples' attitude towards the insane:

> Victorian society was content to ignore the problem of mental illness once the public asylum system had been established.[5]

Certainly, this seemed to be happening in Sussex for after the asylum's first ten years, the local newspapers rarely printed any substantial information about it. Admittedly, the opening of the new Brighton Workhouse in 1867 – when 12,000 members of the public had visited its buildings during the "open" week – had deflected some attention away from the asylum, but in terms of newspaper column inches, interest in it had been declining for some time. Perhaps the local newspapers were merely reflecting a real lack of public interest.

It has been suggested that Robertson was a high flier[6] who was more interested in his own career than in the day-to-day affairs of the asylum. It is true to say that he was deeply committed to the psychiatric profession. Apart from being made the secretary of the Medico-Psychological Association in 1855, he subsequently became the editor of the *Journal of Mental Science* and the president of the former in 1862 and 1867 respectively. But this did not necessarily make him a high flier in a profession which was still incredibly small and where there was not a lot of competition for these time-consuming posts. In fact, Robertson's advancement in the profession had not been particularly fast. He became the medical superintendent of the Sussex Asylum at the age of 34 but two of his peers – Thomas Clouston and Henry Maudsley – had reached the same position by the age of twenty-three.

Robertson was not only an ambitious man but a caring one and he was deeply committed to the belief that lunatics should be treated with kindness and humanity. This was no more evident than in his outspoken attack on the Brighton Guardians for their neglect of workhouse patients. Arguably, upsetting the local dignitaries was not the action of a man solely interested in the advancement of his own career. At Sussex, he frequently implemented new progressive treatments although not all of them were successful. His numerous literary articles reflected his interest in the practical administrative problems of an asylum rather than in academic matters which would have brought him more kudos. He never wrote a book about the subject unlike many of his peers. Instead, he spent much of his spare time visiting asylums at home and abroad in order to get new ideas about treatment.

Overall, Robertson's time at the Sussex Asylum had been a comparative success within the constraints of the circumstances in which the asylum system operated. His achievements had been: to make the asylum relatively self-sufficient; to give patients opportunities for recreation and for learning skills; to experiment with new ideas and treatments; to have imposed a high standard of physical care and hygiene; and to have refrained from using methods of restraint on his patients. On his death, the first chaplain, Henry Hawkins gave this description of his boss at the Sussex Asylum:

> Personally, he was not very much in the wards, his visits being occasional and irregular, but the establishment was maintained in good order, and even when absent, the telegraph, it has been said, conveyed his instructions. Rule, he did, and his strong will made itself felt not only in the wards and household, but also in the committee room. ... He was progressive in ideas and treatment.[7]

Robertson was also "a very truthful and direct critic of any conduct which he considered inconsistent with kind and inhumane treatment of the insane."[8] And it was this basic belief that was his greatest legacy. Of course, he did not eliminate all abuse at the Sussex Asylum but he worked conscientiously to do so. As late as 5th September, 1869, he was writing to a nurse:

> Mrs Hopkins, I have gone into Mrs Ellender's complaints against your treatment of her last night and I have examined her bruises. Nothing can excuse or justify such violence. I neither care to see or to hear your story. You have shown yourself utterly unfit for the charge I have entrusted to you and I hereby discharge you. You must leave the house tomorrow. The steward will pay you up to that date only.[9]

And seven weeks later he wrote to a nurse Broyier:

> I wish to remind you that force in dealing with patients is the last resource of the ignorant.[10]

Robertson was equally strong in his defence of non-restraint which he and others "have for long years so diligently and lovingly built up, which they have, against all comers, defended, and which they yet trust to hand untarnished to their successors in office".[11] He was particularly incensed by an article by a Dr Lauder Lindsay, printed in *The Lancet* in December 1868. In it, Lindsay proposed the use of the 'Protection Bed' or 'Box Bed' – a bed with a lid fastened by a lock – in English asylums in order to restrain patients from getting out of bed at night. It had been in use in several Scottish asylums, and according to Lindsay, was in widespread use in the U.S. Robertson was especially aggrieved because he had once allowed Lindsay to visit the asylum to study its care and treatment. He wrote a strong letter to *The Lancet* on 26th December, 1868:

> Dr Lauder Lindsay has apparently yet to learn that the successful treatment of the non-restraint system is based on the very opposite principle from which guided the small inventive faculty of the originators of straitjackets, strong chairs, leg locks, and which has culminated in the Protection Bed. All these contrivances belong to a system of treatment extinct in the English County Asylums… Their final condemnation was summarised by Dr Conolly – "No fallacy can be greater than that of imagining what is called a moderate use of mechanical restraint to be consistent with a general plan of treatment in all other respects complete and unobjectionable and humane".[12]

Fortunately, Lauder's idea was never permitted in English asylums. It was in his defence of non-restraint that Robertson's autocratic manner and dogmatism became virtues.

The stress involved in running a large asylum placed a heavy burden on one man – especially one who did not have a wife and family to support him – and made the job of medical superintendent extremely stressful. In fact, Robertson's four immediate successors all had serious breakdowns in health and were forced to retire early. Despite Robertson's poor health, he never stopped trying to provide care for pauper lunatics which was based on kindness, an example for all his successors to follow.

ROBERTSON: AFTER THE SUSSEX ASYLUM

As Robertson took up his new position as a Visitor in Lunacy for the Chancery in London, he might have been unaware of one last irony. That year, his old adversary, Samuel Thorncroft, the assistant overseer for Brighton – the man who had publicly taunted him with the jibe of "wrapping patients up like mummies" back in 1864 – went mad, believing himself to be the Emperor of France. Thorncroft, who had ruthlessly dominated poor relief in Brighton both as workhouse governor and overseer for almost 50 years, died later that year. It was reported that his funeral was very poorly attended. True to form, he and his family had been involved in litigation right up to the time of his death. Hero to the ratepayers, scourge of the poor, Samuel Thorncroft would surely make an intriguing subject for a book.

Robertson's new job was less demanding and more lucrative than working as a medical superintendent in a county asylum. He now earned almost three times his previous salary and could claim generous expenses. But he was still in the state system. The job of Lord Chancellor's Visitor entailed visiting the more than 1,000 Chancery lunatics – lunatics with property who were protected by the state – spread over the country. A third of them were

Dr Robertson

in private dwellings and were visited every four months and the rest were in private or public asylums and visited annually. Special extra visits could be arranged if the patients were ill or had specific complaints. Robertson insisted that "he never gave notice at an asylum" prior to visiting. Furthermore, he only occasionally gave notice at a private house, and that was "to a few of the patients who are habitually out driving and walking, but it is not the rule; it is rather the exception than the rule".[13]

Robertson was one of three Chancellor's Visitors and they took it in turns to cover the country which was divided into North, South and West. Half their time was spent travelling and they had no fixed hours. They also had no control over where a lunatic was actually kept. Words that were used to describe another Visitor, Sir James Crighton-Browne, perhaps, may have been as equally applicable to Robertson:

> One might suggest that the Lord Chancellor's Visitorship in Lunacy was perfectly fitted to his love of enquiry, of public activity, and of public pronouncements.[14]

Almost a year after leaving Haywards Heath, Robertson returned to the asylum to take part in an evening's entertainment on 27th February, 1871. He recited a reading about 'love' (see Figure nine). He still maintained his connection with the Brighton Medico-Chirurgical Society and was made an honorary member in 1883. In his job he had to travel a lot visiting lunatics kept at home and in asylums (including Sussex). He also continued to go abroad to visit asylums: in Rome, Munich, Rouen, and the U.S. (Utica Asylum), and wrote numerous articles on the subject. In one article, he defended the use of narcotic and sedative medicines but was against them being used every day for long periods.

In 1881, he gave the presidential address at the Eighth International Medical Congress. His themes were familiar ones. He spoke about the incontestable superiority of public asylums when contrasted with private asylums and their financial speculation. He quoted John Stuart Mill – "insane persons should everywhere be regarded as proper objects of the care of the state" to support his contention that all the insane should be treated in public asylums where no self-interest could arise. He did not want the suppression of private madhouses as he believed they would die out naturally as the public system improved. He spoke also about the "successful application of the English non-restraint system, [which] has gone forth into the whole civilized world, and brought rescue to the most suffering and degraded of our race".[15] Robertson condemned the accumulation of harmless and incurable lunatics in asylums and thought that only 50% of pauper lunatics should be placed there, and that 40% could be held in workhouses and 10% in private dwellings.

But perhaps Robertson's most significant words in the address were those in which he admitted:

> Further reform in the treatment of the insane is not merely a question of whether and how they shall be detained in public or private asylums, but rather whether and when they should be placed in asylums at all, and when and how they shall be liberated from their imprisonment and restored to the freedom of private life. [In the past] I said there was no fit or proper treatment for the insane out of the walls of an asylum. I have since learnt a wider experience… There is, I believe, for a large number of the incurable insane a better lot in store than to drag on their weary days in asylum confinement.[16]

The 'wider experience' he referred to was his work as a Visitor which involved seeing many patients in private dwellings. He was impressed by the care and contentment that benefited both patient and family from this arrangement. Robertson's experience of the public asylum system and his experience as a Visitor placed him in a unique position from which to decide which was the best option in the future. He foresaw that the majority of the insane would benefit most from home treatment. (Although a fellow Visitor, Crighton-Browne, believed that there were far more abuses in private care and preferred private

MONDAY 27th FEBRUARY 1871.

Opening Piece.	"Louisa Polka."	Asylum Band.
Reading.	"Love."	Dr. Robertson.
Song.	"Trifles light as Air."	Mr. Mortlock.
Reading	"The Arab's farewell to his Steed."	Mr. Stuart.
Song.	"On-board the Kangaroo"	Mr. Buckle.
Reading.	Mr Newcastle Apothecary	Rev.d — Crallan.
Waltz.	"Princess Mary"	Asylum Band.
Reading.	"Precepts of Politeness"	Mr. Mortlock
Song.	"The Village Blacksmith."	Dr. Saunders.
Reading.	"Cheap Jack" (a complete Sell)	Dr. Newth.
Song.	"Forget not to Remember"	Mr. Mortlock
Reading.	"John Gilpins ride to Ware"	Dr. Saunders.

Figure nine: Concert programme

asylums). But the main obstacle to this development was, in the words of Henry Maudsley, which are still relevant today, "the public ignorance, the unreasoning fear, and the selfish avoidance of insanity".[17]

How accurate was Robertson's prediction, which he had made in 1867: that in twenty years time there would be no more than 55,000 pauper lunatics; 1 in 400 of the population? By 1st January 1887, there were 80,891 pauper lunatics in the country and the rate of lunacy was 1 in 349 of the population. Almost 50%, were in public asylums. The rest were in workhouses, charitable institutions and private dwellings. Robertson was more accurate with his forecast about how many lunatics there would be at the Sussex Asylum. He had suggested 750 and by 1st January 1887 there were 824. By the time he died in 1897, the number of pauper lunatics in the country had risen to well over 90,000 and the Sussex Asylum had 924 patients; 60 of whom had to be placed in other asylums – Exeter and Fisherton House – due to overcrowding. And public asylums, instead of being places of first resort for treatment (as they were designed to be) had become a place of last resort.

On a personal note, of course, Robertson was no saint. He could be arrogant, overbearing, dogmatic and was undoubtedly a snob. He had been born into an elite family and had married late in life to Mabel, the only daughter of an Indian army colonel. He then lived with her in a very large house situated on the edge of Wimbledon Common in London. Robertson mixed with the upper classes all his life and politically was probably a conservative. He was also a man of contradictions and of contradictory opinions and his ideas such as the use of the wet-sheet and digitalis, with the benefit of hindsight, were dubious. But for all his flaws, there is much to admire in his life, particularly his time at the Sussex Asylum.

Robertson was clearly a great administrator who involved himself in every aspect of asylum life. He was completely consumed by the problem of the poor insane and his dedication to their well-being was total. Nobody reading his daily journal can fail to be impressed by his passionate writing and his genuine interest in the protection and treatment of the mentally ill. His powerful and eloquent attack on the Brighton Guardians for their obvious neglect of John Mockford was particularly striking. The condemnation of his staff when they failed to be kind and tolerant towards patients were models of humanity. Some of Robertson's published articles also illustrated this aspect. His description of the pauper lunatic in the French asylum, who was so restrained that he could do nothing about the flies landing on his face throughout a hot summer, is an image both haunting and moving.

THE ASYLUM – HAYWARDS HEATH
Thursday June 23rd 1870.

MR DAVID SMITHSON,
(THE POPULAR SHAKESPEARIAN READER)

Will give a

DRAMATIC RECITAL,
WITH

MUSICAL ACCOMPANIMENTS;

ASSISTED BY

Miss CLARA VANDELEUR,
FROM THE ST. JAMES'S HALL CONCERTS LONDON.

SIGNOR JULIAN MASI,
THE EMINENT TENOR VOCALIST,
AND

MR HENRY DE VILLE.

DOORS OPEN AT 6·30 P.M. TO COMMENCE AT 7.

Entertainment at the Asylum

But where does Robertson stand within the wider context of psychiatric history in the nineteenth century? In Scull, Mackenzie and Hervey's fascinating book, *Masters of Bedlam*, they trace the careers of many of the leading psychiatrists (although not Robertson) of the period, nearly all of whom worked at some point as medical superintendents in public asylums. It makes depressing reading. Certain characteristics emerge.

Firstly, the majority of these figures, such as Conolly and Maudsley, are initially idealistic and enthusiastic about the state system they work in and attack the private sector. But once cure rates diminish and the asylums fill up (and come more and more to resemble custodial warehouses), they become disillusioned and try and find more lucrative posts in the private sector as soon as they can. Conolly and Maudsley actually end up with private consultancies. They then become more critical of the public system they have just left behind; and in Maudsley's case so pessimistic about the treatment of the insane that eventually he believes that most cases are incurable and nothing can be done for them. By the end of the century some psychiatrists even begin to question the feasibility of non-restraint. So we find that many leading asylum superintendents ended their careers by turning their backs on pauper lunatics, the very section of society, in a sense, on which they had built their reputations.

Secondly, although the Medico-Psychological Association was often divided by different opinions and personality clashes it did help to set up career structures and opportunities for its own members, perhaps at the expense of the profession as a whole. In other words, it encouraged a 'jobs for the boys' mentality.

Was Robertson very different from many of his contemporaries? On the first point, early on in his career he did turn to private practice after failing to obtain the post of medical superintendent at the Glasgow Royal Asylum. But once at Haywards Heath, and for the rest of his career, he worked in the state sector – as a Lord Chancellor's Visitor he was not allowed to work in the private sector. That he eventually became disillusioned with his role as superintendent and pessimistic about the future of county asylums is obviously true and well before he left his post he was publicly announcing that he was looking for another job. Robertson suffered poor health throughout his time at the asylum and by 1870 was clearly worn out and, understandably, switched to an easier option – visiting a privileged group of lunatics ie. Chancery lunatics, was a lot less demanding than daily supervising their pauper counterparts. It was also a job that offered the opportunity to mix with the rich and powerful and useful for its social connections.

On the second point, Robertson was certainly a member of a psychiatric elite and was a protégé and ally of Sir John Bucknill. Bucknill helped him obtain the editorship of the *Journal of Mental Science* in 1862 and played a part in his promotion to the lucrative post of Lord Chancellor's Visitor in 1870. He was also a practical influence on Robertson who adopted many of his innovative schemes i.e., the placing of patients in the homes of attendants and the advocacy of single care. In turn, Robertson helped Henry Maudsley (who acted as a locum for the asylum) become joint editor of the above magazine in 1863. He undoubtedly was also very influential in the career of his successor, Duckworth Williams, who he would later on find some role for on the Chancery Board. And most controversially, he would play a part in the appointment of Williams's successor at Sussex; an appointment which caused an uproar at the time. So, undoubtedly, within the Medico-Psychological Association there was a self-perpetuating elite which clearly Robertson was a part of. But perhaps in a small profession still struggling to establish its respectability within medical science, this was inevitable

Despite the above criticisms, I do not believe that they devalue or invalidate Robertson's achievements as a medical superintendent, especially in the first five years of his office. That he did lose some faith in the county asylum system is not surprising in the light of all the difficulties he faced at the Sussex Asylum. And despite his enhanced position as a Lord Chancellor's Visitor, for the rest of his life he did not waver from his convictions that private asylums should be abolished – as they had a vested interest in prolonging treatment – and that non-restraint was a fundamental principle and a basis for proper care.

I believe Robertson's real legacy to us lies in his great passion and insistence that the insane, whether rich or poor, should be treated humanely and be cared for by the wider society. He was not alone in his objectives. The early Conolly, the early Maudsley and many of Robertson's contemporaries shared the same goal. Perhaps today there is a vacuum of powerful public defenders of the mentally ill such as the men above whose idealism may have eventually died but who, nevertheless, were once inspirational figures to Victorian reformers.

He visited the Sussex Asylum for the last time in 1894 as part of his job, monitoring the progress of Chancery lunatics. Despite his ill-health he continued to work until January 1896. Robertson died on 17th May 1897. He was seventy-two. He had worked unceasingly in his field for fifty years. His obituaries praised his great administrative skills and his enlightened ideas.

The *British Medical Journal* spoke of his kind-heartedness and his benevolence "though he often covered his good deeds with a cloak of cynicism" and made a prediction that, so far, has not come true. Hopefully, this book may help to fulfil it:

> With delicate sensibility and an earnest wish for the welfare of mental sufferers, he leaves a reputation which will probably grow greater rather than less as time enables one to judge fairly of those who directed the great revolution in the treatment of the insane.[16]

It is not possible to end without mentioning one strange twist of fate. In the late 1970s I worked in a large building in south-west London. It was old and spacious with a name all of its own. I had forgotten the name for almost twenty years until I surprisingly came across it during my research for this book. It was called "Gunsgreen" and its address was, The Drive, Wimbledon. For the last few years of his life it had been Robertson's home. Knowing his views on private institutions he would have been gratified to learn that (at least in the 1970s) it had been taken over by the Borough of Fulham and Hammersmith and was being used as an old people's home.

Chapter Thirteen

1870-1904
"DEVELOPMENT AND CHANGE"

SAMUEL DUCKWORTH WILLIAMS 1870-1888

When the mantle of leadership passed from Robertson to Williams (at a salary of £500 pa., £150 less than his predecessor) it was going to a man who had, in practice, probably been running the asylum for at least the previous six months. Williams was just 29 years old, a family man and a passionate sportsman. A fellow writer for the *Journal of Mental Science*, he believed in many of the treatments and ideas that Robertson did. But they had very different characters. Whereas Robertson remained aloof from the local dignitaries, Williams became a prominent Sussex freemason – a fact which undoubtedly ensured him having a better relationship with workhouse guardians. Where Robertson could be dogmatic and severe, Williams was more pragmatic, more emotional. Perhaps this last aspect of his character was best manifested in his great love of music. During his time at the asylum, brass and string bands were formed for patients with musical talents. On the other hand, his less authoritarian character made it much harder for him to stop abuses. But Williams was undoubtedly very dedicated to the asylum and was to become the second longest serving superintendent in its history.

Williams' first official year in office seems to have been quite traumatic. After only a couple of months, he gave his new assistant, Dr Patrick Nichol, three months notice for insulting him. And patient abuse appeared to be getting out of hand:

> Dr Williams is not at all satisfied with the way in which the attendants in male ward 6 do their duty… [a patient] is sure before long to get bruised

or injured in some way. In future a fine of 2s. 6d. for every bruise unless a very good reason can be shown for its presence (18/7/1870).

Dr Williams to nurse Jane Morris – When I came into your ward yesterday you were scolding a patient in a loud voice and had your hand up as if to strike her, but luckily for the patient my entry prevented it (29/7/70).[1]

And later on he reprimands – in a much less severe way than Robertson would have done – a nurse for trying to garotte a patient: "I must beg you to use more gentle means in the future".[2] To be fair to Williams, as well as receiving less money than Robertson, he also received the additional duty of being compelled to visit the wards every day and he probably witnessed far more violence at first hand than his predecessor. Nevertheless, the discipline of the house certainly seemed more lax. In 1872, the head female nurse complained to him about the difficulty of getting nurses out of bed in time for their morning duty and when he visited the farm he found many of the workers inebriated.

It was not just the amount of violence in asylums that was causing concern; it was also its form:

The post mortem discovery of crushed ribs and breast bones in the bodies of the unfortunate lunatics who die in our public Asylums is becoming quite a matter of ordinary routine. It is said that the common Asylum custom is for stout attendants to travel upon their knees up and down the prostrate bodies of unpleasant patients, by way of giving them a hint to cease from troubling. The mystery is that everybody knows this as a piece of abstract information, and that most Asylum superintendents must have abundant proofs of the existence of the practice; but nobody knows anything about any particular instance. Juries are calmly told that a fracture of the sternum and of 6 ribs on each side was caused by the act of the lunatic. Either he sat down suddenly in a chair from which the cushion had been accidentally omitted or he "strained himself" in coughing, or he was in the habit of beating his chest with his hands. It is high time that a stop be put to this kind of thing, and we beg leave to suggest a simple and practical remedy. The fault, of course, rests entirely with the Visiting Justices and with the Commissioners in Lunacy. The former appoint and the latter sanction the appointment of so-called superintendents, who are so over-worked that they cannot superintend and whose medical functions are suppressed and pushed out of sight by their routine tasks as clerks and stewards. But with them rests the responsibility, although not the fault.

We would have a post mortem examination of every patient in an Asylum, and we would insist that whenever mortal injuries were discovered, the superintendent should either prosecute an attendant to conviction, or should be himself dismissed together with all its subordinates. The attendants who were dismissed because some among them had committed a brutal murder would not readily find employment elsewhere, and a public opinion hostile to the practices we denounce would be created among their class by the irresistible force of self-interest. With regard to the superintendent, we would take his successor from among the general ranks of the profession to the absolute exclusion of men trained from early life in an Asylum, and habituated to the existence of its evil customs. In a word, we would infuse new blood into a somewhat effete speciality, and would try to raise up a race of younger Conollys who like him, should bring fresh minds to their work.[3]

This article – reprinted in a local newspaper from *The Times* – came in the light of three recent 'broken ribs' cases. At the Lancaster Asylum, two attendants had been convicted of the manslaughter of a patient who had died from fractures and bruises. Another patient, from the Hanwell Asylum, had died ten days after his admission due to eight broken ribs and a bruised chest. But the jury was forced to return an open verdict due to lack of evidence. And in a more recent case a patient had died with fractured ribs attributed by the staff to him falling against a chair. The public began to ask why asylum chairs seemed to be more dangerous than those found in the ordinary home and why lunatics in asylums were so liable to getting their ribs broken. And if some of these injuries were self-inflicted, why were patients not prevented from hurting themselves in institutions specifically set up for that very purpose?

The Sussex Asylum had its own case in 1870 when Sarah Lucas died with two broken ribs. The inquest jury returned a verdict of 'death from natural causes' but the question still remained, how were the woman's ribs broken? The jury decided, rather unconvincingly, that they were probably self-inflicted. The case caused Williams much anxiety and he promoted a full and searching enquiry conducted by Dr Ormerod and Dr Jowers from Brighton. It was inconclusive. Afterwards, he reminded his staff that the ill-treatment of a lunatic was an imprisonable offence. The recommendation in the article above about having a post mortem on every death in an asylum was an idea that most superintendents agreed with. But the truth was that only a minority of the patients' relatives ever gave permission for post mortems. In 1880, Williams applied for permission after each death that year – 88 in total – but only 26 families agreed. There was still widespread fear and suspicion about such a procedure. As to the suggestion that a superintendent should be selected from outside the system, this is in fact what happened with Williams' successor and the Sussex Visitors' decision almost led to questions being raised in the House of Commons.

The accusation that superintendents were spending too much time in the office was supported by Williams' own diary entries. Below is his typical daily routine, recorded on 26th April, 1878: [4]

8.45 am – At the Office Writing – Received Reports.

11 am – Visited wards, shops, dormitories, kitchen.

12.30 – Office Writing.

2 pm – Visited wards etc.

5 pm – Office Writing.

8 pm – Engagements.

This last activity often involved going to the asylum band practice, which he always attended. And on one occasion, Williams wrote that he did not finish visiting the wards till 1.30 in the morning.

But the controversy about broken ribs did not go away and for the rest of the century many asylum superintendents (including Williams) tried to prove that lunatics, through disease, were more likely to have brittle bones than sane people and therefore were more susceptible to injury. In 1877, Williams recorded that a patient had died of fractured ribs, probably after a struggle with an attendant. He asked the attendant to resign. However, despite the worst aspects of asylums, life was still better in them than some of the alternatives. One patient, who escaped in 1870, begged to be re-admitted after three weeks and was found to be in "a deplorable state of filth and dirt, and half-famished". [5]

Of course, there were also examples of patients attacking staff. A cowman, William Boniface, suffered seven severe scalp wounds after a patient had attacked him with a broom handle, and William Buckle – who had replaced William Knox as Head Attendant in 1869 – was attacked violently on at least two occasions by a patient, William Bell. And in 1883, Thomas Soper attacked attendant Paddington at the urinals, in an attempt to get his keys off him.

SOLUTIONS TO OVERCROWDING

By the end of 1870, with the asylum population reaching almost 700, Williams started vigorously to apply a policy that, in truth, Robertson had already initiated. Selected long term chronic cases – incurables – were returned to workhouses or their friends and relatives. The first option depended on workhouse facilities for lunatics. In this respect, the Sussex Asylum was fortunate that the Brighton Workhouse eventually had specialist wards which had room for a total of 150 lunatics. Later, Williams told a parliamentary enquiry that he felt that the return of incurables to relatives had done away with a lot of the prejudices against the Sussex Asylum. People could now see that they could get their relatives out of the asylum without any difficulty. And he added that the families and friends were more satisfied with the arrangement and that it was better for patients to be at home rather than in a life-long confinement in an asylum, however much their stay there might be softened by kind treatment. Most of the families were given money to maintain their relatives but it was rarely as high as the asylum maintenance rate.

For all Williams' good intentions, the policy did have some defects. In 1873, he recorded that out of 50 chronic cases he had sent home in the last 2½ years, 20 were with their families, 6 had returned to the asylum, 2 were dead, 10 had started in life again, 1 was in a workhouse, and 8 were unknown. Statistically this policy was successful but what had happened to the 'unknowns'? And it was this failure to apply Hawkins' dictum that "after-care has no time limit" that was a concern at the time. By January 1878, Williams had sent 200 chronic patients away in seven years and in that time only 10% had returned to the asylum. But despite this success, apart from a fall in numbers from 691 to 602 in 1871, the asylum population began to increase again.

What happened was that once the asylum had more room it started to resume its practice of offering its spare accommodation to outside boroughs and counties. In 1872, 81 admissions came from Maidstone and the St Pancras Union, London and 14 private patients were received. This bumped up the numbers to 715, an increase in just one year of 113. Obviously, financially speaking it was advantageous. The out-of-county patients were charged 14s. per week and the private patients 16s; whereas the county rate was only 9s. 6d. The more the asylum could get from non-county patients; the more it could keep its own county rate down. But were financial considerations overshadowing the importance of treatment? The Sussex Asylum was not alone in conducting such a policy. Most public asylums followed the same path.

Williams' policy suffered a setback in 1874 when the government decided to give unions a 4s. grant towards each pauper who was accommodated in an asylum. Suddenly, a stream of chronic cases were arriving from, instead of going to, workhouses. That year 237 were admitted to the asylum of whom only 44 were deemed curable and 33 of them died very quickly. Williams recorded that:

> During the whole course of his connection with asylums... he never remembers to have seen such a set of miserable, hopeless, helpless cases as comprise the admissions for 1874.[6]

The following year, admissions rose to a new record of 258, few of whom were considered curable. This meant that the out-of-county patients had to be

> *Medical Superintendent's Office – Memorandum –*
> *December 31st 1871*
>
> *A dense volume of black smoke was proceeding from the engine house this morning between 8 & 9 – I have often spoken of this. It is due to carelessness and is moreover a waste of fuel. My speaking seems of no use, so you will tell the stoker that I shall in future fine him 1/– each time it recurs.*
>
> *(Signed)   S. W. D. W.*
> *Medical Superintendent*

Two pages from the Medical Superintendent's Order Book

sent away again to make room for the county patients. And when overcrowded, the asylum itself had to send its own Sussex patients to other asylums, even as far away as Exeter. Victorian train travellers soon became used to the sight of large batches of pauper lunatics being herded on and off station platforms as they were shifted and swapped around the country. They were often the incurables and it is likely that their friends and relatives had little say in their fate. Williams tried to send some of these cases back to the workhouses but some, like Brighton, refused to admit them. Ironically, sixteen years later it would be the only one to admit chronic cases. In 1895, the asylum's Visiting Committee was still commenting on this traffic in lunacy:

> It is truly pathetic to see the distress of some patients who have to be removed to other Asylums; and conversely it is agreeable to witness the satisfaction they evince when brought back to this.[7]

By 1879, the existing population on the female wing had almost reached saturation point as there were now a record 437 female patients in the asylum. The Commissioners decided to sacrifice the principle that had so annoyed Robertson. They decided to allow a separate house to be built for the medical

Memorandum   19 April 1872

The chief nurse reports to me that in going round
this morning she found many of the nurses not out
of their bed rooms.   This cannot be allowed and in
future any nurse reported to me as being in her bedroom after 6 a.m. in summer 6·30 in winter
will be fined 1/-

                              Signed   S.W.D.W.
To The Nurses.   Medical Superintendent

Memorandum   23 April 1872

In January last I posted a notice stating that any
nurse found with her light burning, after 10·15 p.m. unless
for a good reason would be requested to resign her situation.
Notwithstanding this, you are reported as having up light
burning at 10·23 p.m. on 20th Inst.   You state that
this was an accident, and I am willing to believe you,
and so will not enforce my threat of requesting resignation, but as such accidents show carelessness, I fine
you 2/-

                              Signed S.W.D.W.
To Annie Rolset   Medical Superintendent

SUSSEX COUNTY LUNATIC ASYLUM.

Workmen's Wages for the Week ending *3rd August* 18*78*.

Name and Signature.	Employment.	Days.	Wages. s. d.	To what Account charged.								Remarks.
				County Rate. £ s. d.			Maintenance. £ s. d.			Farm and Garden. £ s. d.		
J Rice for G Kinnard	Farm Attt	1 m	£ 30							2 10 -		
I Wright	do	1 m	£ 26							2 3 4		left Aug 1st
W Gater	Cabinetmaker	6	9/4	1 12								
G Thomas	Cow Boy	6	1/6							9		
E Wright	Shoemaker	6	4/-				1 4					
George Goldsmith	Basket maker	6	4/-				1 4					
J Gentleman	Mat maker	6	4/4				1 6					
G Mitchell	Stockman	6	3/10							17		
C Bonyfull G Mitchell	Cow Man	6	3/10							17		
H Ralph	Bricklayer	6	5/2	1 11								
Ja Pilkington	Engineer	6	6/4	1 18								
Ayre	Painter	6	4/6	1 7								
M X Bothing	Labourer	6	3/4	1								
G Purvey	Office Boy	6	7/2				7					
J J Smith	Tailor	6	4/-				1 4					

Wages sheet from the Wages Register for 1878

superintendent who no longer had to live in the main asylum building. It was a decision made with a view to financial considerations. Instead of having to build yet another extension, the old superintendent's apartments could be converted into patient accommodation. In January 1880, Williams moved into the new house and 61 patients were placed in his old rooms.

As the overcrowding once again became a problem, Williams repeated Robertson's constant lament during his term of office: that many patients were sent to the asylum who were either incurable or sent in to die and that new cases were not admitted quickly enough thereby lessening their chances of recovery. Even the Visitor's Committee were becoming pessimistic. In their Annual Report for 1879, just twenty years after the asylum had opened, they declared that:

> The Committee are strongly of the opinion that our County Asylums are losing the character and the objects for which they were primarily intended viz. – : as places for the sanitary treatment and cure of insane persons and are becoming in a great degree mere receptacles for the chronic and imbecile patients who are detained within their precincts… this interferes with the due separation of the different forms of insanity so essential to the alleviation or the cure of brain disease.[8]

Moral treatment had finally become a casualty through overwhelming numbers and financial considerations and the asylum was becoming a place of custody rather than a place of cure. In 1881, the Visitors set up a sub-committee to look for a long term solution to overcrowding as another extension to the asylum was considered impractical. It concluded that, as Brighton had the most patients there – over 230 – it ought to build its own asylum. But the Brighton Guardians turned down the idea claiming that they had no funds for such a project.

ASYLUM NEWS

Williams had inherited a virtually full asylum from his predecessor and the large numbers made personal contact between staff and patients much more difficult. One gets an impression of patients being escorted here and there in large groups for different activities, prisoners rather than patients. In such a large congested institution, apathy was a problem. In April 1870, Thomas Crallan the chaplain, was complaining that the:

> patients are very listless and inattentive during the chapel service. Therefore in future the nurses and attendants are desired to sit more with the patients and not congregate at the bottom of the chapel… The nurses are also urged to persuade more patients to stand up during the service.[9]

Of course, the behaviour of the patients and the staff in the chapel could have been a reflection on the quality of Crallan's service!

Under Williams, entertainments increased as concerts, readings and fancy dress balls became more frequent. Train trips to Crystal Palace – started by Robertson – also continued and asylum cricket matches flourished. And in 1883, the asylum was spending £20 on books every six months and was providing for its residents: 18 daily newspapers, 50 weekly publications and 38 monthly ones. Gifts from local people also became common – parrots, pianos, a billiard table and food and fruit. The asylum's relationship with the local people throughout its history seems to have been a good one. In many ways – especially in the early years – the asylum *was* the community when one remembers that when it had opened the population of Haywards Heath had been little over 200.

Williams' policy of returning the harmless and chronic cases to the workhouses or to their homes led to the admission of the more violent insanity cases. This inevitably led to the employment of more staff to control them. By the end of Williams' term his staff had almost doubled to nearly 120. Like Robertson, he always had difficulty in replacing good personnel:

Sussex Lunatic Asylum.
Haywards Heath. Dec   1871

CHRISMAS ARRANGEMENTS.

CHRISTMAS DAY.

Workshops and Laundry closed, Patients not to go to work.

Divine Service at 11. a.m.

Patients Extra Dinner at 1. p.m.

Country walk in Afternoon.

Nurses attendants and Servants will meet in the

Class Room from 8 to 11 p.m.

The Porter will lock the divisional doors

punctually at 11 and ring the bell,

for all lights out at 11.15 p.m.

DECEMBER 26th

Entertainment in Recreation Hall at 7 p.m.

by the Asylum Christy Minstrels (See Programme)

DECEMBER 27th

Patients Christmas Ball

Dancing and Refreshments 7 p.m to 9.45 p.m.

JANUARY 2nd 1872   Ball for the Household

Christmas Arrangements for 1871

Every year it becomes increasingly difficult to replace such, and the questions where to find really respectable and efficient nurses and attendants appears yearly more troublesome to solve.[10]

According to Henry Hawkins, medical superintendents had a strong prejudice against taking into their service those who had been trained in other institutions. They didn't want staff to arrive with bad practices – something the 'Bruised Ribs' article above had accused the superintendents themselves of doing – and Williams preferred to train his asylum servants to become nurses and attendants. Only in the immediate aftermath of two wage increases in 1872 and 1876 was the exodus in staff briefly halted.

There remained a wide discrepancy in wages between male and female employees. In 1876, an ordinary male attendant started on £30 a year which could rise to a maximum of £40, whereas an ordinary female nurse started on £18 a year which could only rise to a maximum of £20. And each year a male attendant received one coat, one waistcoat, one cap and two pairs of trousers though they remained the property of the asylum. Whereas, nurses received three sets of uniform a year but had to pay 6d a week for them. Only their hats were freely provided. In 1884, Williams was recording that there were too many changes amongst the female staff and that only ten had long experience in asylum service.

As chronic cases were discharged they were increasingly replaced by epileptic and suicidal patients who needed a lot more supervision. In 1873, after the death of an epileptic patient during the night, the commissioners recommended that all suicide and epilepsy cases should be kept in one ward. Williams initially resisted this suggestion arguing that the lumping together of this group of patients could make their condition worse. But by 1878, they were placed in two wards and were supervised by four nurses during the night. The wards – consisted of 44 beds, six single rooms and one padded room – were so arranged that the nurses could see the occupant of each bed from every part of the ward.

Williams had a particular interest in epilepsy and experimented with treatments such as the nitrite of amy and bromide of potassium which were used to shorten and reduce the number of epileptic seizures. Like Robertson, he believed that these patients needed a specialist hospital with a lot more supervision but this facility was scarce. By 1874, there were as many as 78 epileptics at the asylum. So many in fact, that they enabled Thomas Crallan to make a three-year study of the influence of the moon and weather on the occurrence of fits and mental illness in general. He concluded that it was the change of weather, not the moon, which directly affected the epileptic patients:

> Any marked change of atmospheric pressure, solar radiation, or both, either in the same or contrary directions, is almost certain to be followed by increased number of fits among the epileptics, or by a development of mania or melancholia.[11]

Thomas Crallan's study also produced other interesting theories. He showed that admissions were much more numerous in the winter and summer than in Spring and Autumn. He attributed this to the winter struggle against poverty and the effects of high radiation in the summer. Crallan retired from the chaplaincy in 1884, aged 59. One of his achievements had been to start a savings bank for the staff.

Wet-packing continued to be used although it frequently came under attack from the Lunacy Commissioners who considered it restraint. Eventually, they insisted that Williams must record it as such. He complied even though he felt this was a misnomer. It was abandoned as a method of treatment after he resigned. The principle drugs used to sedate patients were digitalis, cannabis and morphia. If these failed, as a last resort, patients were placed in seclusion – a padded room – and the duration of their stay had to be officially recorded. Few patients received medical treatment for their mental disease and usually only received medication for physical ailments.

Inquests continued to be held on any patient who died under suspicious circumstances. In 1870, a male patient, Emery Clayton, was discovered to have died as a result of eating poisonous berries. In 1872, at an inquest on Charles Ernstring, it was revealed that he had eaten knotted shoe laces, fragments of a tobacco pipe and rusty nails although he had poisoned himself by other means. And another patient, John Butler, after his death, was found to have 57 pebbles lodged inside his intestines.

In 1877, a male patient hanged himself in the shrubbery. Although suicides were rare, this form of suicide became the most common. In 1884, a man hanged himself from a towel in the toilets and the following year another man suffered the same fate using a handkerchief. Escape attempts continued to be fairly frequent and staff were often fined for not being vigilant enough. After Ann Sharpe escaped during a walk in 1871, the nurses claimed that she had been enticed away by her friends but Williams did not believe them and fined five of them 1s. each. One persistent escapee was Hannah Hoad and special precautions were taken with her. She was not allowed to keep her day clothes at night; she was not allowed any money and had to wear very plain clothes well marked with the 'SLA' (Sussex Lunatic Asylum) insignia. Hoad eventually died at the asylum in January 1878.

Perhaps one of the most unusual escapees was Albert Jenner. In August 1885, he made a key out of a piece of brass and escaped during the night. Next day he was recaptured a few miles away. He tried again later that year on the night of 2nd December. This time he made a key out of an old brass button, tied it onto a piece of stick, and slipped away by opening the dormitory door. But it was a bitterly cold night and he was discovered the next day shivering in nearby bushes. He was in a pitiable condition: bruised, cut and bleeding all over and had only a shirt and blanket on him.

The decline of interest in the asylum on the part of the local newspapers continued during Williams' period of office. There are no more reports heralding asylum conditions or treatment and no more descriptive accounts of patient activity. And at the annual feasts – at Christmas and on 25th July – it was the staff dinners (and the local dignitaries who attended them) which received more publicity than the inmate dinners which were only given a cursory mention. Even inquests were rarely reported or even mentioned.

By 1886, the female side of the asylum was so full that Williams was instructed to admit female patients only as beds became vacant by discharges or deaths. In fact, he was forced to transfer 34 females to Camberwell House Asylum, London. And it is in these decisions that we see the often repeated cyclical nature of care for the mentally ill. One of the reasons why the asylum was built in the first place was so that the county would no longer have to send its pauper lunatics to London asylums.

Williams' health started to break down severely in June 1887. His condition was described by his doctors – Dr Lander Brunton and his former master, Dr Charles Lockhart Robertson:

> He is suffering from a severe form of nervous prostration from which results an entire inability to turn his mind to the duties of his office, or to carry out any systematic work. These symptoms are most painful, and are accompanied by frequent feelings of faintness and depression of the most alarming kind.[12]

Williams made several attempts to continue work but his breakdowns became increasingly severe. He resigned in December 1887, and did not work during his period of official notice which ended on 24th March 1888. His resignation letter speaks for itself:

> My work in this Asylum has been so entirely the one absorbing motive of my life, and I have so completely devoted what energy and talents I possess to its execution, that to have thus to separate myself from it is a matter of profound grief to me.

I grieve beyond words at the hard necessity which now compels me to sever a connection which I had fondly hoped would have lasted for many years to come. It is now no small trial to sign the letter which brings my life's work to an end.[13]

The Committee of Visitors thanked him for making money on non-county patients which had financed asylum alterations and additions – including a new Recreation Hall and a twenty-bed detached hospital – and for discharging patients to their homes or to workhouses thus sparing them the expense of building another asylum. Unfortunately, Williams' legacy would be that of a man who had "rendered highly valuable services to the ratepayers of the County of Sussex"[14] by the juggling around of patients for financial reasons rather than a legacy of humanitarian progress. And by discharging patients into home care and workhouses had he not divested the asylum of its traditional role of protecting patients from abuse. But, given the circumstances, how much choice did men like Williams have in the decisions that they made?

Although not as strict as Robertson, Williams did try to impose high standards on his staff. On 16th March 1886, he had even called on three nurses to resign for quarrelling and using bad language to one another in front of the patients. When he left the asylum it was still considered to be one of the best in the country and it had a lower maintenance rate – 8s. 3d. – than any other asylum in the south-east of England. It had its own fire brigade and even a post office which also served local people. And despite the overcrowding, almost all the patients were regularly escorted outside the asylum grounds.

By the time Williams resigned in 1888, the asylum contained almost 900 patients. Since its opening 6,000 had been admitted, over 2,000 had died and 1,800 had been discharged 'recovered'. The sheer size of the institution was making its control by one man an almost impossible job. Williams left the asylum a broken man but, without the exhaustive responsibility of the post, he went on to live to 75 years of age, dying in 1916.

1888-1904 TWO CHANGES OF OWNERSHIP

During Williams' sick leave, his assistant, Dr Walker, had been in charge for almost six months and had worked at the asylum since 1882. But the Visitors' Committee decided that the new medical superintendent must have the double qualification of having been to a British university and be a member of the Royal College of Physicians. This excluded most assistant medical officers working in public asylums and they were outraged when a local doctor, Charles Edward Saunders, with no direct asylum experience, was appointed. They protested publicly about this 'miscarriage of justice'. Saunders had never been in charge of any type of institution and had only been a licensed visitor to private madhouses. Sixty-four assistant medical officers signed a petition of protest which included a reference to possible favouritism from the Lord Chancellor's Medical Visitors Office, and which also demanded that questions be asked in the House of Commons. They sent the petition to the Medico-Psychological Association which was sympathetic but declined to support it and the protest fizzled out.

So why had the Visitors' chosen Saunders? Firstly, he was a well known local visitor to the asylum who, since at least 1870, had been participating in concerts and cricket matches there. Secondly, Robertson knew him well and perhaps the petition, which hinted at interference from the Lord Chancellor's office, saw his hand in the appointment. And thirdly, the Visitor's employed Saunders at a greatly reduced salary – £600 pa. as opposed to Williams' £1,000 pa. – and although the same thing had happened on Robertson's resignation, perhaps the scale of difference was much wider than might have been acceptable to other candidates for the job.

It was no easy task to follow Williams and the Visitors' Committee recorded that:

> A gloom pervaded the entire establishment for some days after Williams left.[15]

Saunders inherited an overcrowded asylum, full of increasingly difficult patients, with little hope of a diminution in the demand for places. Admissions continued apace – there were 288 in 1890 – a new record, as more elderly patients were received. The short term solution was to send patients to other asylums at Oxford, Northampton, Exeter and Salisbury. But this was costly and only reduced overcrowding temporarily. It also involved great hardship on both patients and their relatives. Many relatives lacked the means to visit distant asylums on a regular basis.

Although the asylum was described in 1891 as one of the best of the old asylums and the patients were looked after – weighing more on discharge than on admission – the overcrowding did lead to a deterioration in their quality of life. They often sat back to back in the dining halls, and whereas the guidelines suggested that there should be one toilet for every ten patients, there were in fact only two for every 75 and no separate ones for the staff. Escape attempts and suicide attempts increased and there were not enough staff to control the diffi-cult patients.

In 1890, there were 85 epileptic and 46 suicidal cases. These patients really needed round-the-clock supervision. Many of them were on male ward 6 and it was no coincidence that staff abuse was highest there. Saunders believed that epileptic patients found it extremely difficult to stay at the asylum between their fits. As more staff were re-allocated to supervise the dangerous inmates, activities with other patients suffered. Five years later, only 30% of patients were being taken out on walks outside the grounds, the majority's exercise being confined to the small courtyards. And only 28% were participating in entertainments. This lack of exercise led to a dramatic increase in lung disease – 27 patients dying of this in 1894 – and in bed sores, found on 7% of the dead in 1890. There was also an increase in breakages and in 1893, the chaplain lamented that the "loss and destruction of books on the male side is very great".[16]

Although restraint and seclusion were still very rare, there were other signs that the asylum was becoming merely a place of custody. In 1892, the Lunacy Commissioners complained about the meagre entries in the medical case books and recorded that the attendance at the chapel service had become extremely low. In fact, one chaplain resigned in 1890 after Saunders accused him of showing no interest in the asylum and his successor only lasted a year. The commissioners also received more complaints from the patients about rough usage at the hands of the male attendants, especially in male ward 6. And on female ward 6, they discovered too many women being placed in extra-strong but unattractive clothing.

A temporary solution to overcrowding was found when (through a parliamentary Act) the partnership between West and East Sussex was dissolved in 1892, requiring West Sussex to build its own asylum by December 1893. As the West opened its new asylum, Graylingwell at Chichester, the Haywards Heath institution was renamed the 'East Sussex County Lunatic Asylum". Despite 178 patients being transferred to Graylingwell; the asylum quickly filled up again and the Commissioners continued to complain about the poor staffing ratio – 1 male attendant per 12½ patients and 1 female nurse per 17 patients:

> It was sufficient for custody but inadequate for the proper treatment of the patients in the way of daily extended outdoor exercise, which so materially conduces to the recovery of the curable and to the amelioration of the condition of the chronic cases.[17]

Next year, Saunders was ill and had three months' leave. He had taken over amidst controversy over his appointment and had soon discovered one of the realities of asylum life. His desk diary recorded on 15th May, 1889 that:

> I was struck a violent blow on the nose by Joseph Friend, he being under the delusion that he was my crowned king.[18]

Saunders recorded very little about asylum events compared to his two predecessors and one gets the impression (perhaps unfairly) that he was a much less interesting character. When he returned from leave, he presented the mortuary with an ornamental window which he had designed himself.

It can not be understated how difficult it was to work as a nurse or attendant in a Victorian asylum. "Apart from the readiness to work for very low wages, the most desirable qualification was usually the strength needed to impose physical restraint".[19] That some of the staff over-stepped the boundaries of physical restraint was not surprising. But violent incidents had to be recorded whilst acts of kindness were not and this can give a distorted view of asylum life. On one occasion, a Nurse Gresswell even risked her life by jumping into the pond at the farm to rescue a patient, Emily Shepherd, who had tried to drown herself. The nurse was awarded £2. Saunders believed "harassing, unpleasant and even dangerous duties have to be performed by everyone".[20] In fact, in 1897 two nurses had mental breakdowns. Nurses had far harsher conditions than attendants. Their wages were lower and they had a higher proportion of patients to look after. And only by petitioning the Visitors' Committee in August 1889, were they able to obtain free uniforms, a right their male colleagues had always had.

The intake of more difficult patients did have two beneficial side-effects. Firstly, it made the Visitors (with some pressure from the Commissioners), employ more staff and in 1896, the asylum employed eight more. Secondly, it reinforced the necessity for some sort of nursing training. Dr Walker, Saunders' assistant, gave a series of lectures to the staff with the result that eight nurses and 13 attendants sat an exam in 1899 and gained the "Nursing Certificate of the Medico-Psychological Association". This qualification was a small step towards the recognition that asylum nursing could be more than just a casual, menial job. Two years later, the Visitors' Committee offered an extra £1 per year for those who obtained it. Training staff in asylums had been introduced fifteen years before and was an imitation of the system which had been adopted and practised in general hospitals for some time. The Commissioners had always attributed the poor quality of asylum staff to the poor wages on offer, but general nursing training had proved that gaining knowledge was, in some ways, a more important incentive.

At the Sussex Asylum, according to a petition signed by most of the staff and presented to the Visitors' in March 1901, working conditions were inferior to those in other asylums. The petition, which is reproduced in full below, complained about the pay, the long hours, the short holidays and the poor food ration. As a result, their leave was increased, their diet scale was improved and qualified nurses were given an extra £2 per year.

HAYWARDS HEATH SUSSEX

March 1901

GENTLEMEN,

The HUMBLE PETITION of the undersigned Sheweth that

First With regard to leave

At present we are allowed one day off duty in every thirteen days. Our hours on duty are from 6.30 a.m. to 8 p.m. and once per week and occasionally on Entertainment Nights from 6.30 a.m. to 9.30 p.m. In the Summer Months we are on duty fourteen hours daily viz from 6 a.m. to 8 p.m. It is not necessary for us to tell you of the monotony of our lives or of the gloomy surroundings in which we work. The majority of Asylums allow much more leave than we get, and our duties here are equally as trying and repulsive as theirs. We think it necessary both for our mental and physical health that we should have more relaxation. Gentlemen most earnestly we beg you to give this matter serious consideration with a view to increasing our present amount of leave.

Secondly Re our scale of pay

This to each and all of us is an all important subject. An Attendant on engagement commences at Twenty six pounds per Annum and rises One pound yearly to Thirty pounds. On promotion to the second grade he rises One pound yearly from Thirty pounds to Thirty six pounds and on becoming a Charge Attendant One pound yearly from Thirty six to Forty pounds. On reaching the maximum pay of his grade he does not then get an increase of Salary until he has Twenty years service in the Institution. And as to ration allowance whilst on sick leave — You kindly granted the Married Attendants One Shilling per day in lieu of their rations, which are stopped as soon as they fall ill, but unless they have been ill for seven days, or upwards, they have hitherto received no ration allowance. Gentlemen, as in our first item we would respectfully call your attention to the condition of other Asylums, their scale of pay rises far above ours, and especially amongst the Married Attendants here we can truly say that the wage is almost a starvation one. Coal and many other necessaries have gone up very much in price and House rent is really exorbitant. We feel confident that the matter needs but to be properly explained to you for you to allow the Married Attendants their sick pay, as soon as they fall sick, whether for broken periods or not. And to in some way alter our scale of pay, and so make our lot a correspondingly happier one.

Lastly. As to our diet..

This may seem somewhat a small matter, but we assure you, that to us it is equally as important as either of the foregoing. The cash value of this emolument is 10/6 per week per Man, and Gentlemen we get nothing for breakfast and tea, year in year out, but bread and butter, and a second course for Dinner only on Sundays, and for that a portion of our day's ration of Meat is forfeited, and we are not ashamed to own that we cannot afford to buy all the little extras that are necessary to complete our diet. When a Married Attendant is off duty his ration of Meat is drawn with the remainder of his Mess, and he does not receive it until he comes on duty the following day, when in very hot weather it would be useless to him after being carved from the Joint twenty four hours, and in any case he would not require two rations of Meat in one day. Gentlemen we beg that our whole dietary be raised from its present standard, to one that will enable us to execute in a still more satisfactory manner, our anxious and multifarious duties. And that Married Attendants may receive their ration of Meat uncooked on going off duty, so that they can have it for the day it is issued, and when it is of most value to them,

GENTLEMEN these facts are indisputable and we trust that you will see we are pleading a most righteous cause. We therefore most Humbly and very earnestly beg you to give them your very Kindest consideration and by granting us some alteration in the existing conditions you will guarantee to all of us a brighter, freer and better life than we are leading today, which is the full enjoyment of the produce of our labour. We have appointed a small but representative deputation of Attendants, and we shall be very thankful if you will receive them at your next Meeting, when they will explain these matters more fully than we can do in our Humble Petition.

We are Gentlemen

Your Obedient Servants.

S. Coles	G. Catchlove	F. Farr	I.H. McArdell
F.W. Rants	0. Peirce	I. Hollingdale	F. Check
W. Thomas	W. Pelling	P. Quinn	G. Russell
F.I. Ralph	S.W. Tomb	W. Tuttle	W. Gales
A.E. Hunt	0. Bells	E. Cottingham	H. Spray
R. Barton	H. Hollingdale	H.I. Pearce	S. Cloughton
F. Cook	I. Pattenden	A. Bristow	C. New
I.L. Bull	W. Mills	A. Frost	I.F. Hatley
A.H. Smith	0. Hudson	H. Kemp	F. Godden
F. Butler	S. Clements	F. Dean	H. Evans

As the asylum population grew to almost 1,000, temporary buildings for 100 persons had to be erected within the grounds as other asylums – over-crowded themselves – had no more room for Sussex patients. The Borough of Brighton again came under pressure from the Commissioners to build their own asylum. Meanwhile Saunders became seriously ill in 1899 and took three months' sick leave. The following year he was given another six months before eventually resigning due to ill-health on 27th July, 1900. Saunders died later that year. He had become pessimistic about the asylum's therapeutic value because of its great number of long term chronic cases. In January 1897, he had considered only eight males and 20 females out of 896 had a hope of recovery. And only just over 10% were receiving any medicine at all. He was succeeded by Dr Walker (who had worked at the asylum since 1882) at a reduced rate of £600 a year.

In 1900, the East Sussex Asylum contained 969 patients with another 93 placed in asylums in Essex, Exeter and Chichester. It had been forced to take on a third medical assistant to cope with such large numbers. And with the employment of extra nursing staff the maintenance rate had started, for the first time, to increase. The staff ratio now was 1:10 on the male side and 1:13 on the female side. By 1900, more than 9,000 patients had been admitted into the asylum; over 2,500 had been discharged 'recovered' and well-over 3,000 had died. The large number of deaths meant an extension of the cemetery had to be made in 1889 although many families still preferred to make their own interment arrangements.

In 1901 the daily allowance of beer for staff and patients was stopped. It was replaced by extra money for

A Victorian parlour setting for nurse A.M. Dumdell, probably staged on the occasion of her qualification in 1900

the staff and more cheese and jam for the patients. Walker recorded that the decision "caused but slight expressed discontent on the part of a few patients".[21] And in order to accommodate patients in the chapel for the Sunday service, seven or eight services had to be held.

In October 1900, Thomas Whale, an attendant accused a charge nurse of striking patients himself and ordering him to do so. And two years later, an assistant medical officer saw an attendant hitting an imbecile boy with a stick. An indication of the demanding nature of the assistant's job came in 1902 when there were only four applicants for the second officer's post. The vacancy of storekeeper the same year, received 182 applications. In June 1902, John Frazer, an ex-patient served Walker with a writ and claimed damages for wrongful reception, detention and improper treatment. Not surprisingly, his claim failed.

On 21st March, 1902, the numbers in the asylum exceeded 1,000 for the first time. But after many years of wrangling, Brighton and East Sussex had finally come to an agreement. Brighton would take control of the asylum on 1st September 1903, and East Sussex would move their patients to a new asylum being built at Hellingly near Eastbourne. As a result, the temporary buildings were closed and dismantled and several of the attendants and nurses received notice to leave as the population dramatically dropped. So, after 44 years, the asylum had its third major change of ownership and now became known as the Brighton County Borough Asylum.

Over a hundred patients were transferred from Haywards Heath to Hellingly in July even before Brighton officially took control of the asylum. Their ages ranged from nine to ninety-four and some claimed that they had only been informed about the transfer at the last minute. On their arrival at Hellingly all of them had their photographs taken and were given a medical examination and asked a series of simple questions: what the day was, what the date was, where did they think they were, and what they had done at the asylum. They were also tested on reading, writing and simple maths.

The photos reveal the patients dressed in their best clothes, with a look, for the most part, of bewilderment on their faces. Three had their hands tied behind their backs and in several instances staff hands could be seen holding the patients' head straight for the camera. Almost every male had a beard as razors had been banned at the asylum for some time.

The look of bewilderment was not surprising for many patients appeared not to know where they were or how far they were from Haywards Heath. Some thought they were near London. And weeks after her transfer one female patient was still referring to Haywards Heath as "here" instead of "there". During the medical examination and interviews at Hellingly (which by law for every new admission had to take place within seven days) the medical officers recorded notes. Below is a sample:

> Interviews with female patients from Haywards Heath on their arrival at Hellingly on 20th and 21st July and September 10th 1903.[23]
>
> 41 year old – chronic mania.
>
> Is restless. She sits or lies about with her hands to the side of her neck and the ball of her middle fingers stuffed into her ears. Seems quite awake but her position suggests auditory hallucinations. She blinks a good deal and looks away and is restless. She is quite intelligent when spoken to and answers shortly and rapidly and sharply with much facial movement. Her memory of past events is good but for recent is poor. Readily does what she is told.
>
> 51 year old – dementia
>
> Patient is dull and stupid in appearance but at times looks up though she otherwise takes little or no notice of anything. She does not know where she is or day or month but thinks it is a long way from H.H. Knows she was in the laundry at H.H. and did "dirty work" but has relatively little memory or is too dull and apathetic to exert herself to answer questions. She is clean and is no trouble. Does as she is told.
>
> 41 year old with acute mania
>
> Lies in bed and looks ill. Hands cold. Face expressionless. Last night was restless to 10 pm. Refused to eat and was rather spiteful and bad tempered. Took only fluid. This morning refused to be brought out of side room at first but then gave way. Seized hold of Dr. T's coat and was rather frantic. Tries to push me away from the bed. Does not answer questions but looks dull and confused. Asks for a drink as her mouth is dirty. Waves her arms about. – objects to a patient opposite "standing there grinning". Asks if my medicine is doing her good (forgetting her refusal to take it and spilling it) and asks if she can get home in a cab and seek husband.
>
> Then wants to know what I am writing and pushes at me and when I say "All right" says "Right" and tries to stop me writing and then says I am self-important. Surly-faced. If one coughs she mocks it and makes faces and then tends to stick her tongue out. She talks of going to heaven and begins to sing, "Holy, holy, holy, Lord God Almighty". Sings with a good contralto voice but gets stuck for words at times. Beats time and is quite in tune. Sings with good expression and modulates her voice well. Was wet at 8 pm yesterday. Fed at noon by nasal tube. Slept well afterwards and was not sick.

29 year old – mania

A pleasant-looking girl. Upper face quite blank and apparently she is a chronic case. To questions she laughs and says "Shan't tell you." Asked where she came from, says Eastbourne and laughs. Either doesn't know or won't say correctly in reply to every question or answers deliberately at random.

39 year old – chronic mania

A pleasant and intelligent woman. Knows where she is but not the day or date. Says she was in Haywards Heath and was then 16 years old. Worked in laundry last three years – seems to have been anxious to go home. Accuses Dr Walker of 'telling stories'. Quite rational, shows no sign at all of dementia. Denies ever being insane. Accuses her husband of infidelity, before she came to Haywards Heath. Another woman had a child of his and wanted to get rid of his wife for this reason and the law allowed it. One day they were all in a beer shop and – – asked her husband to make her a baby for six shillings and she heard her. Her husband denied the connection with her but she had a child nine months after so must have been his.

56 year old – dementia

Dull, miserable and despondent. Looks up when spoken to. Tends to sit up in bed but not restless. Puts out tongue when motioned but not when asked to. Is passive to what she is asked to do and only takes notice when touched, not when spoken to and has a most forlorn and hopeless way of behaving. Resists examination of her legs as if from sexual delusion. Most strongly resents examination of abdomen and holds her hands down and resists attempts to move them. After examination she gets depressed and weeps.

35 year old – mania

A vacant looking woman. She does not speak at first but only grins. I ask her her name and after a time she says 'Well, my name's, what it is, I don't know'. I ask her how old she is but she will not answer. After inspection she slaps her thighs and calls out 'He doesn't know his name'. She snatches at my coat with her hand and also snatches at my stethoscope. The nurse says 'Doctor's in a hurry, tell him your name'. She replies 'Doctor's in a hurry'. She looks at what I am writing, grins and points with her finger at it. Puts out her tongue at me and makes a face. Will not put out her tongue when asked to do so but immediately does so when I put mine out. Says I am her uncle.

51 year old – mania

Has rather a grandiose manner and tends to strike attitudes of a more or less devotional type. Lies curled up in bed and takes no notice of her surroundings till spoken to when she smiles … She insists that the year is 1998 or 1999 and denies it is so early as 1903. "She is going to be born again by God's almighty hands and wine". Asked whether she was married replied – "we do not find it necessary to answer that question".

65 year old – melancholia

A thin, vacant-looking woman who lies in her bed holding the sheet tightly round her neck. On an attempt at examination she swears, screams and spits at me.

Male Patients[24]

62 year old – chronic mania

'Shouts loudly and is deaf. Makes a whistling noise with his tongue as he speaks. Says his deafness is from a blow on the head with a shovel. Knows where he came from and where he is. "Strongly objects to the name Hellingly. Thinks Heavenly might tend to the good of the patients. The name is blasphemy. There is plenty of obscenity on the earth without making it by such a name. There is too much dancing etc. at music halls… Knows day and date without newspapers. He then attacked the press generally. …favouritism is given to some patients and not to others… Has hallucinations at night. His mother comes and talks to him at night. She weeps over him and he has found her tears on his cheeks. Gets very emotional over this.

32 year old – chronic mania

A dull looking man, knows where he came from. What is the name of this place? 'T'aint heaven, is it? I guess it's East Croydon'. Has been violent occasionally. Hears voices at night. Says he was sent to Haywards Heath because his mother nearly cut his head off. He sits playing with a thread and will not answer question.

46 year old draper – dementia

Bobs about in bed and talks at a great pace. What is your name? 'I am a gypsy or any bloody name you like'. Picks at his legs which are in consequence covered with sore places. Picks off the scabs and eats them. Asked where he came from he says 'My mother's womb'. I ask him his name again and he says 'I was Ishmael, now I am Ishi'. He roars with laughter and says 'That's damned you, hasn't it?'

37 year old art student – chronic mania

He speaks intelligently and in rather a superior manner. Knows where he came from and can read name of this place on his sheet. Already knew it was Eastbourne. Doesn't know day of week at first then works from Thursday and says Saturday (correct). Worked not very hard at Haywards Heath. Helped at ward work and scrubbing. They only gave him half an ounce of tobacco. Has no hallucinations. Can read and write and can draw very well. His father kept a school, he went there. Age is 37. Thinks there is a weakness in his left eye. Says when his left knee was bad he had visions of females marching in regiments. He only went with women 3-4 times.

57 year old – chronic melancholia

Knows where he is – what day it is. A lively-looking man, looks more than his age. Became very angry at being asked such childish questions. Refuses to answer and says "I've been all over the world and I'm not going to be asked such b_____ childish questions. Says he has "had quite enough humbugging about since he has been here". When I am examining him physically he suddenly turns round and says "You were born with a silver spoon in your mouth" "You never knew misery". He weeps and cries out "Not one eye not one left". Weeps for some time.

12 year old – idiocy

A mischievous little shrimp. Is sharp and takes notice of everything going on around. Points to my writing and laughs. Says he is 8 years old. Does as he is told. Calls me "Daddy". Starts singing "Dolly Gray". Plays with stethoscope. He does as he is told and can imitate simple actions. Cannot write and cannot count fingers. Is not wet and dirty and 'can make a shape' in dressing himself.

In contrast to the Sussex Asylum, the new asylum was electrically wired and, what was a progressive development, detached cottages were on site for convalescent patients. By October 1903, of the nearly 300 patients transferred to Hellingly, less than 30 would ever be discharged recovered. And eventually, 21 of those transferred would return to the asylum they had just left.

As the new century arrived, deep pessimism about the 'asylum solution' had replaced the optimism of 50 years previously. As the numbers of pauper lunatics headed towards the 100,000 mark nationally, there was still widespread bemusement over the causes of this rise. Perhaps though, the value of statistical data was put into perspective by the 1901 census conducted over the entire British Empire. It was discovered that India, with a far greater population than Britain, and with hardly any specialist treatment of the insane, had only a seventh of the number of insane cases as the mother country.[22]

Chapter Fourteen

1904-1930
HARD TIMES

With the dawning of the new century, the Brighton authorities had become the sole governors of the asylum. One wonders what Robertson and his old adversaries from Brighton – Thorncroft, Marchant and Woollett – would have made of this turn of events. Perhaps only the indefatigable Miss Buckle, the head attendant on the female side who had been at the asylum virtually since its opening, could have appreciated the significance of the change. But the new ownership did not make any impact on the trends that had been hindering asylum care and treatment for some time – overcrowding, staff abuses, the movement of patients for financial reasons, understaffing and the difficulty of attracting competent employees. In fact some of the trends worsened and there is evidence to suggest that the quality of life at the asylum deteriorated further.

The immediate consequence of Brighton taking over was a welcome but brief period of liberal space for the patients. The numbers dropped from 983 on 31st December, 1902, to 570 a year later, as East Sussex withdrew its patients and placed them in their new asylum at Hellingly. Correspondingly, the asylum's maintenance rate went up from 10s. to 12s. 6d. despite staff – ten attendants, eight nurses and three artisans – being laid off as the number of patients fell dramatically. But the asylum soon filled up again with the arrival of non-county patients, 60 from West Ham and 110 from Cardiff. This was a rapid reversal of the recent policy of sending patients from Sussex far afield. By 1906, there were 880 patients, more staff were employed, and the maintenance rate fell to 9s. 6d. It could not, though, have been a coincidence that during 1904, the year that the asylum had the most room for its patients, the death rate fell to its lowest point since its opening, only 5.9%.

Weeks before the changeover, Brighton's Workhouse Guardians had been reprimanded by the Lunacy Commission over the death of a female lunatic who had died minutes after her reception at the asylum from the workhouse. To save money, she had been transported in the horse-drawn ambulance with two other lunatics and the stress of the journey was thought to have contributed to her death. Consequently, the Guardians agreed to allow all acute cases to be transported separately. One of the Guardians, William Jarvis, also publicly criticized the Brighton Board's policy of hiring the cheapest conveyances for these trips. This inevitably led to the patients being given a severe jolting for almost $1\frac{1}{2}$ hours as the drivers attempted to do the journey in record times (in order to make a reasonable profit). Jarvis was overruled. Two months later, a male lunatic died during his transfer from the Brighton Workhouse to the asylum. At the inquest, the jury recommended that the Guardians should provide better facilities aboard their vans. Afterwards, rubber protective coverings were placed over some of the rougher edges of their internal compartments.

Under the governorship of the Borough of Brighton the asylum consistently received larger numbers of out-of-county patients. As already mentioned, they paid a higher maintenance rate than the home patients – those paid for by Sussex authorities – and were economically attractive. By the end of 1907, out of 895 patients as many as 266 were maintained by other counties. And when this number fell, they were replaced by an increasing number of private patients. But the Borough of Brighton was reluctant to increase staffing levels and even reduced the number of assistant medical officers from three to two. At times, the asylum was chronically short-staffed. For example, between 8 pm and 10 pm non-duty staff were allowed to leave the premises. This left only twelve staff to look after as many as 900 patients. An obviously insufficient number, especially with the high risk of fire.

By 1908, the fiftieth year of its existence, 11,095 patients had been admitted into the asylum:

> 3,935 patients had died there.
>
> 3,117 had been released 'recovered'.
>
> 1,421 had been released 'relieved'.
>
> 1,895 had been released 'not improved'
>
> 727 patients were still in the asylum.
>
> Total 11,095.[1]

The staff totalled 159, comprising 11 officer posts, 108 attendants and servants, and 40 artisans. The maintenance rate was 11s. and the asylum now had room for 916 patients.

Walker, like his three predecessors, took lengthy sick leave before retiring early in May 1910. He died a year later from a stroke at the age of 53. He had been a neat, methodical man but the asylum's order and quality of life may have suffered under his leadership. When he had been Dr Williams' assistant, all but a handful of patients were taking walks beyond the asylum walls. By the time he left, only 19% were. But in fairness, this probably had more to do with the increasing number of infirm and elderly patients than with his management. Nor could he do much about Brighton's policy of seeking non-county and private patients which made inmate numbers fluctuate dramatically, not helping the institution's stability. He was succeeded by Dr Charles Planck who had been an assistant medical officer at the asylum since 1894. In their report for 1910, the Lunacy Commissioners indicated how far the institution had slipped from being one of the best in the country:

> Dr Planck… will have no easy task to bring the asylum up to the standard of modern requirements.[2]

Complaints became common: about the quantity and quality of food (especially at breakfast); about rats being very numerous; about the shabbiness of the women's dresses; about noisy wards; and the lack of verandas for patients with pulmonary difficulties. And the year before, the Commissioners had even complained about an aspect of the asylum that had traditionally been one of its strong points: its bright interior surroundings:

> Some of the day rooms were dull and wanting in comfort and objects of various kinds to interest the patients.[3]

In 1911, they found that the attendance in chapel and at the weekly entertainments were below the national average and that an unsatisfactory percentage of male patients were employed. And despite an improvement in the staff/patient ratio – 1:11.6 on the female side; 1:8 on the male side – the commissioners admitted in 1910 that the asylum administration left a lot to be desired and had warned about the poor quality of nursing:

> We hope, however, that the necessity of behaving with the utmost kindness and forbearance to even the most irritating and trying patients will be strongly impressed upon the nurses, as some of the complaints which we received from the female patients seemed to indicate something wanting in that respect.[4]

But finding nurses was becoming a major problem. In the immediate pre-

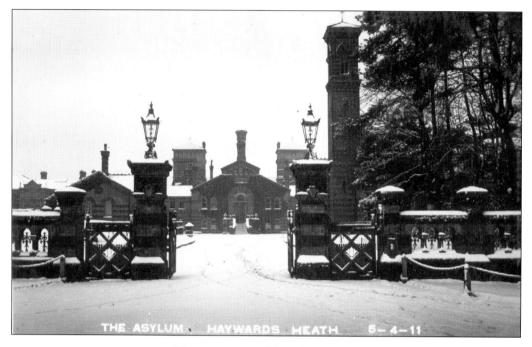

The main entrance of the asylum in 1911

war years, 30 nurses on average resigned each year. This figure did not include those who were dismissed or who absconded. On two occasions in 1913, three gave in their notice on the same day. By contrast few male attendants resigned. In fact, in 1913, 62% of them had more than 5 years service at the asylum in comparison with only 13% of female staff. As we have seen, the nurses had a significantly harder life at the asylum than their male counterparts. Their lower wages, their higher patient ratio, and their obligation to live in the main building (at least until the nurses' home was completed in 1914), all put a heavy strain on female staff, especially the laundry maids among whom there was a particularly high turnover. Now that male attendants were often being chosen for their sporting or musical abilities – posts for musical attendants were frequently advertised – and therefore could get added stimulation from the job, it made the drudgery of the female staff seem even starker. And this was often reflected in the behaviour of the patients under their care. On 13th June 1913, the Visitors' Committee found that:

> There was much noisy confusion in some of the wards on the female side, and generally much restlessness among the women… There were less complaints from the male side.[5]

In this period, the asylum admitted to using seclusion and mechanical restraint only on a few occasions. But the lunacy regulations were helpful in this respect. If patients were kept in single rooms with a split barn-type door, as long as the top half of the door was left open, it was not considered to be seclusion. Cases of fractured bones being caused by falls with staff were also recorded. In the immediate pre-war years, at least six of the nursing staff were sacked for striking patients. There were also complaints about staff not intervening when patients were being attacked by other inmates.

Although the staff/patient ratio had improved, less than 20% of patients were regularly walked outside the asylum grounds. The number of working patients still stayed above 60% but the nature of the work was predominantly menial. The majority of men now worked in the wards rather than on the farm and in the gardens and the majority of the working female patients were employed in sewing – as many as 200 in 1906. Learning trades such as basket-making, mat-making, book-binding and printing seems to have been discontinued. And when the commissioners visited the asylum in 1913 they found 64 inmates in bed. Moral treatment, with its emphasis on the individual within a stimulating environment, was a distant memory.

Even the release of patients on trial was reduced and few were given any money to help their rehabilitation. Occasionally, patients were still returned to the workhouse 'relieved' but nothing on the scale of Duckworth Williams' day. Suicides still occurred, but not that many considering the asylum's population was often 900. One particularly poignant case happened in August 1911. Fred Lewis (not his real name) was a railway worker, married with two children, living in Brighton. One day he had a serious scalding accident at work and spent the next six months at the Royal Sussex County hospital in Brighton. When he was allowed home he discovered that during his time away his wife had been flirting with other men. He divorced her and for the next two years reputedly always carried a razor blade in his pocket just in case he met her again. In 1909, Lewis eventually had a breakdown and was admitted into the Sussex Asylum. There, he apparently worked quite happily on the farm until 14th August 1911. That day he went to a water tank used by the cattle. Lewis, who was a tall man, climbed inside the tank and by kneeling down and stooping forward managed to drown himself in just two feet of water. The level of the water was only four inches above his head.

THE FIRST WORLD WAR

The lack of local newspaper coverage given to the asylum in the pre-war period gives credence to the belief that the late Victorians and their successors had tried to forget about asylums and that the subject of insanity became, even more, a taboo one. That there was even less media coverage in war-time is not surprising as newspapers were wholly focused on what was going on over the other side of the channel. News about the asylum was limited to the names and occupations of staff who were applying for exemption from military service. There was nothing about conditions or events at the asylum. In fact, the summer fetes were suspended till the end of the war. Even the arrival of military service (private) patients in 1917, who were paid for by the Ministry of Defence, was not given any publicity despite their being victims of war and rather conspicuous in their special uniforms of blue serge. They received pocket money of 2s. 6d. per week and were given a richer and more varied diet than the other inmates. By 1921, there were 21 of them at the asylum.

Most of the service patients were suffering from shellshock, a generic term used to describe soldiers who had mental breakdowns during the war. It is perhaps surprising that as there were at least 30,000 cases who ended up in institutions, more did not come to Sussex. In total, anything up to 200,000 service personnel were given the shellshock label. The success of psychoanalysis and psychotherapy – using many of Freud's ideas – in treating this disorder did encourage asylum doctors to look outside the medical model of insanity which saw its cause as a disease of the brain.

Conditions at the asylum seemed to have reached their nadir during the First World War and for the first time its patients actually lost weight after food restrictions were introduced in 1917. What local collections and donations there were, went to the general and military hospitals. And in 1915, the Visitors' Committee reported that only 51% of patients were usefully employed and that many, (especially females) were appealing to be discharged. Patients had little exercise and apparently spent hours walking round and round the small courtyards. At the best of times, asylums have rarely had a high social profile; during wartime, if the Sussex Asylum is anything to go by, they were forgotten. Symbolic of its neglect was the new practice of burying patients under the garden paths. This had to be done until the consecration of a further extension to the cemetery was completed.

The wartime reports of the Board of Control (which had replaced the Lunacy Commissioners in 1914) make pretty sorry reading. In 1916, the number of insane people under care in the country actually fell for the first time

since records had begun, from 140,000 to 137,000. And the numbers continued to fall for the duration of the war. The board believed this was due to the
exceptional conditions caused by the war. Firstly, admissions were limited to
only the most severe cases as some asylums were taken over for military purposes
thus creating a shortage of places. Secondly, male insanity decreased as a large
proportion of males were lost to the war. And thirdly, and probably most importantly, asylum populations fell as conditions deteriorated so much that death
rates soared to record levels – from 10% in 1914 to nearly 20% by the end of
the war. In 1918, the Sussex Asylum recorded 190 deaths, 20% of its total
number.

The Board of Control believed that the severe winter weather of 1916-17
allied with overcrowding and the unavoidable reduction in the quality and quantity of food supplied to the patients (especially flour) were the main reasons for
the high death rates and sickness. But they concluded that even if the diet had
been normal, the conditions in asylums were still too harsh. There had been a
large increase in tuberculosis and dysentery, illnesses which reflected the lower
standard of hygiene in asylums. And yet, paradoxically, for a short period the
First World War and its psychiatric casualties did focus public attention on the
quality of life of asylum inmates and, in the long run, was responsible for many
of the advances in their treatment and care. The new attitudes were reflected in
the gradual phrasing out of the word asylum. Indeed in 1919, the Brighton
Borough Asylum was renamed The Brighton County Borough Mental Hospital.
In the year after the war ended, the numbers in asylums rose slightly and continued to rise annually for many years. Deaths fell during this year from 18,330 in
1918, to 11,317 in 1919 and did not go up significantly until the Second World
War.

By January 1915, the asylum had lost 31 men to military service. Soon the
only men working there were either over military age or medically unfit for
action. But, the real nursing shortage during the war continued to be on the
female side with their number of resignations rising to as many as 42 in 1916
alone. Local women could find much better conditions working in some of the
traditional male jobs now open to them due to the chronic shortage of male
manpower. At Haywards Heath, for example, women were employed at the
railway station and the post office. Consequently, the local newspaper based in
that area, the *Mid-Sussex Times*, frequently printed the following advertisement:
'Asylum Nurses Wanted Immediately', in which one-month trials were offered.

During the war there were more signs of discontent amongst the staff
about their conditions: an increase of resignations (not just on the female side);

Miss Ruby Cheffins, a nurse at the asylum shortly after the First World War.

refusals to do certain duties; and sudden abscondings. By August 1918, all of the staff, apart from the officers, were members of the National Asylum Workers' Union – which had been formed in 1911 and which had its own magazine *The Asylum Record* – and during the war they held several meetings at the asylum. The union had a national membership of 10,000 and should be seen as part of the general working class movement for reform. It did manage to improve working conditions. By the end of the war, the asylum had adopted its recommendation of allowing staff 2½ days holiday a week and four weeks' annual holiday. They now worked a 60-hour week including meal breaks, which was the average working time in that period, but their wages were still low considering the unattractive nature of the job. In particular, the female staff on the whole were paid 20% less than their male counterparts.

General unrest amongst asylum staff nationally peaked in 1919 when 41 union members, without warning, went on strike at the Exeter Asylum. It did not last long as it was easy for the authorities to find replacements out of the mass of unemployed ex-military personnel.

In the autumn of 1918, the asylum was hit by the notorious influenza epidemic which was sweeping Europe. With no vaccine available, there was little to stop it. At the asylum, 28 patients and two staff died and 180 patients were affected. At one time, it caused half the male staff to be off sick. The following year a second but less virulent wave of influenza hit the asylum. This time 11 patients died. Allied to wartime food shortages, these attacks must have left the asylum in a pretty miserable state. And again, it was seriously overcrowded with well over a thousand patients. The cramped conditions were most apparent in the winter evenings and on wet days when patients were confined indoors.

Although the overall number of patients in asylums had fallen during the war; at the Sussex Asylum they had increased. In 1915, it had received patients from Graylingwell (the West Sussex Asylum) which was taken over by the War Office, and from the Eastbourne and Brighton workhouses which had been temporarily converted into military hospitals. And in 1918, 207 patients arrived from the Portsmouth Asylum which was now being used by the American Red Cross. By 1918, the asylum contained 1,021 patients – 395 males and 626 females – over 200 more than at the outbreak of war. But after the war, the numbers fell again and conditions began to improve. Three of the asylum staff were killed whilst away on military duty but one of its officers, Dr Harper-Smith, Planck's assistant, returned unscathed after having served at Gallipoli.

Pulmonary diseases such as tuberculosis increased during the war and as there were still no verandas, some patients – enough staff permitting – were placed on mattresses on the lawns during the sunny weather. By 1918, the number of patients permanently in bed had risen to well over a hundred. The majority of them were old and infirm women. And the following year Robertson's old Roman (Turkish) bath was converted into a disinfector for the

The staff in 1919, the oldest group photograph known to be in existence.
The male attendants are in the peaked caps.

asylum's mounting bed linen. The maintenance rate had also shot up to 25s., one of the highest weekly charges in the country – another stark contrast to the days of Robertson and Williams.

THE POST-WAR PERIOD

The 1920s started on a symbolically positive note with the repair of the asylum clock (installed in 1858 by a London firm) which had not worked for many years. But staff morale remained low. In 1920, one nurse was forced to resign for mistreating a patient and five other nurses absconded. As a result, the medical superintendent insisted that staff going on annual leave must leave their address behind before departing. And in January 1922, Planck recorded in his monthly report to the Visitors that:

> I regret to report that no less than 19 of the nurse probationers who are eligible to enter for the Preliminary Examination of the Medico-Psychological Association in May, have refused to attend lectures or sit for the exam, although one of the conditions of their engagement is that they obtained the Nursing Certificate within four years of joining the institution.

From August 1922, asylum workers in rural areas in England and Wales received a wage cut of 3s. per week and the hours of the nursing staff were raised from 60 to 66. Three years later, one of the main organisers of the National Asylum Workers' Union, the Reverend Stanley Morgan, addressed the asylum's workers and urged them "to make the people outside understand the miserable atmosphere of life in mental hospitals".[6] (See Appendix 2 for an account of what it was like for a young girl from Wales starting work at the asylum in 1924).

In October 1922, Mr Wellman, a Brighton Guardian and a member of the asylum's management committee, paid an unofficial visit and was horrified by what he saw. No repairs or decorations had been done to the buildings since before the war and living conditions were poor:

> In urging the importance of a woman being appointed to the Committee of Management, Mr Wellman said that he found that when the inmates had apple tart for dinner they had nothing else, and he thought they should be supplied with meat, either for breakfast or tea on such days. Sometimes, he said, they had only soup for dinner. With regard to the clothing of the inmates, he said the material was good, but the patterns were absolutely antediluvian. "Just fancy", he said, "a nightshirt only down to your hips, and puckered round the neck so that when you bend down it will make a mark". The nurses' sleeping rooms were a disgrace, and he urged that the Town Council should be approached in regard to these matters.[7]

Although some of the other Guardians congratulated him on having the courage to bring these matters out in the open, an official enquiry the following month declared that his allegations were groundless. The diet was undoubtedly inadequate – one patient who escaped that year was recaptured in nearby fields eating cabbages, and eight patients had actually signed a petition requesting better food. Official visits by the management committee from Brighton tended to ignore the complaints made about asylum life although they admitted in 1924 that the public were sceptical about its advantages. Interestingly enough, Brighton Management Committees' day trips to the asylum in the 1920s (as in the 1860s) were still regarded by some as wasting ratepayers money on extravagant meals in the countryside. On the Mayor of Brighton's visit there in September 1924, one of the Guardians pointed out that the visits were "no picnic" and that they took place on Saturdays, when people were usually enjoying leisure activities.

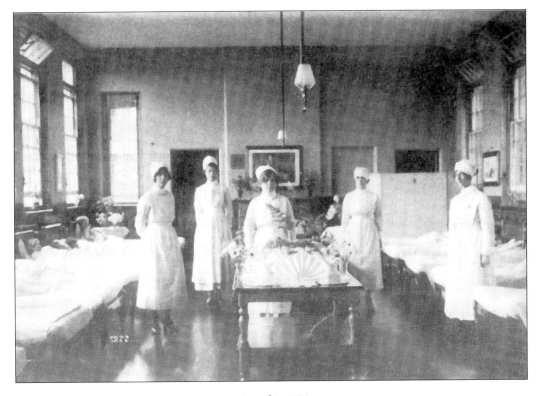

A ward in 1922

In August 1923, Charles Planck, the medical superintendent finally retired after years of ill health. He had been in charge of the asylum during one of its

The cricket team, 1925

most difficult periods. One of his staff paid tribute to him in a letter to the *Mid-Sussex Times,* dated 24/8/1923. It spoke of his "nearly thirty years of strenuous and devoted service":

> His devotion to duty was his greatest asset, but, alas, his greatest failure. He practically broke down in harness, stricken with a painful malady. Between you and me the patients loved him, the staff adored him. He was a friend to the oppressed and a foe to the oppressor. As an administrator in a disciplinary way he was always firm, but for ever just. Any person appearing before him with biased opinions he could read like a book. His sole ambition throughout his life was his scrupulous fairness to all.

He lived on in poor health until 1935, dying at the age of 78. In his obituaries the unmarried Charles Planck was described as a man of wide culture and attainments. He had been a keen rose grower, chess player, book collector and reputedly possessed a rich bass voice. He was succeeded by his assistant, George

Harper-Smith, who had specialised in neurology.

Harper-Smith and his wife threw themselves into improving the social life of the asylum. They increased the number of events and encouraged the organisation of fancy dress balls, non-stop dancing competitions and money raising fetes for the Patients' Amusement Fund. These included many 'Sales in the Park' where most of the objects were made by the patients, donated by relatives and friends or local shopkeepers. Unlike the other major hospitals in the area (including hospitals in Brighton), the asylum did not benefit from the Mid-Sussex Bank Holiday Hospitals' Fetes which took place in Haywards Heath.

The 1920s saw some technical advances. The arrival of electricity, central heating, radio and a cinema all helped to brighten the lives of patients and staff alike. During the Radio Evenings – held in the Recreation Hall – female patients often repaired staff clothing while they listened to a broadcast. It is doubtful whether they were officially rewarded for this work. More significantly, a tutor was hired to instruct the nurses and a dressmaker arrived to supervise the dressmaking and make the clothes less institutional. The diet was improved and a part-time dentist was employed for the first time. He found the patients in a very poor condition with most of them suffering from shrinking gums and loose teeth. In one year alone he saw 442 patients and extracted 821 teeth.

The nature of patient escapes changed during the decade. With the advent of the motor car (and the end of the compulsion to wear only asylum clothing in October 1923) it was not unknown for patients to hitch lifts to Brighton and other places thereby making a quick getaway. On the other hand, with the wide availability of the telephone, the local police were soon notified and the patients usually recaptured within hours. They were often discovered at their family homes or at the Brighton Races or on one of Brighton's two piers. One remarkable attempt was made by Olive Burgess in May 1921. She managed to escape through a window pane measuring only nine inches by eleven and then climbed over several trees. She was recaptured two hours later. One of the least

The main asylum kitchen early in the century.

247

successful escape attempts was made by John James in 1926:

> From the patient's statements, it is evident that after climbing the fence,
> he walked off in a westerly direction intending to reach Brighton, but as
> he kept turning to the left, he completed a circle, arriving back almost at
> the place where he got over the fence. He has sustained no injury.[8]

In terms of staff recruitment, the 1920s saw an even greater emphasis on
the sporting and musical ability of the male nurses. It became a fundamental
qualification as the asylum staff cricket and football teams built up strong reputations and the band gave frequent concerts. For male staff, being part of a team
could mean working fewer hours. If they were involved in a home match they
were expected to be back on duty within an hour of its finish; but if the match
was away they were not expected to return to their shift at all. The staff sportsman were undoubtedly privileged and their colleagues who did not play hardly
ever had a Saturday off.

In contrast to the days of Robertson, fewer patients seemed to play sport.
Indeed, Planck had banned the formation of a patient football team and had
only reluctantly allowed the staff to play a game which he considered to be
"unsuitable for a mental hospital". But patients often accompanied staff teams
to their away matches and in 1926 Harper-Smith recorded that football, cricket
and stoolball matches had been played by them. Stoolball, an old game resem-
bling cricket, was the only sport female patients were allowed to participate in.

Few patients were now involved in the band although it was still open to
them as this extract from 1920 proves:

> The Band shall be composed of such Male Nurses and Patients as have a
> knowledge of Music. Every Artisan, Nurse, and Servant, is required, if
> able, to take part in the band. This qualification has always been taken
> into consideration, and the Visitors consider themselves entitled to use
> this gift, when and how it may best benefit the Patients.[9]

The local branch of the National Asylum Workers' Union became increasingly active during the 1920s and their meetings were given wide coverage in the
local newspaper at least until the end of 1927. In February 1921, they managed
to persuade the management committee to allow, for the first time, the 'indoor'
staff to use the Recreation Hall for whist drives and dances. This was of particular benefit to the female staff who had little or no recreational facilities. The
Union also helped set up a Social and Sports Club in 1924 and organised
numerous activities to raise money for the patients and the staff football club.
Unsurprisingly, it campaigned to shorten the working week and to increase
wages. But it was not in favour of female nurses being employed on male wards.

Nurses on the main entrance stairs in 1925.

The asylum's Union members do not appear to have taken part in the General Strike in May 1926. An asylum spokesman declared at the time that:

> apart from the fact that we are receiving no parcels or the ordinary news-papers the strike is making but little difference to us. Even relatives and friends are still coming. News is broadcast from a loud speaker in the Recreation Hall. Later it is posted in various places.[10]

This was a period which saw a great improvement in the training of nurses. At the asylum in 1926, even if nurses survived the six month probationary period, they remained a probationer until passing the Preliminary Examination of the Medico-Psychological Association after which they became Senior Probationers. Only after passing the Final Examination did they become staff nurses. All nurses had to pay their own examination fees. And in 1921, despite Union objections, for the first time female nurses started to work on male wards. By 1927, there were 230 staff (of whom 144 were nursing) looking after about 880 patients, almost double the ratio of the late Victorian period.

Conditions for the patients remained harsh. In 1926 it was recorded that clothing in male ward 6 was being eaten by rats. The diet was still thought to be inferior to other mental hospitals and treatment facilities were limited or non-existent. Patients requiring malarial inoculation as a treatment for syphilis were temporarily transferred to Hellingly where there was a special room for this

The asylum fire brigade in 1925. (formed in 1911).
The Medical Superintendent, George Harper-Smith, is seated in the centre of the front row.

purpose. And the asylum still had no admissions hospital where new patients could be treated separately from the long-stay cases. Harper-Smith believed that such a hospital would help break down the prejudices that existed against coming to a mental institution. In 1929, he did introduce artificial sunlight treatment which he found to be beneficial to patients during their recovery.

Perhaps the most significant change in the decade was the expansion of treatment before and after admission. The huge number of shellshock cases had caused a boom in out-patient services which had had to deal with as many as 100,000 patients in 1922. This, in turn, focused attention on the importance of quick treatment and also the necessity for an effective after-care service. In 1923, a critical report appeared in the asylum's Visitors' Book about the lack of patients on trial[11] – nine – only two of whom received any financial assistance; about the need for an after-care branch in Brighton; about the need for a properly equipped admissions hospital, and a laboratory pathologist. It added that:

> There are certain other deficiencies for giving treatment in accordance with the demands of modern medicine. For example, the meagre supply of surgical instruments at the hospital.[12]

Some of these deficiencies were rectified by the end of the decade. In 1926, three social workers were employed at the asylum and a local branch of the Mental After-Care Association was set up in Brighton. The following year, Harper-Smith attended an out-patients clinic in Brighton and a nurse was employed to visit patients in their homes. The emphasis of care was gradually moving towards the prevention of asylum admission and to the welfare of patients once they had been discharged, as envisaged by Robertson and Hawkins. But a visiting pathologist was not appointed until 1935 and a proper admissions hospital was not in use until 1957.

The first signs of an open-door principle appeared in this decade. In 1924, a system of parole and full parole was introduced. Parole patients could wander around the grounds and full parole patients were able to go outside the asylum

A patient in apparent despair, although he may simply have been warming his hands.

estate. In 1928, 54 males were given parole, while 16 male and 24 female patients were given full parole. That year, one ward on the female side and one ward on the male side were unlocked and patients were allowed to enter and

Medico-Psychological Association
of
Great Britain and Ireland.

 This is to Certify that

William Gladstone Harris

having been duly trained at

Spigston

according to the Regulations of the Association has shewn in examination Proficiency in Mental Nursing

Signed _Frederick W. Neall_   President.

G. H. Harper Smith   Examining Superintendent.

David F. Rambant   Registrar.

Dated _May 1935_

Nº _19129_

leave them freely. By the end of the decade there had only been one case of abuse of this new freedom. But at the same time as this liberalisation was occurring, more patients were being confined to bed – almost 150 by 1930 – and out of 872 patients, only 3 were out on trial. The asylum was still seriously over-crowded and that year there were 145 out-of-county patients and 84 private patients in residence. Admitting private patients was increasingly profitable and so when the nearby Beechmont Estate was acquired by the asylum in 1929 to build an admissions hospital, the existing house was converted for the use of private patients only.

The policy of trying to attract out-of-county and private patients to the asylum had been much more pronounced since the Borough of Brighton had become its sole owner. It meant that the asylum was permanently overcrowded but for financial reasons, as one of the Brighton Guardians admitted, "it would be foolish to turn the private patients out". The overcrowding obviously affected the quality of care, and incidences of staff cruelty to patients appeared to be as high as ever and dismissals were common. However, this was only one side of the story. One elderly woman who I recently spoke to, remembered going to the asylum as a young girl in the 1920s. She had to meet a girlfriend who worked there as a nurse. This friend asked her to come with her while she went to check on one of 'her' patients. They eventually arrived at a padded cell where there lay a middle-aged woman. On seeing her, the nurse smothered the patient with kisses and cuddles. And one man who worked at the asylum in the 1930s told me that the ward sisters then really doted on 'their' patients and he remembered one bringing in her own best china and cutlery whenever anybody on her ward had a birthday.

But for all the good intentions of benign asylum doctors and kind staff, asylums could still be dominated by an unkind minority who ruled their patients through fear. According to ex-asylum staff, this was still happening on some wards in the 1950s.

Generally, the decade ended on a much more positive note than it had begun, with many new developments. Now, practically the whole staff were trained or were on courses. Their accommodation was improved by the building of 16 staff cottages for married nursing staff. On the wards themselves, Harper-Smith's wife started a system where 'godmothers' were appointed to each ward. They were local women who volunteered to help with patient problems on a

Opposite page: Mental Nurse Certificate, 1925.

253

weekly basis, perhaps writing a letter on their behalf or helping them to keep in touch with relatives. The system was instigated in an attempt "to get rid of that feeling of repulsion",[13] a common attitude among the general public. Mrs Harper-Smith was also very active in organising jumble sales, whist drives and communal singing in order to raise funds for the asylum. Social activities, such as dances, concerts, charabanc rides and theatre visits seemed to increase during the 1920s, although the staff rather than the patients were the principal participants.

So, as the next decade began, there were grounds for believing that asylum life was improving even if 'life' was beginning to literally mean life for many patients. (In 1926, Harper-Smith had claimed that were a large number of very old people living in the hospital). One female admitted in 1861 at the age of twenty-two, died there in 1924 aged 85. She had spent $62\frac{1}{2}$ years in the asylum and had lived under all six of its medical superintendents. An over-zealous council official in Brighton calculated that she had cost the town's ratepayers £1,200.

Chapter Fifteen

1930-95
INTEGRATION INTO THE COMMUNITY

The Mental Health Treatment Act of 1930 (which came into effect on 1st January 1931) aimed to enable patients to be assessed and to receive treatment in the early stages of their illness without the need for certification and compulsory admission into an asylum. Psychiatric units in general hospitals and out-patient clinics were set up for this purpose. But if this early treatment failed, patients could then be admitted to a mental institution on a voluntary, temporary or certified basis.

A 'voluntary' patient was required to make a written application to the institution's medical superintendent accompanied by a medical recommendation. The patient could leave only after giving 72 hours written notice or within the 28 day period allowed. A 'temporary' patient was one who was unable to express their willingness to enter as a voluntary patient. They could do so only with a medical recommendation signed by two GPs and an application from the family. Their treatment was limited to six months which could be extended to a year after which they were certified. The 1930 Act, by abolishing certification for all, hoped to eradicate mass long term asylum confinement.

As we have seen, Harper-Smith was already holding out-patient clinics in Brighton (at 8 Grand Parade and at the Royal Sussex County Hospital) before the Act came into force. These appeared to have been very successful. In 1933, only 24 out of 661 patients attending them were eventually certified. But the asylum's lack of an admission hospital meant that voluntary and certified patients, once admitted, had to be treated in the same wards. Perhaps, for this reason, the institution was initially slow to use the Act.[1] Nevertheless, by 1937, fifty-five percent of its direct admissions were voluntary. On the other hand, few temporary patients were admitted. Harper-Smith believed that this was a category which was little understood.

The asylum eventually opened its own admission villa in May 1938. It was called Hurstwood Park Hospital and was deliberately constructed on a single level so as not to obstruct the view of the private patients living nearby in Beechmont House. It was intended as a reception centre for the treatment of newly admitted (mainly voluntary) patients considered to have a good prospect of recovery. Containing 50 beds, it included a fully equipped laboratory set up to investigate suspected causes of mental illness. William McCartan, who succeeded Harper-Smith in 1938, was a great believer in neuro-psychiatry and hoped to use some of the hospital for experimental operations. Unfortunately, war broke out the year after its opening and it was used as an emergency neuro-surgical unit for the duration of the conflict. Yet again, the asylum was without an admissions hospital and, in fact, Hurstwood Park was never used for that purpose again.

Another serious problem was the asylum's lack of verandas. In relation to this, the Board of Control had recorded in 1931 that:

> we note that the ratio both of incidence and mortality from TB are high in this hospital compared with the corresponding rates for all mental hospitals; 10.4 per 1,000 here whereas 8. 0 per 1,000 for all other mental hospitals.[2]

The death rate at the Sussex Asylum was also higher than average for much of the decade. For example, in 1934 it was 11.2% whereas nationally it was only 7%. Harper-Smith attributed this to the lack of facilities and the overcrowding. Verandas were eventually constructed on the main asylum building before the Second World War.

In the 1930s, half a dozen of the nursing staff were sent to art school in Brighton to learn about basketry, hand crafts and book binding in order to instruct patients. A full-time female occupational therapist was also appointed and by 1937 Harper-Smith was claiming that every patient had a chance of learning a trade. That year 290 male patients (and 108 females) were engaged in arts and crafts daily and even the 60 male patients in bed were knitting scarves or making envelopes.

Harper-Smith had already been overseas to study asylums and their work facilities. In 1933, he had visited Sautpoort in Holland which contained 1,517 patients. He had been very impressed to learn that 98% of them were employed in some trade; less so when he learnt that those who refused to work were kept isolated in dark rooms on a restricted diet until they agreed to do so. In the same

Staff Dance, February 1938.

year, only 42% of the asylum's patients were working but over half of these were employed on the wards. Sautpoort did have ten assistant medical officers compared to the asylum's two which gave them a ratio of 1:150 patients to the latter's 1:450.

Patient work was obviously important to Harper-Smith as he reduced the visiting times for relatives from all day Wednesdays to just the afternoon in 1934 because he felt the morning visits disrupted work too much. But he was also keen on patient rehabilitation and advised the setting up of group boarding homes where patients could be looked after by 'guardians'. He believed that this was a better alternative than simply returning them to their relatives. This idea is very much in practice today involving some patients with mental health problems living in the community in small staff-run group homes.

Harper-Smith resigned in January 1938 after 33½ years service in mental hospitals. He was the asylum's first superintendent since Robertson not to retire through ill health. He had re-invigorated the social life of the asylum, encouraging a vast range of events. The Christmas celebrations alone lasted from almost the beginning of December to the middle of January, including what the local paper described as "the largest New Year Party in Mid-Sussex". Many patients were given the customary Home Leave over Christmas but those who remained were not neglected. On Christmas morning, patients awoke to find an array of presents from friends, relatives, godmothers and local people. And the more than a hundred male patients who had served in the First World War each received a card and cigarettes from the Ex-Service Welfare Society. In the afternoon, between 500 and 600 local people regularly came to the asylum just to look at the decorations. Staff, too often brought their families in to spend the day with the patients. Visitors, then, were not allowed on Christmas day.

In 1932, Harper-Smith had managed to persuade the Mayor of Brighton, for the first time, to attend a Patient's Fancy Dress Dance. Apart from some male nurses dressed up as female nurses, two hundred out of the 340 patients present were in costume:

> To give anything but a vague description of the characters portrayed or the ingenuity of the patients in disguising themselves would be impossible but it was noticed that the women for the most part chose bright colours, while a large number of the men were resplendent in uniforms and deported themselves in true soldierly style. There were English, French and German soldiers, a Beefeater, a fireman, a footballer, two dudes complete with top hats, morning coats and walking sticks, a realistic Chinaman, many male and female French clowns with pointed hats, ballet girls, Victorian ladies, "Buy British" and other advertising costumes, while one male patient, who represented a flower girl, bore the label "Back to Eros". The most prominent of all, perhaps, was a male patient who represented Gandhi. With his practically bald head, his spectacles and his white robes he was almost Gandhi's double. A huge block of salt gave a finishing touch to this impersonation.[3]

The 'finishing touch' represented Gandhi's opposition to the salt tax imposed on the Indian people by the British Empire. These social occasions often gave patients a temporary if small taste of freedom. The *Mid-Sussex Times* rather paternally described the fetes as:

> … an opportunity to "make whoopee". Patients can roam about the sports field in which the fete is held – at random, take part in races, competitions and games arranged for their amusement, don paper hats and make noises with carnival novelties to their heart's content. They are also permitted to mingle with friends.[4]

Reputedly, Harper-Smith never missed an asylum football match, home or away. He left an asylum which was undoubtedly still a very grim place for the inmates with little treatment but at least its unremitting monotony was alleviated by social occasions which everybody seemed to look forward to. He was succeeded by 38-year-old William McCartan, an austere Ulsterman who arrived from the deputy post at the Banstead Asylum in Surrey. He was keen on neuro-psychiatry and had also been to Switzerland and Germany to study insulin and shock therapy treatment. McCartan has been described as autocratic and a martinet and was the last superintendent to have control of the nursing staff before the post of nursing officer was introduced in the late 1950s.

During the 1930s more wards were unlocked and at the 'wireless' concerts selected female and male patients were, for the first time, allowed to mix freely. On the female side, The Nondescript Club (run by an ex-patient) organized meetings for debates and talks from outside speakers. They were held in winter and were attended by 40 to 50 patients. Godmothers also entertained female patients in their own homes. And physical training was organized for both sexes. The following timetable appeared in the medical superintendent's order book for 5th May, 1938:[5]

PHYSICAL TRAINING (except Sundays)

7 – 7.30 am (optional classes) daily. In ward gardens if fine; Recreation Hall if wet.

2.15 – 3 pm In ward gardens, unless bad weather.

6 – 6.30 pm (optional classes) – In ward gardens, daily in summer. In the Recreation Hall, twice weekly in winter. Patients to wear slips/shorts and to have a shower bath afterwards.

But conditions in the asylum in the 1930s were still difficult for both staff and patients. In 1931, those of the nursing staff who earned between £150 and £200 per annum had their wages reduced by 2½% as part of the government's anti-recession policy. And according to staff reminiscences, (later recorded in the *Hospital News* magazine), they were still obliged to work 13 hour shifts from 7 am in the morning to 7.45 pm in the evening. Both medical superintendents lamented the poor standard of nurses due to their extremely low pay. It also became harder to attract local people and most of the nursing staff now came from those parts of the country most hit by the economic depression: Wales, Scotland and the North of England. By the end of the decade, patient numbers were just below the 1,000 mark with only

A patient buffing the floor before the Second World War

The south face of the hospital from the air.

three medical officers and an overworked staff to look after them.

The asylum still contained many 'mental defectives' (mentally handicapped) and the presence of children was not uncommon. By 1938, over 14% of male and 18% of female patients were permanently in bed. Accidental falls and injuries due to violence were still high, particularly on the more overcrowded female wards. These were often full of the old and infirm, a group particularly vulnerable to abuse. Staff themselves sometimes reported their own colleagues for mistreating patients. On 15th March 1933:

> Staff Nurse Noakes stated that a female patient, Lillian Exley, was sitting on the commode and Nurse Hunter was putting her into bed; the patient started to struggle and Nurse Hunter smacked her face. Nurse Noakes told her not to do it and then when she went into the bathroom, she saw Nurse Hunter strike the patient again.[6]

Abuse of patients was difficult to prove and witnesses were often reluctant to come forward. The case below illustrates the potential violence of asylum life:

> C. Martin [a patient] states he tried to stick a knife into Mr Keeling (chief male nurse) at dinner time and afterwards threw his dinner over him. Put in a single room. He states that male nurse Roper hit him several times on the chin and on the right eye. On examination – he has bruises round

the right eye, many contusions and abrasions on the chest and pain on the right hand side. Charge Nurse Fuller states he heard no signs of a struggle but saw Martin having a fit.

In my opinion, and also that of Dr Lang, the medical officer on the male side, the injuries which Martin sustained cannot be accounted for as a result of a fit, but no confirmation can be obtained of Martin's statements, as there was no one in the vicinity.

Dr Guppy, Assistant Medical Officer, 23/9/1931.[7]

In November 1938, the first qualified psychiatric social worker was employed at the asylum. The job entailed: obtaining histories of patients prior to their admission, visiting homes to ascertain conditions for their discharge, visiting patients after their discharge, and assisting at out-patient clinics. A psychotherapist was also appointed and psychotherapy quickly became the main line treatment although it was difficult for enough patients to receive it on any significant scale.

As the decade came to a close more than half the patients were admitted direct from their own homes and in 1939, sixty-four percent of them were voluntary. That year a Child Guidance Clinic was opened in Brighton to work alongside the other out-patient clinics. McCartan and an assistant worked at one of the clinics on a voluntary basis. And the asylum finally had its own mosquito-proof room (kept at Hurstwood Park Hospital) for the treatment of syphilis by malaria inoculation and so no longer had to temporarily transfer patients elsewhere to receive it (although the introduction of penicillin during the war soon made this treatment out of date). There was also a Hydrotherapy Department which was reputedly very popular with the patients. And McCartan began to treat schizophrenic cases with shock-convulsive therapy – injections of a strong chemical called cardiazol. (Convulsive therapies were a group of medical procedures whose objective was the treatment of certain mental disorders by means of an induced fit. They were based on the hypothesis that there was a negative correlation between schizophrenia and epilepsy.) But although any new treatments were welcome, therapy was still undermined by overcrowding.

On 1st January 1939, there were 133,596 patients in asylums out of a total of 158,723 people suffering from mental disorder in England and Wales. That year, the Board of Control estimated that the public asylums were over-crowded by at least 3,000 and that 20% of asylum staff were still sleeping in main buildings. In the Sussex Asylum's case, there may have been a *Catch 22* situation. In order to fund research, it had to accept private patients – as many as 108 in April 1938 – and yet these patients were taking up precious space and contributing to the overcrowding.

Another worsening trend was the increasing number of elderly people in the asylum who had little chance of being discharged not least because there was nowhere else for them to go. Almost 50% who died there were over 60 years old. The new treatments could make little impact on the older residents. And when the Second World War broke out in 1939, the emphasis on preventing poor mental health and treating the patient in the community was temporarily halted. Meanwhile, with the prospect of another war of an unknown length ahead of them, the asylum (and its inmates) – virtually self-sufficient in everything except tea and sugar and still relying on horse-drawn transport – faced a bleak future.

THE SECOND WORLD WAR

Unlike the First World War, which had developed in a matter of weeks, the second had been half-expected for a considerable number of months. (Indeed, locally, the district council had appointed an Air Raid sub-committee as early as April 1936). In the autumn of 1937, all the asylum staff were given instructions on air raid precautions by a Home Office official. By October 1938, almost a year before the outbreak of war, 1,000 gas masks were already in store at the hospital, each carefully marked with the patient's name. Coverings for the black-out were made, sandbags were put in place, wire netting was fitted on certain windows, and anti-shatter paint was also used on some of them although it was later discovered to be ineffective. The asylum chapel was rendered gas proof and was used to house the wives and young children of staff called on duty during an air raid. A decontamination and demolition squad (composed of staff) was trained and equipped with steel helmets and protective clothing and gas masks.

Before war broke out a letter was sent to the German Embassy suggesting that a patient, Otti Hammer, be transferred to her home in Germany through a neutral country. For some reason she was not discharged until September 1943 when the police took her into custody and made arrangements for her repatriation. Some voluntary patients were sent home to make space for the expected 300 civilian casualties. They were to be treated as out-patients and the asylum's social worker was told to curtail her other work and to concentrate on visiting them frequently. If any showed any sign of deterioration she was to return them in her own car immediately.

Fire watchers were appointed to the top of the main building every night and Brighton General Hospital agreed to have up to 200 patients in the event of the asylum being struck by a bomb. It was the extra threat of the bombers – which had hardly existed in World War 1 – that made conditions particularly stressful for people confined in institutions. The black-out led to bad ventilation which in turn increased the levels of sickness. (McCartan was determined that there should be no lights on in the quarter of a mile main building to act as a marker for the German bombers on their way to London. There is evidence to suggest, though, that they used the asylum's huge water tower instead). Worst of all was the lack of sleep caused by the constant air raid alerts:

> All during the summer of 1940 the Battle of Britain raged in the skies over southern England. As far as the Asylum was concerned the most harrowing time were the nights of 7-9th September, the start of the London Blitz. All the patients were moved from the top floor and spent the entire three nights huddled in the shelters on the ground floor and in the laundry and basement. At the end of the third night some of the elderly patients were so exhausted that it was decided to evacuate the top floor for as long as the nightly air raids continued. Instead the patients had to be accommodated on mattresses laid out in the general bathrooms, the laundry and the main corridor.[8]

Fortunately, during the whole of the war the main building only suffered minor damage as a result of a flying bomb exploding one mile away in July 1944. These bombs were particularly disruptive as they operated day and night. The year before, a spitfire had crashed seventy yards from Hurstwood Park Hospital but luckily the pilot managed to parachute out and only suffered a fractured arm. The threat of bombs meant that patients had to bring shoes and overcoats to their bedsides every night until the threat subsided in February 1945.

As the asylum's new admission hospital, Hurstwood Park, was used as a neuro-surgical unit for victims of war and for ordinary neurological practices for the duration of the war, it meant that newly admitted patients to the asylum had to be mixed with long-stay cases. The Sanatorium and one of the male wards were also evacuated and prepared as emergency neuro-surgical units. The evacuees were squeezed into other wards and the Recreation Hall was converted into a dormitory. Without a Sanatorium, the asylum had to send its infectious cases to other hospitals with isolation facilities.

War meant an immediate harshening of conditions for patients and staff alike. Firstly, the Southern Railway Company decided to withdraw its cheap Special Fare facilities which it had provided for asylum visitors travelling from Eastbourne, London Bridge and Victoria stations. (The offer had already been withdrawn from Brighton as that station's fares were considered cheap enough). McCartan believed that fewer visits would cause distress not only to the visitors but also to the patients but his appeal to the company fell on deaf ears. Secondly, all nursing staff appointments and promotions during the war and for six months after were made temporary. This made it much harder to attract staff, especially nurses. Many local women were lost to the better paid factory jobs (dedicated to the war effort) and also, no doubt, to looking after some of the 10,000 evacuees who flooded into Mid-Sussex in September 1939, almost doubling its population.

The asylum social worker resigned in February 1940 and she was not replaced until two years later. As the staff shortage grew, by November that year, McCartan was asking his committee if people who wore glasses could be considered for nursing posts. Traditionally, staff (who could afford them) had been allowed to wear glasses for reading and writing purposes only. In 1930, a nurse actually made a claim for a new pair. He also received permission to employ 16-year-old girls in 1941 but only after informing the committee that the proportion of nursing staff to patients was approaching danger point. Because of the extra duties imposed on the former, such as fire-watching, he even considered boarding out patients with nearby families. By the end of 1944 he was forced to ask some male ward porters to do nursing duties.

During the first year of the war, entertainments were cut back and one meatless day a week was imposed. A sample of patients weighed the following year revealed that 70% of males had lost on average 7lbs, whilst 55% of females had lost 9lbs. Rationing was introduced and only patients with specified physical diseases were allowed one pint of milk a day. Later, the Board of Control claimed that 45-50% of patients lost weight over a period of two years even in peace time. In September 1944, after an outbreak of diarrhoea, 32 patients signed a petition claiming that the food lacked nourishment. The asylum was also a colder place to live in as ward temperatures were lowered in an attempt to reduce fuel bills. And accidents on the female side of the asylum increased to such an extent that McCartan ordered the domestic staff there to reduce the amount of floor polish they used by 50%.

Most of the wartime admissions were elderly and in 1940 the death rate at the asylum went up to 10%. But as the numbers fell – from 943 in 1939 to 846 in 1945 – the death rate also went down to 7.4% by the end of the war. Compared to the First World War, the death rate was generally much lower in asylums in the Second due to an improved and better balanced diet.

During the war many male patients were employed searching for wood and then sawing it for firewood. Whilst female patients often spent time picking fruit and digging up potatoes and even working in the gardens or on the farm. Occupational therapy continued despite the lack of proper facilities. Three classes of folk dancing were started, one of which was mixed. But generally, asylum life was hard and pretty mundane with no fetes and few of the usual entertainments to look forward to. Even asylum football was suspended.

With the use of Hurstwood Park, McCartan experimented extensively with electro-convulsive therapy (ECT). (It was introduced as a variant of cardiazol, rather than as a new treatment.) The hospital was one of the first in the country to do so and had to import an ECT machine from America. But its effectiveness was very much a hit-and-miss affair as the amount of voltage to use and its duration was very imprecise. After doctors, with the assistance of the hospital engineer, had tried it out on animals (mainly rabbits) in Brighton, it was used on patients. In 1942, McCartan treated 31 patients with ECT and claimed that eight of them were cured and six were improved. But one man sustained a fractured leg during his treatment. Until effective anaesthetics were introduced, there was always a risk of injury. (The first effective muscle relaxant employed was curare, a substance used by the American Red Indians on the tips of their spears to paralyse animals.) Some patients found it a beneficial treatment and some did not. One of the latter vividly described its effects:

> You feel like the bottom's falling out of your world. It's like stalling in an
> aircraft. Your aircraft drops away, the aircraft loses weight as it falls into
> the atmosphere and the instruments come up into your mouth. For years
> after you could feel electricity passing through your head.

In 1943, Samuel undertook a study of patients who had received ECT treatment and found that 3% has sustained fractures as a result of the treatment. So, in spite of the early optimism of ECT having only minor side-effects, it was becoming clear that fractures were a real problem.

As recently as 1961, an elderly patient at the asylum died after fractures incurred during ECT. But McCartan did find it effective in treating patients suffering from depression (and it is still used today). He also experimented with leucotomy operations – the surgical cutting of nerve fibres in the brain – in November 1942, though, he considered these to be less successful.

The prolonged use of narcotics, particularly somnifane, on manic depressive patients was also employed. This meant putting patients to sleep for anything up to ten days. When they awoke they were given a big plate of cooked potatoes to eat. This treatment had little significant success. The main focus of treatment was on schizophrenic patients. Some were injected with cardiazol but this often produced strong tremors which caused fractures or blood clots and so was discontinued after a couple of years. It was replaced by insulin therapy which was the first prolonged attempt to eliminate schizophrenic symptoms. Its aim was to put the patient briefly into a restful state and so that when they came round they would be calmer and might obtain some remission from their illness. Harold Barnett, a senior nurse at the time, described the process:

> You had a special ward which patients came to first thing in the morning. Some had been recognized as schizophrenics for a year or so; others were in the very early stages. Insulin was injected directly into the blood stream. You started with a very small dose. You increased the dose until the patient went into coma. Now this had to be judged very carefully. Once in coma you had to judge the amount of time you wanted them to remain in coma because you've got to get them out again by using a saline drip. The maximum time a patient could be left in coma was between 30 to 40 minutes. You had to be careful that you did not push them too far or you had an irreversible coma. Patients would come every day for three or four weeks and sometimes came back for a second treatment.

Insulin therapy had some success in calming patients down but the treatment was also potentially dangerous. It was used at the hospital up until the drugs revolution of the early 1950s. Perhaps one of the most important war-time developments was the appointment of an educational psychologist, Miss Kent, in 1943. She was employed to visit the asylum when requested and to carry out intelligence tests and give advice on vocations.

When the war finally ended in 1945, there were 846 patients – 318 males and 528 females – in the asylum. Of these, 189 were out-of-county patients and 84 were private. The maintenance rate for Brighton or home patients was a little over £2 per week whereas the authorities could receive as much as five times that amount for private ones. The staff/patient ratio had worsened from 1:6 on the female side and 1:4.4 on the male side pre-war, to 1:10.5 and 1:7 respectively by the end of it. 'Victory in Europe' and 'Victory in Japan' celebration teas and dances were held although the decorations were pretty sparse; only the water tower and the asylum entrance were decorated with fairy lights and they were borrowed from a firm in Brighton.

The war did halt progress on the attempt to treat more people in the community and the practice of preventative treatment – attendances at the out-patient clinics in Brighton had fallen. But it also boosted the Sussex Asylum's reputation as an important place for research into neuro-surgery and psycho-surgery. This rested almost entirely on the success of its original admission hospital, Hurstwood Park. During the war over 5,000 patients were admitted there and over 2,000 major neuro-surgical operations were performed. It closed in August 1945 as an Emergency War Hospital with a view to re-opening the following year as a neuro-psychiatric unit. So, the Sussex Asylum was again still without an admission hospital

POST-WAR AND THE DRUG REVOLUTION

Hurstwood Park Hospital was re-opened in 1946 and became a neuro-surgical unit with a psychiatric presence. McCartan had been determined to use part of it for psycho-surgery and had retained a neurologist and a core of people to start a neurology department. This brought together the sister specialities of neurology and psychiatry under one roof. At the same time, Beechmont House (previously containing private patients) was converted into a cafeteria and a social centre. It also provided some accommodation for nursing staff.

The first annual patient fete since 1939 was held on 19th July 1946 as gradually the asylum entertainments picked up. In January 1947, Max Miller, the famous comedian who lived in Brighton (and the first entertainer to earn £1,000 a week at the London Palladium before the war), came to a patient dance. The following month he returned with some friends and performed for the patients and the staff. A few months later 'humour' was the subject of McCartan's talk to a local rotary club. It was reported in the *Mid-Sussex Times* on 16th April 1947:

> "Mental Illness jokes 'anti-social'"
>
> The help we can give mental patients and the efficacy of methods of treatment, will not become one hundred percent unless we have the compassion of the general public, and that we have not got at the moment… A lot of the jokes were based on the erroneous assumption that a person who was mentally ill was different from other people. It is unkind and also anti-social for it prevents people going into hospital for (early) treatment.

The Commissioners from the Board of Control visited the asylum on 13th February, 1947 and reported on the medical developments:

> The standard of medical treatment and nursing care is high and there is a pleasant atmosphere of therapeutic activity. Clinical conferences, which the nursing as well as the medical staff can attend, are held weekly and there is a course of lectures and demonstrations arranged in the evenings. It is hoped soon to hold at the hospital monthly clinical meetings with doctors in the neighbourhood. The out-patient clinics are increasing and there is excellent liaison between the hospital and the social welfare department in Brighton.[9]

And since 1945 it had been possible to get ECT treatment at the hospital as an out-patient.

On 5th July, 1948, nearly 90 years of local government control ended with the establishment of the National Health Service. The asylum was now run by a Management Committee appointed by the Regional Hospital Board and it was re-named St Francis Hospital. The name came from its chapel which had been dedicated to St Francis of Assisi in 1941. The Medical Superintendent was still a key figure but was now part of a management team. One immediate effect was Brighton Library's request that all their pictures loaned to the Hospital should be returned. In fact, some remained unreturned until the day it closed in 1995.

The change of management had little immediate effect on the hospital's problems although there was greater interest now that the general community, not just the Brighton ratepayers, had a stake in its future. In particular, local people felt the hospital was more part of their community. Previously, because it had been primarily for Brighton patients, Haywards Heath people who needed asylum treatment had usually been sent to Hellingly, the East Sussex asylum. The changeover radically reduced the number of private patients – only ten were left a year later – but overcrowding and staff shortages were still much in evidence. The death rate remained higher than average – 8.6%; an ever growing number of elderly patients were confined to their beds, and the age range of patients was wide, from 80 to just under two years old in 1948. Conditions were still harsh. Some patients received no drinks between 5.30 pm and breakfast at 7.45 am the next day. (Supper was only provided for those who stayed up after 7.30 pm). And although there was a system of rewards (money and tobacco) for male patients who worked, there was none for female patients.

The most significant development was the dramatic increase in the number of yearly admissions and, consequently, discharges. In 1948 alone, there were 660 admissions and 533 discharges. Under the National Health Service, St Francis now had a 25% larger catchment area with a population of 270,000 (of whom 200,000 lived in Brighton and Hove), hence the increase in admissions. Looking at the records, it is clear that most of the discharges were of people recently admitted rather than those who had been there for more than a year. In the early 1950s the asylum population again went over the thousand mark and, as before, serious overcrowding meant a high death rate – 12.4% in 1952. In July that year the hospital was close to turning patients away. The situation was particularly bad on the female wards which often contained almost 100 patients. This meant that few of them could be unlocked, in contrast to the male side where only one was closed. This placed a heavy burden on the staff. In fact, female nurses increasingly began to be part-time – over half in 1952 – whilst the male nurses all remained full-time.

The problem of female staff shortage dominated the 1950s. Just after the war McCartan had recruited nurses from Ireland. But some had quickly resigned from their posts saying that they had only joined the hospital to obtain an exit visa. Advertising locally and further afield in 1950 attracted few applicants. In 1952, the Ministry of Health agreed to pay the travelling expenses of junior nursing staff arriving from Northern Ireland. It did not for the rest of the United Kingdom. Two years later the Ministry permitted the hospital to do the same for

The Staff Band at the Coronation Ball in 1953.

girls coming from Austria. They were to be employed as 'assistant nurses' until they learnt sufficient English to become 'student nurses'. And in the mid-1950s St Francis began to canvas local secondary schools and meet with parent-teacher associations in order to recruit 16 and 17 olds as nursing cadets. In 1955 it held a Mental Nursing Exhibition in Brighton and Haywards Heath. The same year, the Matron was sent to the Italian Embassy in London and to Ireland for two weeks ("because of her local knowledge") on a recruitment drive.

But all these measures seemed not to have been particularly successful. In 1956, despite the presence of nurses from Nigeria, Holland and France, the hospital was still 70 female nurses short. Thirty male nurses were also needed due to the introduction of a three-shift system of work. The female nurses' day was still divided in two. In 1958, the hospital tried to get girls from Scotland, the only place "not tried yet". In contrast, it never had a problem finding local domestic female staff.

McCartan believed it was not just the pay and conditions which made it difficult to attract staff. It was also the stigma of working in such an institution. (The hospital even found it almost impossible to get another pharmacist. The post had been downgraded and the pay and conditions were inferior to the same job in general hospitals). The acute staff shortage was partially resolved by recruiting nurses from the Commonwealth from the late 1950s onwards. But this policy was not without its difficulties. The environment of a mental hospital situated in an all white country town was not an easy one to adapt to. Sometimes, they came from countries which had little defence against European infection. In 1957, a 20-year-old Nigerian nurse died of acute bronchial pneumonia. At the inquest, the angry relatives (who had to be physically restrained) blamed the hospital for the lack of treatment and for not taking the early symptoms seriously enough.

As the decade progressed, McCartan's faith in psycho-surgery was losing ground to social psychiatry. The discovery of major tranquillisers such as Chlorpromazine in 1952 had a major impact on mental hospitals. Though far from perfect, they relieved distressing symptoms – suffered particularly by schizophrenics – and enabled patients to benefit more from the hospital facilities. These drugs also allowed more patients to live at home and control their illnesses themselves. They became self-medicating or received depot injections – drugs lasting weeks – from a local psychiatric unit. A charge nurse at the hospital then, later claimed that:

> … it was the coming of Chlorpromazine in the 1950s which heralded the real changes in our mental hospitals. It can be likened to the effect which Penicillin had on non-viral infections… The more far-sighted medical and nursing staff saw the coming of the tranquilliser as the means whereby the previously closed hospitals could become more open.[10]

The change did precipitate more patients being allowed back into the community. But it also began what has been described as a revolving door situation: new patients at the hospital were treated quickly, released, but later often readmitted (as their illnesses re-occurred) again and again.

In 1954, 911 patients were admitted into St Francis (most of whom were voluntary) and 859 were discharged. De-carceration did not lead to the expected drastic decline in admissions. Firstly, the effects of hospital institutionalisation had probably been underestimated. Secondly, in Sussex, there was a lack of community psychiatric services and rehabilitation facilities to support the extra number of patients released back into the community. By 1957, there were 160 new admissions a month compared with 250 per year before the war. In other words, the hospital was dealing in a month with more than half the number dealt with in a pre-war year.

One of the asylum's doctors in the late 1870s had attributed a sudden rise in admissions to the reaction caused by a powerful evangelical speaker preaching in the vicinity. In 1957, McCartan attributed one such rise to a TV series 'The Hurt Mind' which highlighted mental health problems although he admitted to the *Mid-Sussex Times* on 6th March, 1957, that:

> … for some unknown reason, quite unconnected with anything national
> or local, the rate of admissions and attendances suddenly soars.

McCartan's successor, Dr Liddell, was also at a loss to explain the doubling of admissions in July and August 1960 as compared to any other previous year.

In 1955, St Francis contained 897 patients who were looked after by a nursing staff of 212 and nine doctors including McCartan. The weekly maintenance rate was high – well over £6 a week. This was largely due to the cost of the neurological unit at Hurstwood Park Hospital. In 1957, Dr W. Liddell replaced McCartan as the medical superintendent. In many ways the latter was the last of the old style superintendents. He had been rather unbending in his views and had perhaps placed too much faith in psycho-surgery but his pronouncements on mental illness had often showed a passion reminiscent of Charles Lockhart Robertson.

McCartan had continued Harper-Smith's concentration on hospital entertainment. A Patient's Committee had been formed in 1953 to run social functions during the winter. That June, a pageant 'In the Days of Liz' was staged with 90 players composed of patients, staff and their children. The following April patients put on the first art exhibition held at the hospital. Opened to the public, it contained 240 exhibits of mainly original paintings and sketches. And the Christmas programme for 1954 began on 10th December and lasted until 12th February!

McCartan also helped set up a Mental Health Exhibition in Brighton in May 1956. Its aim was to dispel ignorance and misunderstanding and to show the progress made in the fight against mental illness. It included films, pictorial display shows, photos and

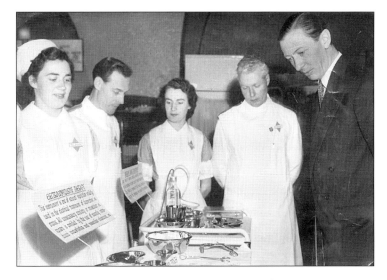

Health Exhibition at the Corn Exchange, Brighton, 1956.

captions to explain "the nature of mental illness and deficiency" and:

> the vital part which X-ray plays in the work as demonstrated, details were given of insulin shock treatments, and various apparatus showing mental and physical reactions of patients were displayed. Visitors were most interested in a realistic model of a woman patient having a blood transfusion, while models of brains such as were used for the training of students were explained by members of the staff.[11]

Despite being poorly advertised, the free exhibition attracted 5,239 visitors over a four-day period. For McCartan, it "showed the fine spirit of the staff which was more important than the buildings and the new equipment".[12] Apart from his attempts to interest the public in the hospital, McCartan's main achievement was to make the facilities at Hurstwood Park as good as anywhere in the country. It was ironic though, that this hospital would eventually be separated off from St Francis, lose its psychiatric unit, and become self-governing.

The year Liddell took over, 60% or more of the female patients were near or over 65 years of age and the death rate was 14.2% – the highest since World War One – in a hospital containing almost 900 patients. There were twice as many female patients as male patients and 24 women and eight men suffered fractures that year as a result of accidents. This was more than average but largely due to falls associated with old age. The following year the death rate reached over 16% – above the average of all mental hospitals – and most residents were 'elderly' or 'very elderly'.

At this time, St Francis was described as a very good hospital in very poor, outdated buildings. And it was still chronically overcrowded. One of Liddell's assistants and his eventual successor, Dr Richard Wheeler, remembers seeing one female ward containing over 100 patients and described it as an "absolute snakepit".[13] The most important event of 1957 was the opening of the long awaited Admission Villa – 34 years after the Visitors' had written a report strongly recommending one. At last St Francis had a place to treat easily curable cases or cases of short duration. There, uniforms were dispensed with and the principles of custodial care were less apparent.

THE 1959 MENTAL HEALTH ACT AND AFTER

The 1950s saw a number of developments – the use of major tranquillisers, new occupational therapy departments and the introduction of day hospitals. A Royal Commission on Mental Health and Mental Deficiency was set up in 1954. Three years later, it recommended sweeping changes which included a far greater flexibility in the identification of the disease and its appropriate treatment. It also recommended that the community rather than the mental hospital should be the centre of treatment. The result of their report was the Mental Health Act of 1959 which set out clearly the rules under which patients could be detained and established their rights of appeal. It ended the status of certified, voluntary, and temporary patients and introduced informal admission for observation (section 25) and admission for treatment (section 26). The Board of Control's Commissioners were replaced by Hospital Management Committee Visitors. The latter carried out monthly visits but their reports contained less information than those of their predecessors.

The commission predicted that mental illness would gradually decline in the future thus lessening the need for mental hospitals. This prediction has proved to be wrong as since their report the mental health of the population has probably worsened. Nevertheless, the report and subsequent Act signalled that the wheel of mental care had come full circle, placing the patient back to be cared for within the community. Robertson himself had predicted almost a hundred years before that, one day, asylums might be replaced by psychiatric wards in general hospitals and that more patients could be looked after at home. His only reservation had been about the lack of supervision and support for the patient in the community. He considered asylums, for all their faults, to be centres of care. In fact, the Mental Health Exhibition held in Brighton in October 1960 (Mental Health Year) still saw a role for them. Opened by the then Minister of Health, Enoch Powell, it portrayed the hospital as a place of care and treatment rather than custody. And, echoing the spirit of moral treatment, Liddell spoke of the Mental Hospital as a "quiet refuge where gentleness reigns".

The changes that mental health Acts encourage are sometimes more apparent than real. After 1959, St Francis still faced considerable practical difficulties in trying to improve hospital conditions whilst at the same time trying to rehabilitate patients back into the community. Physically, the main building continued to be in a poor state. In 1961, the Visitors' Report book recorded that in one 86-bed ward there was only one bath, three toilets and four wash basins. By their own guidelines, there should have been four baths, fourteen toilets and fourteen wash basins. They also found toilets with no doors – a situation which still existed when this author worked there as a student twelve years later. In 1962, one female ward had only one bath for 96 patients. And one of the Visitors, Dr C. F Macquire commented that:

> It can hardly be considered a mental up-lift for mentally sick patients to
> have to sleep in these large, barren, prison-like dormitories.[14]

In 1963, another Visitor found radiators not working (in September) and one ward's decoration deplorable. And his colleagues spent the whole day investigating the shortage of accommodation for resident female staff.

Though there were many new developments at St Francis during the 1960s such as the opening of a new occupational therapy department in 1963, the construction of an adolescent unit for 30 boys and girls, Colwood, and the appointment of music and art therapists, conditions for staff and patients – who were overwhelmingly elderly – remained poor. One of the medical officers, Dr Klaus Bergman, wrote in August 1968 that:

> Those of us who care for the elderly know how unsatisfactory conditions still are. To give our patients a fairer deal we need one thing above all, tangible evidence that the community cares.[15]

Bergman was echoing the sentiments voiced by Henry Maudsley more than a hundred years before. But public apathy and indifference towards mental health was no more apparent than when the hospital tried to obtain a house in Brighton to use as a social club for ex-patients. The NIMBY (not in my back yard) factor resulted in the hospital only obtaining premises after being refused permission to buy other ones on seventeen separate occasions, all due to local objections. Rather fittingly, the address of the house they eventually acquired was 18 Preston Park Avenue and it soon became known as the '18 Club'.

The 1960s was a period when asylums everywhere were under attack for their institutionalisation, drug dependency and poor living conditions. Books such as Ken Kesey's *One Flew Over the Cuckoo's Nest* and R. D. Laing's *The Politics of Experience and the Bird of Paradise* and *The Divided Self* all attacked the asylum solution. Not that the staff at St Francis themselves necessarily disagreed with some of the critical sentiments expressed. Their own and the patients' plight was highlighted by a local newspaper the *Evening Argus* in an article entitled "An Affront to Human Dignity" which appeared on 9th April 1969. Although the article was a bit sensational and although the editor apologised the following week for a misleading headline, much of its content was uncontested. Part of the article was based on an interview with Dr Richard Wheeler, the Medical or Physician Superintendent (as the post was now called) since 1961. Below are some extracts:

> I [reporter John Marley] found that overcrowding is such that some patients sleep in beds only a foot apart. In some cases sleeping quarters consist of cell-like rooms with stark stone walls, bare boards, windows that won't shut properly and no effective heating. The hospital's dedicated staff are doing their best against overwhelming odds. But with constant overcrowding and lack of money, it is an uphill struggle.

Dr Wheeler told me that: "This hospital is only suitable for 700 patients but we have 900 beds… There is no opportunity to give people the privacy or decent conditions that anyone would expect. The effect of the conditions here must be to dehumanise patients. The conditions are an affront to human dignity… It is not right that people should be cooped up like this. It is abhorrent. There are wards here with 70 patients in them, although the maximum for any ward should be 40. We do what we can but the planning policy is not to expand the fabric of the hospital. These places are doomed eventually. Big mammoth institutes for mental patients are a dying concept. It is a question of keeping them going until alternative hospitals take over their function."

Dr Wheeler went on to describe how understaffing meant that two or three times a month a member of staff was attacked on the disturbed wards. He also admitted that although 92% of admissions were discharged within a year; over half of them returned later. Wheeler finished the interview by saying that:

> There is terrific pressure on us to take more patients all the time. Only a rigorous admission policy and determined efforts towards patients' discharge keeps the numbers under control. About half the patients here are over 65, and this makes our task all the more difficult… There is not a single home for the elderly mentally infirm in the Brighton area. As a result, we have to bear the burden of a lot of elderly patients who do not really need full hospitalisation.

The reporter was then shown the hospital's industrial therapy unit which was described as "grossly inadequate and in contravention of the Factories Act". His article was corroborated later on in the year by one of the hospital's own doctors, Dr Jacobson, who wrote in the November issue of *Hospital News* that:

> There seems to be a steady levelling down of the hospital to penury, depression and gloom… Its buildings are long outdated and its amenities are shabby and backward.[16]

But the *Evening Argus* reporter also acknowledged that:

> There is another story that emerges from my visit to St Francis – that of the sterling work done by voluntary effort, which has done much to improve the patients' lot, as well as help the staff in their formidable challenge.

A variety of local organisations such as the Women's Royal Voluntary Service had been helping the hospital for years in various ways. The W. R. V. S alone had been raising on average £4,000 a year and had managed to build a shop, canteen and a swimming pool amongst many other gifts. In fact, even local schoolboys and police cadets had helped erect the latter. And a voluntary organisation called the Summer Fair Association (helped by people like Sally

```
                                        SILVER JUBILEE INTER

                                        Compere:


        "Overture" - Harold Barnett and his Music

    The Ruth Sadler Dancers
    "Introduction to First Aid" by the Professionals
    Mauritian Group
    Extract from Henry V
    Can-Can Dancers
    Table Tennis Exhibition Match - Mauritius v Ireland
    Irish Music and Dancing
    Fashion Parade (day wear)
    The London Scene


             15 MINUTE INTERVAL


    The Ceylonians Group
    Robert Rawat Sings
    David and Anita - Piano Duet
    West Indian Folk Singing and Dancing
    Ruth Sadler Dances
    The Franklanders
    Pilar Cabanban Dances
    Fashion Parade (evening wear)
    Silver Queens and Jubilee Dancers
         Finale - International Assembly
```

Programme for the asylum anniversary fete, 1977.

McEwan) raised thousands of pounds in the last three decades of the hospital's life.

It was the great effort put in by friends and staff – comprising many nationalities, 29 in 1981 – which created what has been described by ex-staff as, at the very least, a friendly communal atmosphere rather than that of a cold, uncaring institution. And, in contrast to today's sometimes desperate pleas from families for more psychiatric treatment for their relatives, the hospital for much

```
NATIONAL VARIETY SHOW

Jim Mable



     Lighting:                    Edward Lacey, Mike Morgan

     Make up:                     Kitty Dennis

     Front of House Manager:      Jack Funnell

     Music Director:              Harold Barnett

     Scenic Design:               Bill Golunski, Colin Small

     Sound:                       John Collins, Andrew Collins
                                  Pat Donahue, Brendon Daniels

     Pianist:                     David Stanley

     Compere and Pianist
     for Fashion Show     :       David and Jane Grey

     Stage Manager and
     Assistant Producer   :       Jim Mable

     Assistant Stage Manager      John Floate

     Our thanks go to all those not named who have
          covered duties and helped in other ways.
```

of its later history rarely turned anyone away. A personnel officer there in the seventies and eighties remembers how people with suitcases would sometimes turn up at the hospital and request to stay over potentially stressful periods of the year such as Christmas. Neither did the hospital necessarily evict people who were no longer mentally ill. As in Robertson's day, staff working (rather than social) conditions remained relatively poor and even in the 1970's new staff were occasionally forced to sleep on the wards due to the lack of decent nursing accommodation.

CLOSURE

As Wheeler had said in the newspaper article, mental hospitals were eventually doomed. Since the 1959 Act, little was invested in trying to modernise the old asylums. The cost of maintaining the buildings and sufficient staffing levels had become enormous. In April 1969, St Francis had 500 members of staff and 800 patients. Also, the drug revolution was an expensive one, an expenditure that had been virtually negligible when the asylum had opened. In January 1969, the hospital's pharmacy department estimated that they spent £60 a day on drugs and that in 1968 the patients had consumed:[17]

260,000 sleeping tablets

150,000 anti-depression tablets

260,000 tranquillisers

160,000 tablets to control side effects.

They had also used 47,000 syringes. As the average resident population was 800, it meant that more than 1,000 tablets per patient were taken that year.

Gradually the number of patients began to fall as emphasis was placed on the rehabilitation of those with chronic illnesses and the treatment of the elderly for whom a specialised service was developed. By the end of the 1960s the numbers fell to under 800 for the first time since the beginning of the century. This was achieved in four ways: more stringent admission assessments, shorter stays, the increase in use of day patient facilities, and the use of community care for long term patients.

In addition, new departments in district general hospitals were set up to provide a comprehensive service and eventually replace the old mental hospitals. As early as 1972, there were banner headlines declaring that St Francis Hospital was to close. In fact, it took another 23 years for this to happen. The hospital farm – one of the success stories of its history – was gradually run down during this period along with the hospital itself. By 1975 there were only 600 beds available.

The policy of getting patients back into the community faced enormous problems. Historically, nursing had focused on caring for the patient on a day-to-day basis. This made patients more dependent and institutionalised. But for the last 25 years of the hospital's life more emphasis was placed on making the patients more independent and preparing them for rehabilitation outside in the community. Now nurses had to give less care without caring less. In 1971, a housing project for discharged patients was instigated and small group homes were set up locally and in Brighton. Over the next few years other houses were bought for the same purpose.

The asylum gradually emptied of its residents to the extent that in 1984, the 125th anniversary of the opening of the asylum, a historical exhibition of artifacts, photos etc. was staged in an empty ward. The same year the male corridor was decorated with a mural designed and painted by patients and Manpower Services staff. In 1992, the asylum changed its name yet again and was now known as the West Wing of the Princess Royal Hospital (the new general hospital constructed in the asylum grounds). It was no doubt politically correct but according to some staff led to people who required general hospital treatment frequently making a mistake and arriving at the Victorian asylum.

By 1994, there were only 100 patients left in Kendall's old building. For many patients, particularly the older ones, the hospital had become their home; a place where they felt protected and secure. Indeed, historically the asylum had always had a problem trying to persuade older patients to leave. For this reason, some were reluctant and afraid to go when the time came. On the other hand, more recent and younger inmates were probably glad to leave the gloominess of the internal surroundings.

The following year, in the weeks before its closure, 40 long-stay elderly patients were placed in temporary wards at Haywards Heath Hospital, awaiting a new privately-run ward to be opened in 1997. Others were placed in small staff-run group homes in Brighton and Haywards Heath. Some patients had little genuine say in their dispersal. Staying where they were was clearly not an option. The Sussex Asylum/St Francis Hospital finally closed on 17th November 1995. That day the last sixteen patients were moved to a psychiatric unit in the recently built Princess Royal Hospital. Like the asylum's first admissions – the 42 female pauper lunatics who had arrived from Bethnal Green private asylum on 25th July 1859 – they were facing an improvement in their material life. But, as then, it was difficult to predict whether they would be any happier.

A week later 200 former St Francis patients and staff attended a special commemorative service held at the Chapel. Meanwhile the whole of the site was placed in the hands of London estate agents. The closure was greeted with very little press comment or public regret. Large old remote mental hospitals had rightly had their day and had become an anachronism in a modern society. The future was "Care in the Community" and enabling patients to remain in their own homes. The worst cases were to be kept in psychiatric units. These were to be places of last resort, just as the Sussex Asylum had been for so much of its history.

A short time before its closure, one long-stay patient was involved in a comic but potentially tragic incident. Just as pall bearers were leaving the asylum

Chapel carrying a coffin, he managed to hijack the hearse and drove it erratically for two miles until he collided head on with another vehicle. Fortunately, no one was seriously hurt. When interviewed afterwards, he expressed fears about being forcibly placed in accommodation where he did not wish to go. He had never driven a car before and what was a final and perhaps symbolic twist: inside the coffin was the body of an ex-member of staff.

CONCLUSION

The care of the mentally ill in Sussex has come a long way since the day William Perfect, the Kent surgeon, first offered to treat the county's "canine and other madnesses" more than two hundred years ago. And a long time has also passed since the asylum's first patient, Jane Woods, arrived from the Bethnal Green private asylum in July 1859. A forty-year-old domestic servant, she had spent several years at Bethnal Green suffering from (amongst other things) visions of angels and devils ascending and descending in rooms.

After the contrasting fortunes of the county's first private madhouses, Ticehurst House for the rich and Ringmer Asylum for the poorer classes, came the Sussex Asylum. It was part of the county asylum system which arose out of the ashes of the failure of the private sector to cater for pauper lunatics. At that time, Haywards Heath only had a population of 200 and the asylum was not only in the community, it largely was the community. This fact led to an extraordinarily good relationship between the town and the institution for the rest of its history. Since 1859, the asylum had largely been the main centre for the care and treatment of the mentally ill in Sussex. Now, the centre has become the wider community, just as it had been in the days before the asylum opened.

It has been argued that the "rise of the county asylum was part of a more general trend towards the isolation of the dangerous, deviant and socially incompetent in total institutions".[1] And that the new industrial world had no place for those who did not contribute to it or fit in. There certainly was a strong 'social control' element in the asylum and workhouse systems, especially in the latter. But there were also genuine elements of benevolence and humanitarianism which we see displayed by men such as Dr Charles Lockhart Robertson. And although the Victorian period is often seen today as a time when moralism dominated society; so did, to a lesser extent, philanthropy.

By the time the Sussex Asylum was founded, there were already serious doubts about large public institutions as a solution to mental illness despite the progress made by moral treatment. However, under Robertson, the asylum really did aim to fulfil the dreams of the reformers. In those early years we see genuine optimism about the prospect of real progress, not only on the part of Robertson but also by the local press. It soon established a reputation as one of the best asylums in the country. But almost from day one it was handicapped by financial constraints which were to undermine its therapeutic capabilities for most of its history.

To his credit, Robertson attempted to criticise workhouses for sending patients to the asylum who had obviously been badly neglected. But in the end, unsupported by his own committee, even he goes quiet on the subject. And indeed, as the problems of the regime mount up, he has to admit in 1867, rather damningly, that whatever advantages his beloved asylum may have over the local workhouses "…the truth is that the insane poor who are sufficiently sane to argue the point, are constantly asking to be sent back to the Union (workhouse)".[2] They preferred to mix with sane people and to be near their families and friends.

Nevertheless, according to Dr Saunders, Robertson, "both by example and precept showed what could be done by the humane treatment of the insane… and did much towards breaking down prejudices and raised the asylum life to a higher level".[3] The asylum's reputation undoubtedly declined after the departure of first Robertson and then Williams. Although it never gained a bad name and indeed was for many years one of the cleanest asylums, it never again became a model for other institutions to follow.

By the end of the nineteenth century, with pauper lunatics making up 98% of those in the county asylum system; with dullness, overcrowding and low cure rates dominant; with disillusioned ex-medical superintendents becoming more and more conservative; and with the early part of the century's dream that specialist state institutions could cure much insanity in tatters, even mechanical restraint starts to be considered again as an unavoidable necessity. And 'moral treatment', the cause of so much optimism and hope, is virtually dead. At the Sussex Asylum, rather symbolically, one of Robertson's favourite treatments, the Roman Bath, is in disuse and will eventually be converted into a disinfector for bed linen.

The gloomiest times for the asylum were probably during the wars, especially World War One. Staff shortages, food rationing and high death rates were common-place. And throughout its history urgent needs such as extra patient accommodation, nurses' homes or occupational therapist units were only met many years after they first became necessary. It would be easy to lay the blame

at the door of the many visitors' committees and latterly management committees who had control over expenditure at the asylum. Undoubtedly, society as a
whole must also be blamed for its indifference and apathy towards asylums and
the mentally ill. However, on a local level, the Sussex Asylum frequently benefited from the generosity of local people in terms of their time, gifts and donations. For example, in January 1953 an anonymous donor left £137 in notes at
the Reception desk; money that in those days could buy a new car.

It is interesting to note that the asylum, although isolated physically from
Haywards Heath, does not appear to have been isolated from it socially. Local
people and the families of staff often visited it not just for the social occasions
but also to help the patients. Since at least the 1920's, mental patients could
frequently be seen wandering the streets of Haywards Heath and yet no letter of
complaint or criticism of their presence has ever appeared in the local newspaper. The asylum community existed in a restricted society which perhaps showed
it far greater compassion and understanding than the wider society.

When the Sussex Asylum (or St Francis Hospital) eventually closed in 1995
it did so in a very different atmosphere than when those two Brighton journalists attended the first Christmas Ball and had been invited by a patient to go
outside and pick strawberries in the dark. Long before the future of public
asylums was first questioned in the 1950s, they were perceived as having failed
to cure insanity and had, in Andrew Scull's words, become "museums of
madness". They had outlived any useful purpose they may have had and were
accused of being outdated in both concept and reality. The mass closure of
asylums in the 1990s was brought about by the dual needs of cost and therapeutic effectiveness. The cost of running large institutions had become astro-
nomical and the huge number of re-admissions was throwing doubt on their
efficacy as places of treatment.

The old Victorian asylums had started out with the intention of trying to
give individual treatment to the insane but, because of the rapid increase in
pauper lunacy, had ended up by trying to treat them en masse. This had obviously failed. For this reason, the main objection to being placed in an asylum
was not that of being illegally confined or the cruelty inflicted; no, it was the
almost non-existent nature of treatment that patients often had to contend with.

When it closed, the Sussex Asylum bore little resemblance to the asylum
that Robertson had known. It had become a series of buildings and extensions
spread over a wide area of ground. But with all its defects, which were apparent
from the day it opened, Kendall's main building has survived and perhaps even
Robertson would have been amused to discover that 140 years later, it would be

a listed building. Another great change was in the staffing levels. By the 1990's, Robertson and his assistant medical officer had been replaced by a medical team of 16 doctors and consultants. And the hospital had just as many administrative staff as nursing staff. Lastly, the vast majority (if not all) the patients at the hospital for the last thirty years were on some form of medication. In Robertson's day medication was extremely rare. And even by the turn of the century less than 10% of the patients were given medicine and this was mainly for epilepsy.

It would be foolish to romanticize life in asylums. They contained too much suffering and sadness for that. And any generalization as to their benefits or detrimental effects would probably be grotesquely inaccurate. Besides, asylums varied enormously. At its best, the Sussex Asylum was undoubtedly one of the best. But there was cruelty there just as there was kindness. It was a prison to some, a home to others. Many of its patients found themselves socially isolated: others, may have found a greater social life inside than outside the asylum. For a minority it did offer the opportunity to get better, but for the vast majority, it did not. The word 'happy' is not one that is usually associated with mental asylums but there were some patients who were quite content to spend the rest of their lives at the Sussex Asylum. And many clearly did.

Of course, many of the asylum's residents were old, infirm or socially inadequate and should never have been sent there in the first place. And this brings us to the question: what was the real alternative? The answer, sadly, must be that for most of the inmates there was none. Few of them by choice would have ever opted to enter an asylum if there had been a better alternative available. The eventual recognition by reformers that asylums were not the ideal solution was one thing; persuading society to provide something better was another.

Not everything about the Sussex Asylum in the early days was negative. Indeed, many of the principles implemented by Robertson and other reformers are re-emerging again today: the recognition of the value of a good diet; the need to build on patients' strengths rather than their weaknesses; the importance of a patient being ready for rehabilitation (as shown by Robertson's flexible policy over discharge); and encouraging patients to widen their capabilities by giving them a diverse range of activities; and above all the importance of kindness as a basis for treatment. And it must not be forgotten that the widespread establishment of asylums did make the study of symptoms of mental illness possible for the first time.

Outdated and outmoded as they may have become, there are further lessons we can learn from the asylum experience. Looking at the Sussex Asylum we can see how much physical space was important to a patient's well-being.

Even though the labrynth of corridors – totalling more than a mile – were depressing places, they did afford patients an opportunity to walk out their anxiety however bad the weather was outside. The asylum also offered patients: occupation, companionship and security. In its heyday, it was a centre of opportunity offering its residents sport, music, art, education, and teaching skills in traditional professions. It emphasized the value of work in restoring the individual's health and self-esteem. At times, the asylum often provided a stable and sometimes lively social life for its residents. It also gave the patients a high level of protection and security. All these are rights that may be more difficult to guarantee in a wider society.

Lastly, life in the asylum was an experience shared by staff and patients alike. Many of the former lived in the same grounds, used the same facilities. On occasion, they even attended each others funerals. This physical closeness, apart from helping to create a communal atmosphere, also produced great dedication on the part of some of the staff who often gave up their free time to help the patients. For them, it was not just a job, it was a vocational interest. They worked in an environment that encouraged a certain amount of befriending and friendship, concepts that, with all the boundaries of today's caring professions, may be difficult to maintain. If community care is to succeed surely it must capture some of the spirit the best asylum workers demonstrated in the past.

Although the Sussex Asylum (or St Francis) is no more its main building still dominates the landscape. It is, at present (1999), being converted into luxury housing – "its developer coyly disguising its stigmatising past"[4] – whilst the chapel's future is uncertain. The latter is bare now except for, rather fittingly, the memorial plaque to Valentine Browne, Robertson's assistant whose dedication to the asylum and its inmates was remarkable. The sensation that the old asylum gives is essentially a Victorian one. If one stands before the front of the old Victorian building one can, perhaps, still feel the spirit of Charles Lockhart Robertson and imagine those early days, can still see the male entrance where, in 1860, poor John Mockford arrived from the Brighton Workhouse in such an appalling condition. And if you enter the nearby chapel, one can imagine the poetic words of a Henry Hawkins' sermon trying to inspire an audience.

In the last few years of its existence, a dedicated body of staff (with the help of patients) set up and maintained a very impressive museum at the hospital. It was full of interesting artifacts and displays which illustrated the history of the asylum and provided a sensation of what life must have been like there. Since the closure, the museum's contents have been stored away. Its trustees believed, as did the South Eastern Museums Service, that the chapel was the natural and most appropriate place for the museum. They believed that it would do justice to the hospital's history and could have become an important institution in Haywards Heath. Unfortunately, the developers have decided to offer a much smaller site which may severely limit the potential of the museum. The local council have endorsed this proposal and so it looks as if a golden opportunity has been missed to use an historic building which could have become a valuable educational resource not just for local people, but for all those interested in the history of mental health care.

There are no memorials to the thousands who died in the Sussex Asylum. Their names and numbers are all that remain. This book is a small memorial to them and to all those who lived and worked there.

APPENDIX 1

Robertson' s reply to the Brighton Guardians, recorded in his Asylum Journal, dated 23/5/1860.

1. I ask the Visitors to test the accuracy of my statement by the examination of Mr Knox, the Head Attendant who had charge of the patient. I further add that the patient had a venerable sore of the existence of which the Brighton Workhouse nurse who had charge of him was ignorant and that so evident had the patient been subject to blows that when spoken to or approached he always held up his arm to protect himself and shrank back. He had a worn emaciated aspect and was quite unable to swallow any solid food during the few days he survived his removal here. I annex here a certificate by Mr Gwynne, the late Assistant Medical Officer, as to the state of the patient on admission.

2. In the report of the Brighton Guardians it is stated by the nurse that he had a change of linen and sheeting every day. Had this change been made six times a day the excoriation of the back would probably have been prevented. A patient like Mockford if changed only once a day is certain to have excoriations.

3. The certificate of Mr Rugg's examination of the body here on the 18th April is at best a biased and partial statement. It is Mr Rugg's neglect of duty which my letter to Mr Hollis is calculated to expose, and he cannot therefore with any equity be permitted to judge of my report. I have never yet heard of the accused being made the judge of the truth of the accusation against him. Had the Guardians really intended to subject my report to a professional scrutiny they would I submit have called in to their aid some independent physician as Dr Ormerod. The certificate of their own surgeon accused by me of neglect of duty cannot I submit be allowed much weight as evidence in the case.

4. The Guardians are mistaken in supposing that death renders bruises more perceptible. The rapid decomposition and discoloration of the body (which occurred in this case) tends to obliterate and render indistinct marks of injury apparent during life.

5. I distinctly disclaim any feelings of hostility (attributed to me) to the Guardians. I do not even know them by sight. They complain that I did not address my report to them. I have no control over the Guardians and have no authority or right to address them. The rules of the Asylum on the contrary require me to communicate with the House Committee when any circumstances requiring immediate attention arises. As Mockford belonged to the Brighton Union I wrote to the Brighton magistrate on the House Committee (if from Cuckfield I would have written to that magistrate). I submit that I was strictly in accordance with the rules and regulations in the step I took. My communication to the Commissioners in Lunacy was only the usual certificate required by the Act of Parliament to be forwarded to that office on the admission of every patient.

6. I equally disdain all intention of discourtesy to the Guardians. It is the first time such an accusation has been brought against me. The Visitors can readily ascertain the feeling of the parochial authorities in the county on my general conduct towards them on their visits here. I had hitherto flattered myself that I had succeeded in gaining their approval. I believe the dissatisfaction on the part of the Brighton Guardians to arise from a misapprehension on their part of our relative position. Thus Mr Marchant is reported to have said that the occasional supervision of the establishment at Haywards Heath has now become part and parcel of their business; that they as Directors and Guardians had the power of going there when they thought proper… and throughout the speeches that day (24th April) there, the impression pervades that the Guardians have a right to visit and supervise this establishment… Now the Committee of Visitors and the Commissioners in Lunacy are the only visitors here recognized by Act of Parliament and there is no obligation on me to be in attendance. The Lunacy Act permits the Brighton Guardians to visit and examine individual patients chargeable to their Parish between the hours of eight and six and does not in any way authorize their official examination of the Asylum or of its management. In some county asylums the patients are on such occasions brought together in the Recreation Hall for this inspection. I have however always opened the wards and every part of the Asylum to the inspection of every Guardian who favoured me with a visit and the Brighton Guardians have been no exception to this rule. I am ready to make an appointment with any of the Guardians or others who may wish to see me regarding their patients. Lastly, my only regret in this case of Mockford's is that I did not communicate with the Coroner and request him to investigate the whole (case). I was unwilling to thus cast a public scandal on the Brighton authorities.

APPENDIX 2

Interview with Eileen Cruttenden conducted on 10/5/1999.

In 1924, I was living in the valleys near Port Talbot in Wales. There was no work for men let alone women. My mother had eleven children and I left school at 14. One day my half-sister – who was several years older than me – saw an advert about vacancies for domestic staff at the Brighton Mental Hospital. My father wrote to the hospital for her. They wrote back and said they would take her and that she would have to go there and have a medical test and all that. I was eighteen, miserable and not working and so I told my father to write back and tell them that he had another daughter who would like a job as well. They wrote back saying they would engage both of us together and they gave us a date to start in October. We told them our circumstances in Wales, you know, not much money. So they said they would transfer our fares to us which we would pay back later.

We had a new tin box for our things. We didn't know what to expect. At Port Talbot station they had never heard of Haywards Heath and told us to get the train to Brighton. It was a long, long journey but we eventually arrived at Brighton. When we found out that the fare to Haywards Heath was one shilling and eight pence, we thought it must be very close. When we arrived at the station there, no one helped us with our luggage and we had to take a taxi to the hospital. From then on it was a nightmare.

We arrived at these big gates at about eight o'clock in the evening. We couldn't see a lot because it was dark. The taxi man dropped us off at the nurses' home. My sister had saved up a lot of threepenny pieces and paid him with these. Of course we had to come from there to the main building and to a door with a chubb lock on. A white-haired lady came along with a big chain around her waist with all those keys. She was the housekeeper. She said it was too late to do anything and that she would see us in the morning. The cook was still on duty, so the housekeeper called her and she took us along to the kitchen. There was a big mess room. There were a lot of staff there. She cooked us eggs on toast and made us tea. The cups were that big I could hardly hold them. Everything was stamped, you know, with the name of the hospital. She then looked at us both and said to me, "Well, you look the healthiest. You can go up to the gallery to sleep and your sister can sleep downstairs."

Well, to get up there was a nightmare. The cook took me up. First of all, we had to get a gas lamp. No electricity, you see. She collected it. Talk about Florence Nightingale! Everything was locked. We unlocked a door, went through it, locked it and so on. Then we went up a lot of stairs, right to the top of the building. When we got there, she gave me keys. Inside the door was a gas jet with a square key on it. She turned it, lit the jet and then we walked through this dormitory, where all the patients were in bed, to where I was to sleep. At the time I did not know that the nurses slept up there as well. I thought I was the only one up there.

We got into this little room. She lit the gas jet there. It had bare boards, brick walls but they were painted in that awful dark brown, and black and green and dark green. And there were shutters on the windows. The bed was clean. It had a wardrobe and a wash-basin, chest of drawers. The bed was made up. Then the cook said to me. "Well, I'll leave you now" , she was off duty, "Be down in the kitchen by half-past six. In the morning, the night nurse will give you a call." Well, the shutters to me were like a prison. I was only used to curtains and open windows.

Next morning, I was dressed at 5 o'clock and so was already up when the nurse gave me a call. Then I opened the door and saw all these patients outside. Some were standing up with nothing on; some were dressing. They were all chattering to one another and calling out. It was all a jumble. I thought, I'm not going through there. I was too scared. So I went back to the bedroom, unlocked the door, then locked it. I waited there until the cook came and fetched me. She wasn't very happy. She had to come all the way up.

That day, there was no work. I had to be in the hall for the doctor to examine us. At a certain time, I had to be down in the female ward. The housekeeper looked all through our hair. That was degrading. After that, she said "I'll take you to the needle room." They fitted us up with aprons, caps, cuffs, collars and there were our dresses, terrible dresses they were. But when they gave us our dresses they weren't sewn. They were cut out to fit you. They were all lined; a few tucks in the bottom to let down if they shrunk. And they gave you this bundle and you had to sew them yourself. I didn't know what to do. Anyway, the cook came to our assistance. She said, "We all had to go through the same thing. There is a patient down in ward six. For half a crown she will sew your dresses for you". She used to do this although she was a very bad patient because ward six was the worst ward. You had to duck when you opened the door in case something came at you! Apart from that, the woman made our dresses for us and we paid her when we got some money.

I then worked in the kitchen. There were eleven staff there and the work was heavy. There was no electricity. Everything was done by hand. One or two patients would work there; sometimes taking the eyes out of the staff potatoes. Everything was cooked on steam boilers. And everything was done by time. Potatoes had to go into the steamers at a certain time. The patients who worked with us would get little extras and have their meals with us. We worked 56 hours a week and were paid nineteen shillings. We had two days off and were given rations for these days. We got half a loaf of bread, a pint of milk, a pat of margerine which we had to do ourselves down at the dairy, three eggs, some kippers… . When I was off I either stayed in bed half the day or got out on my bicycle.

After a while I did the cooking as well. I left after three years and three months to get married to a nurse at the hospital. Later, in 1949, I returned and worked in the hospital for another twelve years until I was sixty. My sister? She didn't pass the medical. Anyway, she had a boyfriend back home. She went back by Christmas. She could have stayed on the staff but she would not have been on the superannuation.

GLOSSARY

asylum	The name given to private or public mental health institutions from the late eighteenth century to the early twentieth century.
attendants	The nineteenth century description for male nurses. Female attendants were usually always referred to as 'nurses'.
bleeding	To draw blood surgically sometimes by using a leech.
Committee of Visitors	A committee composed of locally-appointed magistrates from the county. They regulated and monitored the asylum. Each workhouse which was paying maintenance for patients at the asylum also had their own 'Lunacy Committees' which were entitled to visit and check on their patients. Brighton's Lunacy Committee visited the asylum every three months.
cretin	A person who is deformed and mentally retarded as the result of a thyroid deficiency.
cupping	To bleed a person by using a glass in which a partial vacuum is formed by heating.
dementia	A chronic or persistent disorder of the mental process marked by memory disorders, personality changes, impaired reasoning etc., due to brain disease or injury.
general paralysis of the insane	A disease of the brain, an advanced form of syphilis.
idiot	A person of extremely low intelligence.
imbecile	A person with an intellectual impairment.
insanity, madness, lunacy	Generic terms used to describe to describe mental illness.
Lunacy Commissioners	A government-run board which regulated all public and private asylums. The board consisted of medical, legal and lay members.
madhouse	Usually a private institution for the insane in the 18th and early 19th centuries.
mania	Mental illness marked by periods of great excitement and violence.
mechanical restraint	Restraining patients with leg irons, strait-jackets, shackles or chains.
melancholia	Mental illness marked by depression and ill-founded fears.

mental handicap	Now replaced by the term 'learning disability'.
monomania	Insanity with respect to only one faculty.
moral treatment	Viewing the lunatic not as an irrational, mad animal, but as a human being who retains much of his humanity. The treatment was based on moral rather than medical grounds and emphasised one-to-one communication between staff and patient and the importance of re-education, diet and a healthy daily routine.
non-restraint	Not using mechanical instruments to restrain patients, relying more on communication skills. In its purest form it was the abolition of all forms of mechanical restraint and physical coercion whatsoever.
out-of-county patient	(sometimes known as 'non-county') A patient who was admitted into the Sussex Asylum, whose maintenance was paid for by another county. These charges were always higher than those for 'home' patients from Sussex.
pauper lunatic	Poor whose maintenance came wholly or in part from public funds.
phrenology	The study of the shape and size of the cranium as a supposed indication of character and mental faculties.
seclusion	Placing the patient in a padded cell
union	Two or more parishes consolidated for the administration of the Poor Laws.
workhouse	A public institution where people of a Parish unable to support themselves were housed and (if able-bodied) made to work. After the New Poor Law Act of 1834 it was sometimes referred to as the 'Union House'.
Workhouse Guardians	Elected by the ratepayers to regulate the workhouse and to monitor their 'inmates' placed in other institutions.

CHRONOLOGY

1808   County Asylums Act recommends that a public asylum should be set up in each county.

1815   Counties allowed to borrow money for up to 14 years to encourage them to build their own asylums.

1845   Lunatics Asylums Acts compelled every county in England and Wales to provide adequate accommodation for all pauper lunatics within three years.

1854   March: The East and West Divisions of Sussex agree to unite for the purposes of building an asylum. Brighton becomes a borough just too late and so is annexed to East Sussex for asylum purposes.

1856   February: The architect H.E. Kendall is chosen to build the new asylum.

1858   1st September: Charles Lockhart Robertson is appointed the first medical superintendent.

1859   St James's Day, 25th July: The Sussex Lunatic Asylum opens with 42 female patients arriving from Bethnal Green private asylum in London. By 25th December there are 285 patients in the asylum – 135 males,150 females.

1860   399 patients in the asylum – 172 males,227 females

1862   6th September: The asylum's first suicide.

1864   The thousandth patient arrives at the asylum. Now there are 501 patients: 225 males and 276 females.

1870   January – Lockhart Robertson resigns and is replaced by his assistant Dr Samuel Duckworth Williams. Over 700 patients in the asylum.

1888   December: Williams resigns through ill health and is replaced by Dr Charles Saunders. Over 900 patients in the asylum.

1893   Partnership between East Sussex and West Sussex is dissolved and from the beginning of the following year the asylum is known as the East Sussex County Lunatic Asylum. West Sussex transfers its patients to a new asylum, Graylingwell in Chichester.

1897   17th May: Charles Lockhart Robertson dies at the age of 72.

1900 July: Saunders resigns through ill health and is replaced by his assistant Dr Edward Walker. 969 patients in the asylum with a further 93 placed in asylums in Essex, Exeter and Chichester. 9,000 patients had been admitted since its opening with 2,500 deemed "recovered" and more than 3,000 having died.

1903 1st September: the Borough of Brighton takes control of the asylum with patients from East Sussex being transferred to Hellingly,a new asylum near Eastbourne. The asylum is renamed Brighton County Borough Asylum.

1910 Walker resigns through ill health and is replaced by his assistant Dr Charles Planck.

1918 The asylum population reaches 1,021 – 395 males, 626 females. That year there are 190 deaths.

1919 Name changes to Brighton County Borough Mental Hospital.

1923 Charles Planck resigns through ill health and is succeeded by his assistant George Harper-Smith.

1938 January: Harper-Smith retires and is succeeded by Dr William McCartan. In May a new admission villa, Hurstwood Park Hospital is opened but the following year, with the outbreak of war, it is used as an Emergency War Hospital.

1946 Hurstwood Park opens as a neurosurgical hospital with a psychiatric presence.

1948 5th July: becomes part of the National Health Service and is renamed St Francis Hospital.

1957 McCartan is replaced by Dr W Liddell. An admission villa is built.

1961 Liddell is replaced by Dr Richard Wheeler who becomes the last medical superintendent.

1969 April: the hospital has 800 patients and 500 staff.

1992 The hospital's name is changed for the last time and is now known as the West Wing of the Princess Royal Hospital.

1994 Only 100 patients left.

1995 17th November:the last sixteen patients are removed to a psychiatric unit in the Princess Royal Hospital. The hospital closes.

FOOTNOTES

CHAPTER 1

1. Allderidge, P. 'Bedlam: Fact or Fantasy?', p30, from *The Anatomy of Madness*, Volume 2, ed. Bynum, *et al.* (Tavistock 1985).
2. Ibid. p29
3. Ibid. p25
4. Conolly, J. *An Enquiry Concerning the Indications of Insanity*, pp4-5 (1830)

CHAPTER 2

1. Parry-Jones, W.L. *The Trade in Lunacy. A study of private madhouses in England in the eighteenth and nineteenth centuries*, (London), Routledge & Kegan, 1972.
2. Hodson, L.J. and J. Odell, *Ticehurst: The story of a Sussex parish*, Tunbridge Wells, 'Courier' Co., 1925, page 148.
3. The prospectus, *Views of Messrs. Newington's Private Asylum for the Cure of Insane Persons, Ticehurst, Sussex*, (1830), East Sussex CRO QAL/1/2/E2.
4. East Sussex CRO QAL/1/8/E2.
5. East Sussex CRO QAL/1/3/E5.
6. East Sussex CRO QAL/2/3/4a/4b.
7. East Sussex CRO QAL/2/3/5.
8. Ibid.
9. Smith, L. 'The County Asylum in the Mixed Economy of Care 1808-1845'. Chapter 2 from *Insanity, Institutions and Society. A Social History of Madness in Comparative Perspective*. Ed. J Melling & B Forsythe (Routledge 1999)
10. Boyer, G. *An Economic History of the English Poor Law 1750-1850*, (Cambridge University 1990), See Introduction.
11. Dunkley, P. *The Crisis of the Old Poor Law in England 1795-1834*, (Garland 1982), page 46.
12. The conclusion reached by C. Choomwattana in *Opposition to the New Poor Law in Sussex 1835-37*, (University of Sussex PHD, 1990).
13. West Sussex CRO QAL/2/3/W1.
14. Ibid.
15. Scull, A. *Madhouses, Mad doctors and Madmen*, page 168.
16. East Sussex CRO QAL/2/EW6.
17. *Metropolitan Lunacy Commission Report, 1844*, pp 185-187.
18. East Sussex CRO QAL/2/EW6.
19. Ibid.
20. West Sussex CRO QAL/2/3/W1.
21. East Sussex CRO QAL/2/EW5.

CHAPTER 3

1. Hawkins, H. 'Glimpses of Asylum Life' (1869), from *The Journal of Mental Science*, April 1869, pp 320-323, The Wellcome Institute, London.
2. Kendall, H.E., *Descriptions, specifications and estimates for the building of the Sussex County Lunatic Asylum, East Sussex* CRO ACC 6694/8.
3. Richardson, B.W., 'The Medical History of England' (1864), from *The Medical Times and Gazette* 18/6/1864, page 676, Wellcome Institute.
4. Hunter, R. & I Macalpine, 'Three Hundred Years of Psychiatry 1535-1860' (1963) Oxford University

Press, from *Charles Alexander Lockhart Robertson*, page 981.

5. Ibid. page 983.
6. Obituary notice of C. A. L. Robertson, British Journal of Mental Science, May, 1897.
7. Hawkins, H. 'A reminiscence of the late Dr C Lockhart Robertson', *Journal of Mental Science* vol 43, pages 677-678.
8. East Sussex CRO HC 9/1, *Servants and Attendants Register* of the Sussex County Asylum.
9. East Sussex CRO HC 4/3. A letter from Mr G. Campbell, a Lunacy Commissioner, to Mr W. P. Kell, clerk to the Visitors' Committee, Sussex Asylum.
10. East Sussex CRO HC 3/4, Mr W. P. Kell's papers.
11. West Sussex CRO QAL/2/W7, *Kendall's Completion Report.*
12. Source: Annual Reports of the Lunacy Commissioners. By 1890, there was an average of over 800 patients in the 66 county and borough asylums.
13. Parry-Jones, W.L., 'The Model of the Geel Lunatic Colony and Its influence on the Nineteenth Century Asylum System in Britain', from *Madhouses, Doctors and Madmen*, A. Scull, ch. 8, p. 209.

CHAPTER 4

1. Robertson, C.L. *Asylum Journal*, letter to the Visitors' Committee 30/7/1859. Source: East Sussex CRO HC7/1.
2. Robertson, C.L. ibid 13/8/1859.
3. Robertson, ibid. 10/9/1859.
4. Robertson, ibid. 17/8/1859.
5. Robertson, ibid. 24/9/1859.
6. Robertson, ibid. 7/10/1859.
7. Robertson, ibid. 10/9/1859.

8. Williams, S. *Institutional Care for the Pauper Insane in Sussex 1830-1880*, p. 84.
9. *Medical Superintendent's Order Book*, 29/10/1859. East Sussex CRO HC 10/1.
10. See Figure 1 for diet table for 1859. It remained virtually unchanged for thirty years.
11. Robertson, ibid. 8/10/1859.
12. Robertson, ibid. 17/12/1859.
13. *Sussex Lunatic Asylum First Annual Report 1859*, Medical Superintendent's Report. Most of these reports are kept at the East Sussex CRO.
14. Scull, A. *The Most Solitary of Afflictions 1700-1900, Madness and Society in Britain*, p. 83.
15. Murphy, E. *After the Asylum*, Introduction.
16. *Medical Superintendents Order Book*, 17/12/1859, Sussex CRO HC 10/1
17. Conolly, J. *The Construction and Government of Lunatic Asylums*, (1847), Reprinted edition London: Dawsons, 1968, p. 84.
18. Williams, S. ibid.
19. *Attendants and Servants Register SLA*, East Sussex CRO HC 9/1.
20. Robertson, ibid. 8/10/1859.
21. *Attendants and Servants Register SLA*, East Sussex CRO Hc 9/1.
22. Robertson, ibid. 17/12/1859.
23. See Figure 3
24. See Figure 2.
25. Robertson, ibid. 10/9/1859.
26. Robertson, ibid. 20/11/1859.
27. See Figure 3.
28. Robertson, ibid. 17/12/59.
29. *The Brighton Herald*, 31/12/1859, Brighton Reference Library.
30. Robertson, *Medical Superintendent's Report*, 1st Annual Report, SLA, 1859.

CHAPTER 5

1. Robertson, 'A Case of Homicidal Mania without Disorder of the Intellect', from the *Journal of Mental Science*, July 1860, vol 34, page 385, The Wellcome Institute, London.
2. Ibid. page 389.
3. Robertson recorded in his journal, on 24/3/1860, that the "Assistant Medical Officer, on my advice wants to resign".
4. Robertson, Ibid. 24/3/1860.
5. Ibid.
6. Ibid. 13/6/1860.
7. Ibid.
8. Ibid. 13/4/1860.
9. Ibid.
10. *Brighton Guardian*, 25/4/1860.
11. Ibid.
12. *Brighton Gazette*, 26/4/1860.
13. Ibid.
14. Ibid.
15. *Brighton Gazette*, 26/4/1860.
16. Ibid.
17. Ibid.
18. *Brighton Herald*, 12/5/1860.
19. Robertson, *Asylum Journal*, 23/5/1860. His full reply is printed in the Appendix.
20. Ibid.
21. *Minute Book of Committee of Visitors*, Sussex Lunatic Asylum, 19/5/1860.
22. *Brighton Herald*, 26/5/1860.
23. Ibid.
24. Ibid.
25. Robertson, *Asylum Journal*, 28/7/1860.
26. Ibid. 10/3/1860.
27. Ibid.
28. Ibid. 28/4/1860.
29. *Medical Superintendent's Order Book*, Sussex Lunatic Asylum, 19/5/1860 East Sussex CRO HC 10/1.
30. Digby, A. *Madness, Morality and Medicine*, p. 154.
31. *Minute Book of Committee of Visitors*, 8/12/1860. East Sussex CRO RC 143.
32. Robertson, *Asylum Journal*, 27/10/1860.
33. *Brighton Herald*, 12/5/1860.
34. Robertson, *Asylum Journal*, 13/10/60.
35. 'Medical Superintendent's Report', p. 35, From *1860 SLA Annual Report*.
36. Robertson, *Asylum Journal*, 27/10/1860.
37. *Minute Book of Committee of Visitors*, 27/10/1860.
38. Robertson, ibid. 8/12/1860.
39. Ibid. 11/10/1860.
40. *Minute Book of Committee of Visitors*, 28/1/1860, East Sussex CRO RC 143.
41. *Medical Superintendent's Order Book*, 7/1/1860, East Sussex CRO HC 10/1.
42. *Minute Book of Committee of Visitors*, ibid.
43. See Figures 4 and 5 for Tables V and VI, from *SLA 1860 Annual Report*.
44. *Sussex Lunatic Asylum Annual Report 1860*, The farm had a production worth £1, 174 4s. 9d.
45. See Figure 6, Table IV from the *SLA 1860 Annual Report*.
46. Table VII (Discharges) for *SLA 1860 Annual Report*.
47. 'Medical Superintendent's Report', *SLA 1860 Annual Report*.
48. See Appendix H for Table VIII (Deaths) for *1860 SLA Annual Report*.
49. Medical Superintendent's Report, *1860 SLA Annual Report*.

CHAPTER 6

1. Robertson, *Asylum Journal*, 12/1/1861, East Sussex CRO HC 7/1.

2. Ibid.
3. Ibid. 23/2/1861.
5. Ibid. 12/1/1861. "Gray" could also be "Guy" due to the unclear handwriting.
6. Ibid. 22/6/1861.
7. *Minute Book of Committee of Visitors,* 22/6/1861, East Sussex CRO RC 14/3.
8. Robertson, *Asylum Journal,* 27/4/1861, East Sussex CRO HC 7/1.
9. Ibid. 30/11/1861.
10. *Medical Superintendent's Report* 1863, pp 15-16, East Sussex CRO HC 2/1.
11. *Medical Superintendent's Order Book,* 2/11/1863, East Sussex CRO HC 10/1.
12. *Medical Superintendent's Report,* 1862, page 21. East Sussex CRO HC 2/1.
13. Hawkins, H. *Glimpses of Asylum Life,* (1869).
14. Ibid.
15. Robertson, *Annual Report for 1861,* East Sussex CRO ACC 6694/1.
16. Hawkins, H. *Glimpses of Asylum Life.*
17. Robertson, *The Lancet,* letter, 25/2/1860. Post-Grad. Library, Brighton General Hospital.
18. *Medical Superintendent's Annual Report,* 1863, East Sussex CRO HC 2/1.
19. Robertson. *Journal of Mental Science,* July 1863.
20. Robertson, *Asylum Journal* 31/5/1862, East Sussex CRO HC 7/1.
21. Ibid. 28/9/1861.
22. *Medical Superintendent's Order Book,* Sussex Lunatic Asylum, 3/6/1861, East Sussex CRO HC 10/1.
23. Robertson, *Asylum Journal,* 23/2/1861, East Sussex CRO HC 7/1.
24. Ibid.
25. Ibid. 28/9/1861.
26. Robertson, *Asylum Reports 1859-67,* September 1861. East Sussex CRO HC 7/2.
27. Ibid. 26/10/1861.
28. Robertson, *Annual Report for 1861,* East Sussex CRO ACC 6694/1.

CHAPTER 7

1. Robertson, *Asylum Journal,* 22/12/1860, East Sussex CRO HC 7/1.
2. Robertson, *Medical Superintendent's Order Book,* 24/6/1860, East Sussex.CRO HC 10/1.
3. Robertson, *Asylum Journal,* 28/2/1863, East Sussex CRO HC 7/1.
4. *Medical Superintendent's Order Book,* 18/11/1867, East Sussex CRO HC 10/1.
5. Robertson, *Asylum Journal,* 19//2/61, East Sussex CRO HC 7/1.
6. *Medical Superintendent's Order Book,* 20/1/1861, East Sussex CRO HC 10/1.
7. Ibid. 16/7/1861.
8. Ibid. 4/6/1863. Robertson was annoyed that Browne hadn't placed the patient in the infirmary.
9. Ibid. 6/6/1863.
10. *Minute Book of Committee of Visitors,* 27/6/1863, East Sussex CRO RC 14/3.
11. Robertson, *Asylum Journal,* 25/4/1860, East Sussex CRO HC 7/1.
12. Ibid. 27/12/1862.
13. Robertson, 'A Descriptive Notice of the Sussex Lunatic Asylum', *in Journal of Mental Science,* April 1860, vol. 33, page 254.
14. Robertson, *Asylum Journal,* 8/12/1860, East Sussex CRO HC 7/1.
15. Robertson, JMS article (note 13), page 257.

16. Robertson, *Asylum Journal*, 24/11/1860.

17. Robertson, *Medical Superintendent's Order Book*, 30/10/1860.

18. Robertson, *Asylum Journal*, 19/1/1860.

19. *Medical Superintendent's Order Book*, 3/6/1861.

20. Robertson, *Asylum Journal*, 10/10/1862.

21. Ibid. 22/12/1860, see Figure 7.

22. Ibid.

23. Ibid. 11/10/1860

24. Ibid.

25. *Medical Superintendent's Annual Report* 1862, East Sussex CRO HC 2/1.

26. *Asylum Journal*, 28/11/1861.

27. *Minute Book of Visitors*, 26/10/1861, East Sussex CRO RC 14/3.

28. Robertson, *Asylum Journal*, 22/2/1862.

29. Robertson, Ibid. 25/5/1860.

30. Middleton, J. unpublished book on the Sussex Lunatic Asylum (1995), chap 3.

31. *Medical Superintendent's Annual Report*, 1862, p. 21, East Sussex CRO HC 2/1.

32. *The Fifth Annual Report of the Sussex Lunatic Asylum*, Commissioners Report, pages 49-54, East Sussex CRO HC 2/1.

33. *Medical Superintendent's Order Book*, 1/5/1861.

CHAPTER 8

1. *Medical Superintendent's Annual Report*, 1862, p. 21, East Sussex CRO HC 2/1.

2. Ibid.

3. Robertson, *Journal of Mental Science*, July 1862.

4. *Brighton Guardian*, 17/1/1862,

Brighton Reference Library.

5. Robertson, *Asylum Journal*, 31/5/1862, East Sussex CRO HC 7/1.

6. Hawkins, H. *Glimpses of Asylum Life* (1869).

7. Robertson, *Asylum Journal*, 27/12/1862, East Sussex CRO HC 7/1.

8. Ibid. 22/8/1863.

9. *Sussex Lunatic Asylum Annual Report, 1862*, Visitors' Committee Report.

10. *Minute Book of Committee of Visitors*, 31/1/1863, East Sussex CRO RC 14/3.

11. *The Fifth Annual Report of the SLA*, 'Medical Superintendent's Report', p. 14.

12. *Brighton Guardian*, 25/11/1863, a letter from Robertson, dated 13/11/1863 Brighton Reference Library.

13. *Brighton Gazette*, A report on the Brighton Guardians' meeting of 1/12/1863. Brighton Reference Library.

14. Ibid.

15. Ibid. 17/12/1863.

16. Ibid. Robertson's letter to the Brighton Guardians, dated 10/12/1863.

17. Ibid.

CHAPTER 9

1. The dialogues are taken from reports in the local newspapers in February and March – the *Brighton Herald*, the *Brighton Gazette*, the *Brighton Observer*, the *Brighton Examiner*, the *Brighton Guardian* and the *Sussex Agricultural Express*. The most comprehensive report was in the *Brighton Herald*, 27/2/64. These newspapers are on microfilm in the

Brighton Reference Library.

2. *Brighton Examiner*, 1/3/1864, Brighton Reference Library.

3. *Brighton Examiner*, 15/3/1864, Brighton Reference Library.

4. *Sussex Advertiser*, 30/3/1864, Brighton Reference Library.

5. Robertson, *Asylum Journal*, 27/2/1864, East Sussex CRO HC 7/1.

6. Ibid. 26/2/1864.

7. Robertson, 'Remarks on the Use of Digitalis in the Treatment of Insanity', *British Medical Journal*, 3/10/1863

8. Hunter, R & I. Macalpine, *Three Hundred Years of Psychiatry 1535-1860*, p. 487.

9. Robertson, 'Hydrotherapia in Hospital Practice', letter to *British Medical Journal*, 27/1/1862.

10. Maudsley, H. *Pathology of Mind*(1879), p. 545.

11. The rules were written on 1/3/1864:
The Head Attendant will record:

1. The name & date placed under the water treatment with the form in which it is ordered to be given and also the date on which it is discontinued.

2. The packing in the wet sheet, the cold pails of the douche to be entered.

3. When the sweating process(this dry pack) is induced the patient after $1/2$ hour in the warm bath is then wrapped in a day blanket & then 6 blankets rolled round. He is visited every $1/2$ hour during this time, which lasts 3-4 hours & then taken back to the warm bath. The process may then by medical orders be repeated.

4. Where packing in the wet sheet is ordered $1^{1}/2$ hours is implied as the time unless otherwise ordered.

5. The Head Attendant has authority in cases of sudden excitement or violence to use the bedsheet instead of seclu-

sion/repeating the same in the normal manner for the period of $1^{1}/2$ hours. Later on, in consequence of a death in the bedsheet being reported at Gloucester rule 5 was rescinded – No water treatment shall be used without medical authority on each occasion.
Dr Robertson.
East Sussex CRO HC 10/2.

12. Ibid.

13. Hawkins, H. *Memorial to William Knox*, 18/1/70, circulated privately by Hawkins.

14. *The Lancet*, 21/11/1846.

15. *Brighton Examiner*, 13/9/1864, Brighton Reference Library.

16. *Brighton Herald*, 3/9/1864, Brighton Reference Library.

17. Ibid.

18. Ibid.

19. Ibid.

20. Ibid.

21. Ibid.

22. Ibid.

23. Ibid.

24. Ibid.

25. *Brighton Guardian*, 7/9/1864, Brighton Reference Library.

26. Robertson, *Asylum Reports 1859-67*, 23/11/1864. East Sussex CRO HC 7/2.

27. Ibid. July 1864.

28. *Brighton Guardian*, 5/10/1864, Brighton Reference Library.

29. *Sixth Annual Report SLA*, Superintendent's Report,

CHAPTER 10

1. A tobacco pipe made by a clay-like substance.

2. Robertson, *Asylum Reports 1859-67*, 8/3/1866. East Sussex CRO HC 7/2.

3. Undated letter found in Robertson's Asylum Reports 1859-67, 1865 East

Sussex CRO HC 7/2.

4. *Medical Superintendent's Order Book*, Sussex Lunatic Asylum, 30/7/1865.

5. Ibid. 31/9/1866, East Sussex CRO HC 10/1.

6. Ibid.

7. *Sussex Advertiser*, 27/10/1866, Brighton Reference Library.

8. *Assistant Medical Officer's Daily Notes*, Vol. 1, East Sussex CRO HC 8/1.

9. Ibid. 10/12/1865.

10. Robertson, *Asylum Reports 1859-67*, East Sussex CRO HC 7/2.

11. *Brighton Examiner*, 10/1/1865, The Brighton Reference Library.

12. Ibid.

13. Ibid.

14. Ibid. 20/6/1865.

15. *Brighton Guardian*, 19/5/1865. Report of the Brighton Guardians visit to the asylum on 29/3/1865. Brighton Reference Library.

16. Robertson, *Asylum Reports 1859-67*, 23/12/1865, East Sussex CRO HC 7/2.

17. Ibid. Undated letter from Edward Polhill to Robertson. Edward Polhill was later re-admitted from Battle on 9th March, 1878.

18. *Medical Superintendent's Order Book*, 13/10/1865. East Sussex CRO HC 10/1.

19. Ibid.

20. Robertson, *Asylum Reports 1859-67*, 1865, East Sussex CRO HC 7/2.

21. *Eleventh Annual Report, SLA*. The Lunacy Commissioners Report, page 25, East Sussex CRO HC 2/1.

22. Copies of it were printed and circulated privately. It was reprinted in *the Journal of Mental Science*, pages 1&2, No. 54, July 1865.

23. A work colleague informed me that she had found one a few years ago being used to support a plant in a pot.

24. *Seventh Annual Report, Medical Superintendent's Report*. page 18. East Sussex CRO HC 2/1.

25. See Figure 8 for the "Nominal List of 25 Patients admitted in a Hopeless Dying State during the year 1866", from the *Eighth Annual Report*, East Sussex, CRO HC 2/1.

CHAPTER 11

1. *Seventh Annual Report,* SLA. The Committee of Visitors' Report, page 7 East Sussex CRO HC 2/1.

2. 'THE AMOAHI, MPA & Presidents', by Renvoize, page 62, from *150 years of British Psychiatry 1841-1991* (Gaskell) by E. Berrios & H. Freeman.

3. *Brighton Herald*, 14/5/1864, The Brighton Reference Library.

4. 'The AMOAHI, MPA & Presidents', by Renvoize, page 61, from *150 years of British Psychiatry* by E. Berrios & H. Freeman.

5. Ibid. Renvoize, page 60.

6. *Journal of Mental Science*, January, 1865, (vol 52), page 479.

7. Ibid.

8. *Journal of Mental Science*, October 1867 (vol 63), page 299.

9. Robertson, *Asylum Reports 1859-67*, 29/10/1867, East Sussex CRO HC 7/2.

10. *The Ninth Annual Report of the Sussex Lunatic Asylum*, page 21, East Sussex CRO HC 2/1.

11. *Brighton Gazette*, 7/11/1867, Brighton Reference Library.

12. Ibid.

13. *Journal of Mental Science*, July 1867, Williams, page 176.

14. *Minute Book of Committee of Visitors*, 29/9/1866, East Sussex CRO RC 14/3.

15. Ibid.
16. *Assistant Medical Officer's Daily Notes*, vol 1, 12/10/1867. East Sussex CRO HC 8/1.
17. Ibid.
18. Ibid. 1/3/1867.
19. 'Glimpses of Asylum Life', by Henry Hawkins, reprinted from 'The Churchman' magazine (1869), in the *Journal of Mental Science*, July 1870, page 320.
20. Ibid.
21. Ibid.
22. Hawkins, 'A Reminiscence of the late Dr Robertson', *Journal of Mental Science* (1897), vol. 43, pages 677-8.
23. Robertson, *Journal of Mental Science*, July, 1868, page 192.
24. *The Tenth Annual Report of the Sussex Lunatic Asylum*, Medical Superintendent's report, page 20.
25. *Medical Superintendent's Order Book*, 7/3/1868, East Sussex CRO HC 10/1.
26. *Sussex Agricultural Express*, 23/10/1869, Brighton Reference Library.
27. *The Tenth Annual Report of the Sussex Lunatic Asylum*, See Table X, page 42.
28. *Assistant Medical Officer's Daily Notes*, vol. 1, 3/2/1869, East Sussex CRO HC 8/1.
29. *The Eleventh Annual Report of the Sussex Lunatic Asylum*, Medical Superintendent's report, page 18.
30. *Sussex Agricultural Express*, 2/4/1870.
13. *The Ninth Annual Report of the Sussex Lunatic Asylum*, page 21, East Sussex CRO HC 2/1.
14. *Brighton Gazette*, 7/11/1867, Brighton Reference Library.
15. Ibid.
16. *Journal of Mental Science*, July 1867, Williams, page 176.
17. *Minute Book of Committee of Visitors*, 29/9/1866, East Sussex CRO RC 14/3.
18. Ibid.
19. *Assistant Medical Officer's Daily Notes*, vol 1, 12/10/1867. East Sussex CRO HC 8/1.
20. Ibid.
21. Ibid. 1/3/1867.
22. 'Glimpses of Asylum Life', by Henry Hawkins, reprinted from 'The Churchman' magazine (1869), in the *Journal of Mental Science*, July 1870, page 320.
23. Ibid.
24. Ibid.
25. Hawkins, 'A Reminiscence of the late Dr Robertson', *Journal of Mental Science* (1897), vol. 43, pages 677-8.

CHAPTER 12

1. Robertson, 'The Care and Treatment of the Insane Poor', from the *Journal of Mental Science*, October 1867 (vol. 63), page 299.
2. *The Tenth Annual Report of the Sussex Lunatic Asylum*, 1868.
3. Williams, S. *Institutional Care for the Pauper Insane in Sussex 1830-1880*, page 87.
4. Robertson, *The Lancet*, letter, 18/9/1869, pp. 420-21.
5. Renvoize, 'The AMOAHI, MPA & Presidents', page 75, from *150 years of British Psychiatry* by E. Berrios & H. Freeman.
6. Williams, S. *Institutional Care for the Pauper Insane in Sussex, 1830-1880*. p84
7. Hawkins, 'The Late Dr Lockhart Robertson: A Reminiscence', *Journal of Mental Science* July 1897, pp. 667-668.
8. Robertson's obituary in the *British Medical Journal*, volume 1, page

1385.

9. *Medical Superintendent's Order Book*, 5/9/1869, East Sussex CRO HC 10/1.

10. Ibid. 28/10/1869.

11. Robertson, letter to *The Lancet*, 26/12/1868.

12. Ibid.

13. Robertson's Presidential address, *The Lancet*, 6/8/1881, page 233.

14. Ibid.

15. Robertson, 'The Care and Treatment of the Insane Poor', October 1867, *(Journal of Mental Science)*, quote from Henry Maudsley's 'The Psychology and Pathology of the Mind'.

16. *British Medical Journal* July 1897, vol. 1, page 1385.

CHAPTER 13

1. *Medical Superintendent's Order Book*, East Sussex CRO HC 10/1.

2. Ibid. 12/9/1871.

3. *Sussex Agricultural Express*, 29/1/1870, Brighton Reference Library.

4. *Assistant Medical Officer's Daily Notes*, vol 2, 26/4/1878, East Sussex CRO HC 8/2.

5. *Twelfth Annual Report SLA*, Medical Superintendent's report, page 19.

6. *Sixteenth Annual Report SLA*, Medical Superintendent's report, page 14.

7. *Visiting Committee Reports*, 27/4/1895, East Sussex CRO HC 7/6.

8. *Twenty-first Annual Report SLA*, Visitors' Committee report, page 7.

9. *Medical Superintendent's Order Book*, 7/4/1870, East Sussex, HC 10/1.

10. *Fourteenth Annual Report SLA*, Medical Superintendent's report, page 18.

11. *Thirteenth Annual Report SLA*, Chaplain's report, page 83.

12. *Twenty-ninth Annual Report SLA* , Visitors' Report, page 25.

13. Ibid. page 24.

14. Ibid. page 23.

15. *Visiting Committee Reports*, April 1888, East Sussex CRO HC 7/4.

16. *Thirty-fifth Annual Report SLA*, Chaplain's report.

17. Ibid. *Lunacy Commissioners' Report*, page 53.

18. *Medical Superintendent's Diaries*, 15/5/1889, East Sussex CRO HC 8/6.

19. Lowerson, J. *St Francis in Perspective*, pamphlet, page 5, March 1973, (University of Sussex).

20. *Thirty-eighth Annual Report SLA*, Medical Superintendent's report, page 26.

21. *Forty-third Annual Report SLA*, , Medical Superintendent's report, page 22.

22. *Sussex Daily News*, 2/3/1901, Brighton Reference library.

23. *Admin Case Notes for Pauper Female Patients – Hellingly*. ESRO HE28/1

24. *Admin Case Notes for Pauper Male Patients – Hellingly*. ESRO HE26/1

CHAPTER 14

1. *Brighton County Borough Asylum Report for 1908*, Table A 2, East Sussex CRO HC 13/1.

2. *Brighton County Borough Asylum Report for 1910*, Commissioners Report, p. 58, East Sussex CRO HC 13/2.

3. *Brighton County Borough Asylum Report for 1909*, Commissioners Report, p. 55, East Sussex CRO HC 13/2.

4. *Brighton County Borough Asylum*

Report for 1910, Commissioners Report, p. 56, East Sussex CRO HC 13/2.

5. *Visitors' Book 1903-1938*, 13/6/1913, East Sussex CRO HC 14/1.
6. *Mid-Sussex Times*, 8/9/1925.
7. *Evening Argus*, 20/10/1922.
8. *Medical Superintendent's Desk Diary 1926*, 14/6/1926, East Sussex CRO HC 20/11.
9. Extract from *Asylum News*, December 1977-January 1978, private collection.
10. *Mid-Sussex Times*, 11/5/1926.
11. Patients on 'trial' was an attempt to rehabilitate them back in the community by placing them with family or friends.
12. *Visitors' Book 1903-1938*, 21/8/1923, East Sussex CRO HC 14/1.
13. *Visitors' Book 1903-1938*, 20/6/1930, East Sussex CRO HC 14/1.

CHAPTER 15

1. In their annual report for 1932, the Commissioners noted that very little use had yet been made of the provisions of the Mental Treatment Act 1930, in respect of treatment. *Hospital News* 12/2/1969. Private collection.
2. *Visitors' Book 1903-1938*, 8/12/1931, East Sussex CRO HC 14/1.
3. *Mid-Sussex Times*, 5/1/1932, Mid-Sussex Times Offices, Haywards Heath.
4. Ibid. 24/7/1934.
5. *Medical Superintendent's Order Book*, 5/5/1938, East Sussex CRO HC 26/1.
6. *Desk Diaries*, 15/3/1933, East Sussex CRO HC 20/15.
7. Ibid. 23/9/1931.
8. Middleton, J. *A History of St Francis*

Hospital (1995), unpublished, in Chap. 16 'Brighton County Borough Asylum'.

9. *Board of Control Annual Report*, 13/2/1947, microfilm, University of Sussex.
10. Pate, B. *Reflections from the Community*, October-November 1975, "Hospital News", private collection.
11. *Mid-Sussex Times*, 23/5/1956.
12. Ibid.
13. In an interview between the author and Dr Wheeler in the Summer of 1997.
14. *Visitors' Report*, 18/1/1962.
15. *Hospital News*, St. Francis Hospital, August 1968.
16. Ibid. November 1969.
17. Ibid. January 1969.

CONCLUSION

1. Walton, J.K., 'Casting out and bringing back in Victorian England: Pauper Lunatics 1840-70', from *The Anatomy of Madness*, vol 2, Bynum et al.
2. Journal of Mental Science, October 1867 (Vol 63), page 299.
3. *Visiting Committee Reports*, May 1897, East Sussex CRO HC 7/5.
4. A Scull, 'Rethinking the History of Asylumdom', page 312, from A Scull, C Mackenzie and N Hervey, *Masters of Bedlam: The Transformation of the Mad-doctoring Trade*, Princetown University Press.

BIBLIOGRAPHY

NEWSPAPERS AND JOURNALS

Brighton Examiner
Brighton Gazette
Brighton Guardian
Brighton Herald
Brighton Observer
Mid-Sussex Express
Sussex Agricultural Express
Sussex Weekly Advertiser
Sussex Daily News
British Medical Journal
Journal of Mental Science
Journal of Psychological Medicine & Mental Pathology.
London Medical Times and Gazette
The Lancet

ARTICLES ABOUT THE SUSSEX COUNTY LUNATIC ASYLUM

M. Charman, *The History of the Building of the Sussex County Lunatic Asylum*, unpublished, 1994.

M. Charman, *A Short History of St Francis Hospital*, unpublished, 1994.

J. Lowerson, *St. Francis in Perspective*, University of Sussex, 1973.

J. M. Mable, The most famous landmark in Mid-Sussex, from 'The Life and Work of St. Francis Hospital 1859-1995 in *ON CALL*, Mid-Sussex NHS Trust magazine, Nov. 1995.

St Francis Hospital *Asylum News* 1960-80s

BOOKS

G. E. Berrios and H. Freeman, *150 Years of British Psychiatry 1841-1991*, Vol 1 Gaskell, Royal College of Psychiatrists, 1991.

G. E. Berrios and H. Freeman, *150 Years of British Psychiatry 1841-1991*, Vol 2 Gaskell, Royal College of Psychiatrists, 1996.

G. Boyer, *An Economic History of the English Poor Law 1750-1850*, Cambridge University, 1990.

W. F. Bynum, R. Porter and M. Shepherd (eds), *The Anatomy of Madness, vol I*, London, Tavistock Publications, 1985.

W. F. Bynum, R. Porter and M. Shepherd (eds), *The Anatomy of Madness, vol II*, London, Tavistock Publications, 1985.

W. F. Bynum, R. Porter and M. Shepherd(eds), *The Anatomy of Madness, vol III*, London, Tavistock Publications, 1988.

C. Choomwattana, *Opposition to the New Poor Law in Sussex 1835-37*, University of Sussex, unpublished PhD, 1990.

J. Conolly, *An Enquiry Concerning the Indications of Insanity, 1830*.

J. Conolly, *The Construction and Government of Lunatic Asylums*, London, Dawsons, 1868.

A. Digby, Madness, *Morality and Medicine. A study of the York Retreat, 1796-1914*, Cambridge University Press, 1985.

F. Drewe, *Ticehurst*, Phillimore and Co Ltd., 1991.

P. Dunkley, *The Crisis of the Old Poor Law in England 1795-1834*, Garland, 1982.

E. W. Gilbert, *Brighton, Old Ocean's Bauble*, Methuen, 1954.

L. J. Hodson and J. Odell, *Ticehurst: The Story of a Sussex Parish*, Tunbridge Wells 'Courier'Co. , 1925.

R. Hunter and I. Macalpine, *Three Hundred Years of Psychiatry, 1535-1860*, London, Oxford University Press, 1963.

A. Huxley, *The Witches of Loudon*,

K. Jones, *Lunacy, Law and Conscience, 1744-1845*, London, Routledge & Kegan Paul. 1955.

K. Jones, *A History of the Mental Health Services*, London, Routledge and Kegan Paul 1975.

C. Mackenzie, *Psychiatry for the Rich, A History of Ticehurst Private Asylum*, Routledge, London and New York, 1992.

H. Maudsley, *Pathology of Mind* (1879), London.

J. Melling and B. Forsythe (eds), *Insanity, Institutions and Society. A Social History of Madness in Comparative Perspective*, Routledge 1999.

J. Middleton. *A History of St Francis Hospital*, unpublished, 1995

E. Murphy, *After the Asylum*

M. Neve and T. Turner, 'What the Doctor Thought and Did: Sir James Crichton-Browne (1840-1938)', from *Medical History*, 1995, Volume 39.

W. L. Parry-Jones, *The Trade in Lunacy. A study of private madhouses in England in the eighteenth and nineteenth centuries*, London, Routledge & Kegan Paul, 1972.

G. Parsons, 'Ringmer Lunatic Asylum', *Sussex History*, Vol. 1, no. 9.

R. Porter, *Mind Forg'd Manacles: A History of Madness in England from the Restoration to the Regency*, London: Athlone, 1987.

R. Porter, *The Greatest Benefit to Mankind: A Medical History of Humanity from Antiquity to the Present.* HarperCollins, 1997.

A. Scull, *Museums of Madness. The Social Organization of Insanity in Nineteenth-century England,* Allen Lane, 1979.

A. Scull, *Madhouses, Mad-doctors and Madmen*, The Athlone Press, 1981.

A. Scull, *The Most Solitary of Afflictions 1700-1900,* Madness and Society in Britain,

A. Scull, C. Mackenzie and N. Hervey, *Masters of Bedlam: The Transformation of the Mad-doctoring Trade*, Princetown University Press 1996.

S. Williams, *Institutional Care for the Pauper Insane in Sussex 1830-1880*, unpublished MA. Brighton University, 1990.

RECORD OFFICE DOCUMENTS

WEST SUSSEX - CRO QAL/2/3/W1
EAST SUSSEX - CRO QAL/1/2/E2
 CRO QAL/1/8/E2
 CRO QAL/1/3/E5
 CRO QAL/2/3/4a/4b
 CRO QAL/2/3/5
 CRO QAL/2/E5
 CRO QAL/2/EW6
 CRO ACC 6694/8

PRINCIPLE RECORD OFFICE SOURCES

East Sussex CRO RC 143 "Minute Book of Committee of Visitors".
CRO HC 2/1 "Medical Superintendent's Reports".
CRO HC 3/4 & HC 4/3, Mr W. P. Kell's papers, clerk to the Visitors.
CRO HC 7/1 Robertson's "Asylum Journal".
HC 7/2 Robertson's "Asylum Reports" 1859-1867
HC 7/4 Visiting Committee Reports.
HC 7/5 Visiting Committee Reports.
HC 7/6 Visiting Committee Reports.
HC 8/1 Assistant Medical Officer's Daily notes, vol. 1 & 2.
HC 8/6 Medical Superintendent's Diaries.
East Sussex CRO HC 9/1 "Servants and Attendants Register", Sussex Asylum.

HC 10/1 "Medical Superintendant's Order Book".

HC 13/1 Brighton County Borough Reports.

HC 13/2 Brighton County Borough Reports.

HC 14/1 Visitors'Book 1903-1938

HC 20/11 Medical Superintendent's Desk Diary 1926

HC 20/15 Desk Diaries

HC 26/1 Medical Superintendent's Order Book

West Sussex CRO QAL/2/W7 Kendall's Completion Report

INDEX

References to illustrations and facsimiles are in **bold**, and titles of published works and newspapers are in *italic*.

SUSSEX LUNATIC ASYLUM.

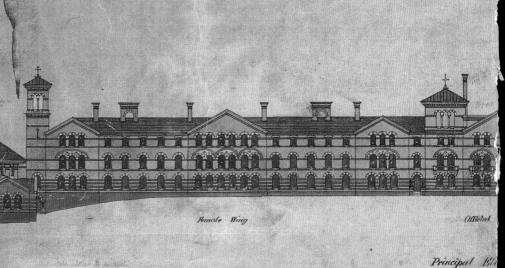

Working Offices (Male)

Male Wing

Centr

Entrance

Infirmary

Female Wing

Official

Principal El